Second Edition

Related Macmillan titles

Start Hairdressing! – The Official Guide to Level 1,
by Martin Green and Leo Palladino

Professional Hairdressing – The Official Guide to Level 3,
by Martin Green, Lesley Howson and Leo Palladino

Beauty Therapy – The Foundations,
by Lorraine Nordmann

The Complete Make-up Artist: Working in Film, Television and Theatre, by Penny Delamar

Manicure, Pedicure and Advanced Nail Techniques,
by Elaine Almond

The Nail File, by Leo Palladino and June Hunt

Science and the Beauty Business:
The Science of Cosmetics, and
The Beauty Salon and its Equipment,
both by John V. Simmons

Principles and Practice of Hairdressing,
by Leo Palladino

THE FOUNDATIONS

The Official Guide to Level 2

Second Edition

NICK ARROJO, WELLA

Leo Palladino

with

Martin Green

First published 1995 by
MACMILLAN PRESS LTD
Houndmills, Basingstoke, Hampshire RG21 2XS
and London
Companies and representatives
throughout the world

ISBN 0–333–63194–3

A catalogue record for this book is available
from the British Library.

10 9 8 7 6 5 4 3 2
04 03 02 01 00 99 98 97 96

Designed by Susan Clarke
Typeset by Tek Art, Croydon, Surrey

Printed in Hong Kong

Note about pronouns

Using 'he or she' and 'him or her' throughout the text would become cumbersome in a book such as this. For simplicity and ease of reading, therefore, we have generally used simply 'she' and 'her', except in passages concerned specifically with men's hairdressing.

CONTENTS

TRESemmé

SPLINTERS EDUCATION LTD

In the fast-moving world of hairdressing, it is important to have a solid foundation on which to build. That's why the Hairdressing Training Board developed national standards for hairdressing. Each level of the NVQ/SVQ framework helps you build up your skill, knowledge and experience. All these provide you with a valuable insight into the world of hairdressing.

There are many techniques that need to be mastered, experiences to be lived and skills to be acquired before you can reach the high standard expected of a hairdresser. If you want to become a world-class hairdresser, then achieving the ability to learn is one of the first steps to take.

This guide is written specifically for learners. It will enable you to learn new skills and take in knowledge. The experience comes from learning.

Alan Goldsbro
Chief Executive, Hairdressing Training Board

INTRODUCTION

REGIS

Hairdressing – the foundations is the Official Level 2 Guide for trainees working towards the NVQ/SVQ qualification recognised and endorsed by the Hairdressing Training Board.

The second edition of this best-selling book continues to emphasise the need for good, basic, practical hairdressing skills and an understanding of what occurs when they are applied.

Chapters on barbering, shaving and face massage have been added since these have now become optional units at NVQ/SVQ Level 2.

Further additions which meet the changing needs of NVQ/SVQ Level 2 include chapters on working together, salon resources, and salon health safety and security.

At the end of each chapter a series of work assignments have been set. These should help you to look into and explore a variety of topics with which you will need to become familiar. These are:

- assignments based on practical techniques
- activities which involve investigating and finding out
- case studies to familiarise you with a variety of likely scenarios.

When you have satisfactorily worked through these assignments you should be ready for assessment.

Guest author Martin Green has also shared his experience to enrich the quality of the book further and to make it a must for everyone working towards a professional career in the hairdressing industry. Your attainment of sound foundations will be the basis of work satisfaction and success.

Leo Palladino

The author and publishers would like to thank the following for providing pictures for the book: Access Brand Limited, American Express, Andrew Collinge, BLM Health, Carol Hayes & Associates, Cheynes Training, Clinique, Clynol Hair, Comby, Computill Ltd, Denman, Depilex/RVB, Dr Andrew L. Wright (Consultant Dermatologist, Bradford Royal Infirmary), Dr Michael H. Beck (Consultant Dermatologist, Salford Royal Hospitals NHS Trust), Ellisons, Errol Douglas at Neville Daniel, Fire Protection Services, Forfex, Freeze Frame Photography, Goldwell (Hair Cosmetics) Ltd, Hairdressers Journal International, Hairdressing Training Board, In Line, Jackie Henry at A Cut Above, Jingles International, John Carne, Joshua Galvin Education and Training, L'Oréal, Mahogany, Marianne Majerus, Micol Group, National Westminster Bank, Nick Jones Hair Design, Paul Mitchell Luxury Haircare, Redken, Regis, Richard Thompson, S. Lewis, Salon Ambience, Schwarzkopf, Sharon Thompson, Luster Products Inc., Sharp, Signs and Labels Ltd, Smith & Nephew, Splinters Education Ltd, Terence Renati, TRESemmé, Vidal Sassoon, Wella Great Britain, Worthingtons.

The author and publishers would also like to thank the following: The Controller of Her Majesty's Stationery Office for Crown copyright material; Peter Hickman, John Phelps and all their colleagues, friends and students who were involved in the various technique photographs taken for this book.

Martin Green, joint author of *Professional Hairdressing*, contributed three chapters to the book.

Salon reception

MARIANNE MAJERUS FOR *HAIRDRESSERS JOURNAL*

Reception area

INTRODUCTION

Before anyone touches your client's hair, she has to be received into the salon. Reception is the point at which she begins her relationship with the salon's staff.

As a receptionist, you can help relationships with clients to be relaxed, friendly and businesslike:

- greet the client politely, pleasantly and courteously
- attend to her promptly and helpfully
- when a client asks for advice and information, give it correctly, accurate and efficiently
- be ready to explain which services the salon can offer, and their benefits to the client
- make sure that a new client knows the salon's name, address and telephone number
- be ready to give the times and costs of services
- look after the client's belongings – coat, parcels and so forth
- be careful when you are making appointments, especially with their timing.

WELLA

Reception area

RECEPTION DUTIES

As a receptionist you must always be ready, available and attentive. Find time to acknowledge the arrival of each client and assure her that she will soon be attended to.

Client satisfaction is the salon's main aim. Here are some important points.

- Specialist hairdressing advice must be given by the hairdresser appointed to that client.
- Know exactly what services the salon offer. A client can be put off by staff who are unsure, or cannot explain, what the salon can provide.
- Allow time for client consultation before hairdressing begins, to avoid any misunderstanding.
- However busy you are, always stay calm but unhurried. This will help you to avoid mistakes at reception.
- Create a good impression through your own appearance, by being neatly dressed and having an attractive hairstyle.
- Confirm each client's appointment, and refer her to the relevant person for action as soon as possible.

TIP

To meet the client's expectations, offer a prompt welcome, efficient service, and attention with the minimum of delay.

- Be helpful to anyone who arrives without an appointment.
- Refer her to a relevant person for action if possible, or make an appointment for a future time.

WELLA

A receptionist and client

DEALING WITH PEOPLE

The client

Every hairdressing business has to have clients. They attend the salon for what they know it has to offer. This includes not only good hairdressing, but clean, pleasant, hygienic surroundings and well-mannered staff.

Good hairdressing is achieved by patient practice and by taking time. The same applies to the skills required for dealing with people. Realising this is the key to your success.

Disagreements and bad manners have no place in successful, harmonious working salons. The client must never be aware of any staff friction there may be, nor must she ever be the subject of it.

Choosing a hairstyle or treatment

In choosing or deciding exactly what is to be done, the client can be helped by the receptionist in several ways.

- Discuss with the client what she wants and expects. Further discussion between the hairdresser and client will determine the actual specialist hairdressing required – this is something the receptionist cannot usually do.
- Communicate with the client by listening to what she tells you and understanding what is required. You must then interpret what is being requested and pass this information on to a competent hairdresser.
- The hairdresser will then examine the client's hair, to determine its length, condition and any other important factors that may affect the services requested.
- The hairdresser will analyse the hair type, facial features and so forth to assess whether the treatment requested is suitable, possible and safe to carry out – if not, further discussion will be needed. The hairdresser may need to take the initiative in guiding the client to a satisfactory decision.
- Make sure that the client understands and agrees to what is finally decided. This avoids any misunderstanding later on.
- Indicate how long the processes will take to complete and the cost of the service. Make sure the client knows, accepts and agrees with these.
- In conjunction with the hairdresser, decide whether tests (for example, a test curl or strand test) should be carried out. If so, try to arrange for them to be made before the appointment. This saves time and helps towards a successful result.

TIP

Never attempt to carry out any hairdressing service without the client's consent.

TIP

Never bill the client for an amount that was not agreed to.

Requests and enquiries

These may be made by a variety of visitors – regular clients, new clients, casual clients hoping for service without an appointment, and others too. Some may have been recommended to come to the salon by friends and have knowledge of the salon; others will not.

Enquiries may be internal, from within the salon organisation, or they may be external, from outside. They may be made directly – face to face, in person – or indirectly, by telephone, letter or via another person or existing client.

Whether enquiries are related to salon services, sales or administration generally, you need to communicate effectively, clearly and precisely in order to avoid problems and difficulties.

Making appointments

TIP

Always try to offer a client a choice of appointment times.

Each salon has its own system for making appointments, which should be familiar to all its staff. It involves allocating the time that is to be given to each client and the services requested. Usually you should book services that take more time, such as perming and colouring, for the early morning or early afternoon. Then you can fit around these appointments others that take less time.

Making appointments

WELLA

Date: Saturday 21 September

Stylist	Kate	Charlotte	Sally	Sarah	David	Tony		
8.30	Jackson	Lisa			Osborn			
8.45	Wedding B/D	Wedding PUT UP	Beatrice	Beatrice	Wedding B/D			
9 00	Smith	Cane	Extensions	Extensions	Burtwell	Morley		
15	CBD	P/W	Top Only	Top Only	B/D	Meche HL		
30	Johnstone	Jacobs			Thomas	Long Hair		
45	P/W	Col			Few Meche			
10 00	Williams	Meek D/C			Garner			
15	CBD	Cooper D/C			CBD			
30	Russell D/C	Cane			Meche			
45	Russell D/C	P/W CBD			CBD	Simmons		
11 00	Johnstone	Jacobs			Jorden	CBD		
15	P/W CBD	Col CBD			Semi Col	Meche HL		
30	Davis	Webster			Godwin D/C	CBD		
45	B/D	CBD	Gibbon	Grace	Semi Col	Jackson D/C		
12 00	LUNCH	Possee	CBD	CBD	CBD	LUNCH		
15		CBD	Jouhét D/C		Medwell			
30		Waldren	LUNCH	LUNCH	B/D			
45		CBD			Casey D/C			
1 00	Watts	LUNCH			LUNCH	Beezer		
15	Meche HL					HL		
30			Gladstone	Crane		Jenkins		
45			Spiral P/W	Straightener		Top P/W		
2 00		Peters	(Long	Corker	Cook	Jarvis		
15	John	Semi Col	hair)	Col	CBD	CBD		
30	CBD	Bone D/C	Payne	Straightener	+ Plait	Beezer		
45	Tyler D/C	Semi Col	S/set	CBD	Masters	HL CBD		
3 00	Watts	CBD	Selwyn D/C	Corker	P/W	Jenkins		
15	Meche CBD	Baker	S/set + Brush	Col CBD	Tozer	P/W CBD		
30	Richmond	P/W	Gladstone	Jennings	HL	Gribble		
45	CBD	Rickets	P/W CBD	CBD	Smith	Put up		
4 00	Hobbs	CBD	Toby	Osborn	CBD			
15	Plait	Griffiths	Put up	CBD	Masters	Salter		
30	Simons	B/D		Adams	P/W CBD	CBD		
45	CBD	Baker	Curtis	CBD	Tozer	Sadler D/C		
5 00	Robins	P/W CBD	CBD	Stevens	HL CBD	Collins		
15	CBD			CBD		CBD		
30								
45								

high Hair

You should bear in mind whether the hairdresser is working alone or with assistance. A hairdresser who is preparing, shampooing, arranging products, tools and materials, and carrying out other tasks by herself requires more time for each appointment than one who has plenty of help.

Some salons allow 30 minutes for cutting, 30 minutes for blow-drying, 15 minutes for setting, and so on. Others may allow more or less time. You must know exactly how much time your salon allows for each service, so that you can make appointments accurately and fit in as many as possible. Wasting time and making mistakes when booking clients can be costly. If in doubt, check with the stylist.

Apart from the process of managing time and the specific service to be booked, there are other factors to be remembered – the date of the service, its cost, its duration, and the staff member to be booked. Finally, complete an appointment card with clearly readable details for the client to take away.

ACTIVITY
Practise timing your own techniques until they are fast enough to be acceptable.

Telephone skills

Preparation

1. Always have pencil and paper to hand, so that you can make notes or take messages.

Answering the telephone

2. Answer the telephone promptly.
3. Speak slowly and clearly into the telephone.
4. State the salon's name and telephone number.
5. Ask how you can help the caller.
6. Listen to what the caller says.
7. Write down the caller's name and telephone number.
8. If there is a message, write it down.
9. Complete the call by thanking the caller.
10. Replace the telephone receiver correctly when finished, so that other callers can get through.
11. Keep calls businesslike, brief and efficient.

TIP
However busy you are, never speak abruptly to a telephone caller, and never rush a call.

TIP
Never ask a telephone caller to 'hold on' without making sure first that she is willing to wait.

Emergency services

You can call the **emergency services** – fire, police and ambulance – free of charge, at any time of the day or night. Dial **999**, then wait for the operator to ask you which service is required. State clearly 'fire', 'police' or 'ambulance', and wait for that service to be connected.

When they answer, be ready to give the salon telephone number if they ask you for it. Give them the full address at which help is needed, and directions to make it easy to find. Speak clearly, and listen carefully. Try not to panic – you will be able to help more if you are calm. Remember to replace the receiver properly when you have finished the call.

TIP

Telephone directories, codebooks and guides to charges provide a great deal of useful information. Read them carefully to make yourself familiar with the telephone services that are available.

Other services

- If you need help getting through to any particular telephone number, dial **100** for **operator services**.
- If you can't find a telephone number in the directory, dial **192** for **directory enquiries**.
- If there is a **fault** on the telephone – if calls cannot be made in or out of the salon – it needs to be reported as soon as possible: any delay could be costly because clients may be trying to make appointments. Call the operator on **151**, on another telephone line.
- Refer to the telephone directory for fuller information about the services available.

Taking messages

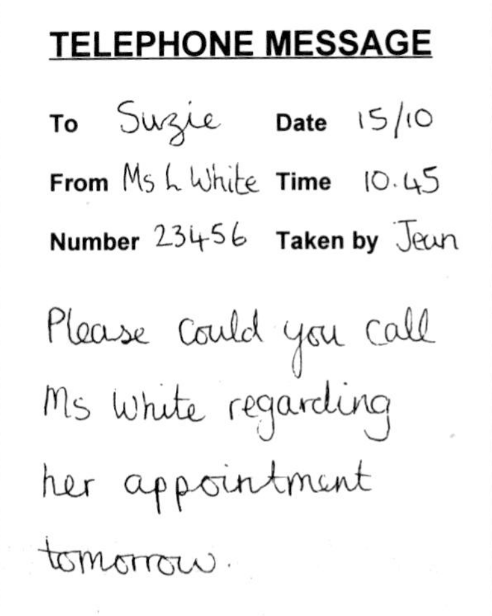
TELEPHONE MESSAGE

To Suzie Date 15/10

From Ms L White Time 10.45

Number 23456 Taken by Jean

Please could you call Ms White regarding her appointment tomorrow.

Taking messages

It is important to keep a written note of any **messages** you take. Use a notebook to record all messages clearly – it may be necessary to refer back to them later.

- Make sure you pass all messages to the people for whom they were intended. Do this immediately, and mark the message book to indicate that this has been done.
- If the person for whom the message is intended is not available, tell others in the salon there is a message waiting for that person. Check later that the message has been received.
- If messages require a reply, or if you have promised to call back, make sure this is done.
- Return calls as soon as possible to avoid unnecessary waiting.
- Listen carefully to the caller, without interrupting, and be helpful and polite in your reply.
- Ensure that all communications are clear, accurate and understood.

TIP

Never leave a telephone caller on the line for longer than a few seconds. Return to let them know what is happening. Being left on the end of a line is frustrating and the caller may hang up.

The cost of calls is based on distance, time of day and duration of call. Keep calls short, and avoid making long-distance calls at peak time if they are not urgent.

If you need to make a personal call from the salon, note how long it took, the distance you called and the time of day, so that your call can be charged to you.

HANDLING PAYMENTS

When a service has been completed, you will need to calculate the client's **bill**. If you have to add up several items, double-check your answer before telling the client how much to pay.

Most salons include **VAT (value added tax)** in their prices. VAT is a percentage of the total bill. It has to be paid to HM Customs and Excise – a government tax collector – quarterly, when the salon's accounts are made up. Make sure you understand the salon's method for calculating VAT, and always ask someone if you are unsure what to do.

Payment methods

Clients may wish to pay their bills in **cash**, by **cheque**, by **credit card** or some other way. You must be familiar with all these forms of payment.

Payments in cash

Legal tender is the name given to money that is legal to use in a country. The notes and coins produced in England, Scotland, Northern Ireland and Jersey are legal tender in the UK and may be taken in the salon. The money of Eire is not legal tender, nor is money of other foreign currencies. The local bank will charge the salon for exchanging it, so you can legally refuse to accept it.

Try to follow a step-by-step procedure each time.

1. Calculate the client's bill and double-check the final amount.
2. Clearly inform the client of the total that needs to be paid.
3. Take the client's money, count how much you have been given, and place it *on* the till, or where the client can see it.
4. Calculate the change required – use a notebook if necessary.
5. State the amount to be paid and count out the change to the client.
6. Double-check the change given and the amount taken.
7. Give the client a receipt.
8. Put the money in the till or cash box.
9. Before the client leaves, make sure that she is satisfied.
10. Check whether further appointments are required.
11. Be courteous and polite throughout.
12. Make sure that takings are recorded, so that the total day's takings can be calculated and checked against the cash in the till.

TIP

Any tips given by a client should be kept separate from money for the bill. A piggy bank on the reception desk is a good idea.

ACTIVITY

In pairs, practise taking cash and giving change. How can you prevent disagreements about how much cash was handed over and whether the change is correct?

Many salons find it convenient to maintain a **float**. This is a sum of money that is kept to ensure that adequate change is available. The amount of the float must always be carefully noted. Remember, it is not part of the takings. When you are totalling monies, during or at the end of the day, you should deduct the total float sum from the takings, or the monies will not balance.

It will help to keep a certain amount of change in the safe to avoid running short. How much is kept there will depend on how much business is usually transacted each day. It can be time-consuming to look for change, and a nuisance when the salon is busy.

Cash registers vary from salon to salon, and may have a variety of features which deal with cash transactions. These are useful in producing receipts, totalling individual takings and salon

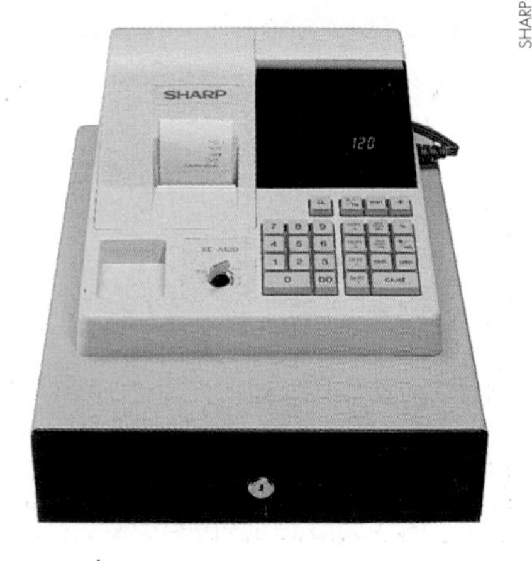

A cash register

SHARP

COMPUTILL LTD

A computerised till

takings, and other features too. Make sure you understand how to use the cash register. Always ask if you have a problem or if you make a mistake.

At the end of the day, record the cash register totals in a book, so that accounts can be kept. In most salons the total takings for hairdressing services and sales of other items are listed separately. Records of **petty cash** and other expenses must be kept so that the final totals can be balanced. Find out how to fill in your salon's **cashbook** accurately. Keep your entries neat and clear to read.

Payments by cheque

Many clients prefer to pay their bills by cheque. This is as good as cash if accompanied by a **cheque guarantee card**. This card guarantees payment up to a certain amount – usually £50.

The cheque is an order from the client to her bank to pay to the salon the amount stated, so it needs to be made out correctly. Help your client by making sure the cheque is correct:

1. Check that the cheque is clearly dated, with the date on which you are receiving it.
2. Check that the name of the salon (or person to be paid) appears on the cheque. If the salon has a stamp for this, offer to print it.
3. Check that the amount to be paid is written both in words and in figures.
4. Check that the cheque has been signed by the client, in your presence.
5. Ask the client for a cheque guarantee card, and write the card number on the back of the cheque. Check that the signature on the card matches the one on the cheque.
6. If the bill is greater than the limit on the cheque guarantee card, ask the client for further identification – such as a driving licence or credit card – so you can double-check the signature.
7. Write the client's address on the back of the cheque, in case any problems arise later.

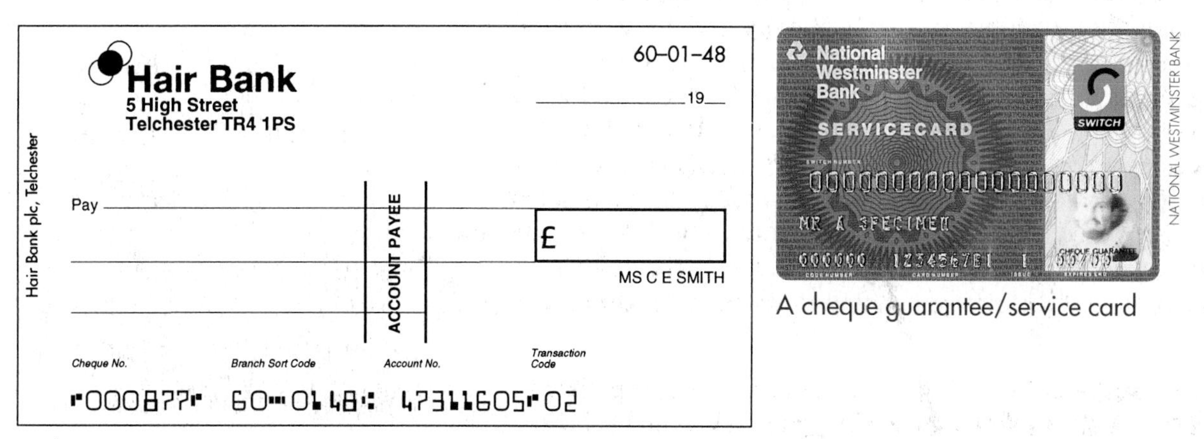

A cheque

NATIONAL WESTMINSTER BANK

A cheque guarantee/service card

8. Check the date of the guarantee card to make sure that the card is valid. If a card is out of date, do not accept the cheque.
9. Put the cheque in the till and return the guarantee card to the client. Give her a receipt.
10. Make sure all cheques are paid into the bank as soon as possible, so that they can be cleared.

ACCESS BRAND LTD

An Access (credit) card

Payments by credit card

Some salons have agreements with companies such as Visa and MasterCard so that clients can make payments using credit cards. The salon pays a small percentage to the credit card companies on all these transactions. It is important that you know which credit cards are accepted by the salon.

If a client wishes to pay by credit card, this is what you do:

1. Check that the card is not out of date. If it is, you cannot accept it.
2. Place the **voucher** and card in the **imprinter** and make sure the card number is transferred clearly to all the carbon copies.
3. Write details of the services and any purchases on the top copy of the voucher.
4. Write the amount charged.
5. Ask the client to sign the voucher. Check this signature against that on the card.
6. Give the *top* copy to the client as a receipt.
7. Put the other copies in the till and throw away the carbon papers. Copies are kept by the salon – one for the credit card company, the other for salon accounting.
8. Return the card and give the client a receipt.

TIP

Use a ball-point pen to fill in credit card vouchers, and press quite hard to make sure that what you write is transferred clearly to all the carbon copies.

Other non-cash payments

Charge cards, debit cards and gift vouchers may all be offered as payment in place of cash. The organisations that issue these also send out information on how to handle them. It is important that you know which of these forms of payment is accepted by your salon. Ask a senior member of staff to show you how to deal with them, what forms you need to fill in, and what to do with the vouchers in the till.

Charge cards such as American Express and Diners Club are used for payments in the same way as credit cards. The charge card companies charge the salon a percentage on all transactions processed.

Debit cards or EFTPOS (Electronic Funds Transfer at Point of Sale) cards such as Switch and Connect serve as a cheque guarantee card and a service card. These cards are convenient, because the client doesn't have to write a cheque. The transaction process is similar to the one used with cheque cards or credit cards but the salon needs a special terminal. When the card is 'swiped' through the terminal, the amount is electronically debited from the client's bank account immediately. The client

TIP

The salon's procedures for recording payment transactions and security of monies are usually the responsibility of the receptionist or cashier. Any discrepancies arising should be immediately reported to senior staff or management.

AMERICAN EXPRESS

A charge card

SHARP

'Swiping' a card through an electronic terminal

signs a slip (called an authority), which is produced automatically by the till and is in two parts. The client keeps one part and the other is kept by the salon. As with all payment cards, you must check the signature on the authority against that on the card. The salon pays a fee for having an electronic terminal.

Gift vouchers are sold by some salons to be used in payment for goods and services. These payments may be treated in the same way as cash or cheque payments. There are different forms of gift voucher; some may be used in other stores. Make sure that you know how to use these.

Traveller's cheques may be offered in payment by some clients. Find out whether or not the salon's policy is to accept these. If so, make sure the client countersigns the cheque in your presence, and check that the signatures match and that the date is correct.

ACTIVITY
Make a list of all the different cards that may be used for payment in your salon, and of the differences between them.

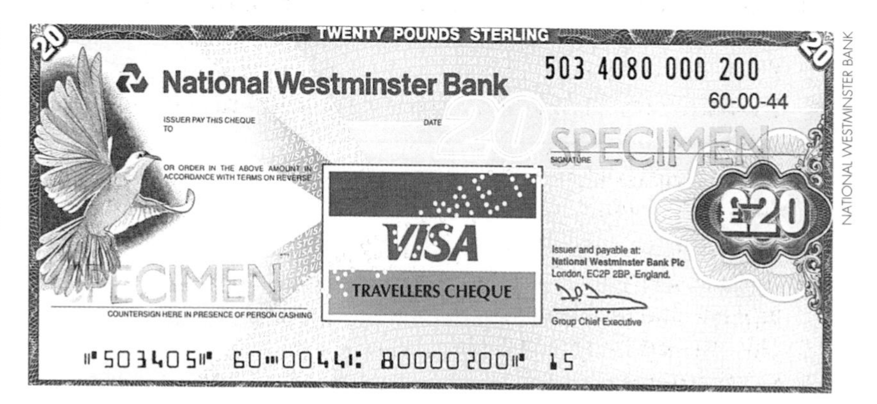

NATIONAL WESTMINSTER BANK

A traveller's cheque

Discrepancies

Inconsistencies, disagreements or differences – invalid currencies being tendered, out-of-date cheque cards or unsigned cheques – should be dealt with as soon as possible. Where a payment card is being fraudulently used or there is a payment dispute, such as a bill totalling more than was previously agreed to, then a senior member of staff should be referred to. Should an illegal transaction be attempted, or even one suspected of being illegal, it may be decided to refer the matter to the police. This should finally be decided only by senior staff members, however. In these instances effective communication is very important, so that everyone concerned understands what is happening.

TIP
All information regarding clients should be handled in strict confidence. This safeguards all concerned and helps to reduce the possibility of embarrassment and loss of clients.

CLIENT RECORD SYSTEMS

An accurate **record system** of all clients ensures that information about hairdressing that has been carried out can be referred to when required. The client's name and telephone number, the stylist's name, the type of perm, the lotion used, the time processed, the results achieved, the date of the last perm, the price charged and so on can all be noted down for future use.

Many salons use **record cards**, filed in alphabetical order in a box or cabinet. These cards should be available to all staff at

CLIENT RECORD CARD		
Name:	Address:	
Telephone numbers: Home: Work:	Date first registered: Stylist:	Age group: ☐5-15 ☐16-30 ☐31-50 ☐ 50+
Hair condition:	Scalp:	Skin type:

Date	Services used	Remarks	Stylist

A client record card

ACTIVITY
Discuss with your colleagues the requirements for a client record card. Design one that meets these requirements.

reception. Make sure you understand your salon's record system and know how to fill in and file the record cards correctly. Remember, too, that personal details must always be kept private and confidential.

Computers

Computer systems are being used in very many salons. Many types are available, and you may be required to operate one.

A computer system consists of **hardware** (the equipment) and **software** (the programs), and each computer system has its own special features. In the salon the computer may be used in taking cash and issuing receipts, to total each person's takings, for general accounting, client records, stock records, storing information, and so on.

Make sure you understand your salon's system and know how to use it. Remember to ask for help if you run into problems – pressing the wrong button could cause even greater problems!

COMPUTILL LTD

Using a computer system

DEALING WITH COMPLAINTS

It is not easy to deal with an unsatisfied client – you will need all your skills of tact and diplomacy. Remember that a client has every right to expect the services agreed and paid for. If the salon is at fault, mistakes might be put right.

It can be difficult to decide what is reasonable or unreasonable. Whatever your personal feelings, try to remain calm, polite and understanding. Arguing back will probably make the client more angry, and is not good for the salon's image. A satisfied client is good business!

If you notice a mistake, don't try to pretend it hasn't happened. Put the situation right before the client leaves the salon. If a client approaches you with a **complaint**, you should:

- deal with the client pleasantly and politely
- discuss the nature of the client's complaint
- analyse the complaint carefully and sympathetically
- diagnose the fault and suggest corrective action
- agree with the client what is to be done
- carry out the correction then and there, or agree a convenient time for the client to return
- record the complaint and the action taken.

If the complaint is serious – such as hair breaking off after a perm, or hair becoming discoloured after tinting – it may be difficult to put right. Give all the details to your employer, who will warn the salon's insurers, as the client has a legal right to claim **compensation**. With tact it may be possible to avoid this by agreeing a course of corrective action and refunding money paid.

TIP

Don't be too hurried in trying to put a problem right – you might make a bad situation worse. Always remain calm and give careful consideration to the problem, making sure the client understands and agrees to any course of corrective action.

ACTIVITY

In threes, use role-play to practise reception duties. One person acts the client, another the receptionist. The third person notes where the duties are done well, and where things go wrong.

Repeat the activity, with the client complaining about the service received.

RECEPTION SECURITY

It is important to maintain a safe and secure environment at the reception area. All monies must be secured, and products on display must be safeguarded. All personal details of clients, such as record systems, should be held under cover. If a client sees record cards lying around, she will have little confidence in the discreetness of the salon staff. The following points should help to ensure adequate reception security:

- The reception area must be staffed at all times.
- Keep all monies securely in the till during the working day.
- Never leave the till drawer open when it is not in use or if you have to leave the reception, even for a moment.
- Check all notes to ensure that both the metal strip and the water mark are present. On a forged note, either or both may be missing.
- When a client hands you a note, put it outside the till until you have accurately counted the change.
- Never leave money in the till overnight.
- Leave the till drawers open, but emptied, at the end of the day to prevent a burglar from damaging them by forcing them open.
- Large amounts of money should be regularly transferred to a secure safe or bank.

HEALTH AND SAFETY

Always keep the reception area uncluttered, allowing free passage for clients and staff.

- Visits to the bank should be irregularly timed to deter 'muggers'. If the receptionist normally does the banking (it could of course be any staff member) someone else must be nominated to take the responsibility while she is absent from work. If possible, she should be accompanied.
- Receipts should be given for all payments and bills retained.
- Remember that all bills, receipts and drawings or additions must be noted so that balance can be achieved.
- At the end of the day all monies must be checked, recorded and either secured in a safe or banked.
- Follow your salon's security procedures at all times.

ASSIGNMENTS: RECEPTION

A practical activity
With the help of your colleagues carry out the following:

1. Practise the different reception duties that you have been shown by your trainers.
2. List any mistakes you made, and what corrections were required.
3. Discuss and make notes on the correct ways of dealing with people.
4. List the different situations that can arise at reception.
5. Think carefully about why there is a need for confidentiality.
6. Make sure you are familiar with the salon's appointment system.

Make careful notes, and keep them in your folder.

For you to find out
Investigate and collect together information concerning reception areas and receptionists' duties. Visit your doctor's and dentist's surgery, or watch other receptionists at work. Explain to them what you are doing before taking notes. Include the following:

- the differences between the different receptionists
- the common aims
- the importance of accurate communication
- ways of dealing with people – new and existing clients, internal and external calls, communicating directly face to face or indirectly by telephone or letter
- the importance of a courteous manner and efficiency.

A case study
A client has returned to complain of services received at your salon. Describe the following:

- the action or actions you would take
- how you would record what the client has told you
- the questions you would need to ask
- what to do if you could not deal with the problem yourself
- what you could do to calm an angry or upset client.

PREPARING FOR ASSESSMENT

In preparing for your assessment on reception work the following checklist may be useful. Check that you have covered and now fully understand these items:

- the need to be clean, hygienic and efficient
- using the telephone efficiently
- receiving clients pleasantly, politely and courteously
- finding out, by questioning and discussion, what services and goods a client requires
- operating the salon's appointment system effectively
- ensuring that safety and security practices are followed
- allowing time for consultations before services are given
- clarifying requests made
- communicating effectively
- recording all information received
- dealing adequately with any discrepancies arising from payment transactions
- remaining calm, composed and unflurried throughout all dealings with clients and visitors
- recording messages and passing them on to the relevant person
- ensuring complete confidentiality.

When you feel that you are ready talk to your trainer and arrange a suitable time for your assessment.

CHAPTER 2

Client care

INTRODUCTION

Client care is essential to your success as a hairdresser. It is an important part of all that you do for your client in the salon. It involves concern for your client, and genuinely wanting to meet all her needs satisfactorily. In doing so, you will reach your own high professional standards of achievement too.

Like most skills, good client care has to be learned, and this requires thought and study. The following are some of the topics covered in this chapter:

- communication between you and your client
- interpretation of your client's needs
- preparation of your client and her hair for different services
- understanding the hair and skin on which you work
- diagnosis of hair and skin conditions
- decision-making and choice – knowing when services should, or should not, be applied.

MAHOGANY

LUSTER

WHAT IS MEANT BY CLIENT CARE?

Client care means what it says: caring for your client, looking after her and making sure that she is comfortable, satisfied with the service and safely attended. This begins when the client enters the salon and continues until she leaves. Helping the client with managing her hair at home is a part of client care. So too is making your expertise available to her, to ensure that when she leaves she will be really happy with the appearance of her hair.

For client care to be fully effective an initial consultation is essential. This applies to both new and existing clients. The importance of consultation with your clients cannot be overemphasised.

CONSULTATION

Consultation – a meeting at which advice is given and taken – consists of talking to the client, listening to her so that you can establish her needs and jointly negotiating a suitable course of action. You will be expected to exchange views with her, and to discuss with her just what is to be done with her hair. You, the professional, already know a lot about hair in general, but your

TIP

To provide hairdressing services without consultation is unprofessional, and unlikely to result in a satisfied client.

TIP

Good client care starts with careful consultation.

client is more familiar than you are with her own hair and how it behaves. Listen to what she tells you, and find out what she has in mind. She may ask for a service which you know will not lead to a satisfactory end-result for her, and this requires careful consideration. Work should only proceed after you have carefully determined what is required, achieved your client's understanding and agreement, and confirmed that her requests are suited to her own wishes and to the services given in your salon.

Consultation includes the following:

ACTIVITY

Explore the use of the computer for the storage of all client details.

- determining exactly what a client wants before and during the application of hairdressing services
- questioning and observing to determine the services and products required
- testing where necessary to ensure safe practices and the client's well-being
- noting and taking account of any limiting factors, such as adverse hair, skin or scalp conditions, the presence of incompatible chemicals, hair that is in a poor state, and so on
- accounting for the client's use of hairpieces and deciding how these might affect the services she has requested.
- referring a client where necessary to a senior member of staff for further action, advice and guidance
- ensuring the client agrees to the services being carried out
- making further information available if the client is still uncertain
- assuring clients of complete confidentiality by keeping their individual records private
- communicating effectively to ensure understanding.

TIP

Record all client information. Ensure that it is easy to retrieve.

HYGIENE – THE SCIENCE OF HEALTH

Clients expect the salon to be clean. They expect towels to have been washed and brushes cleaned. They take it for granted that good **hygiene** is maintained.

You are as responsible as every other member of staff for maintaining the highest standards of cleanliness and hygiene at all times, to safeguard both clients and staff from infection.

REGIS

REGIS

Cross-infection – the passing of disease from one person to another – may follow unhygienic use of washbasins, cups, tools, and so on. If you take sensible precautions the salon can be kept as clean as possible and the risk of cross-infection can be minimised.

- Use only clean towels and gowns for each customer.
- Wash combs and brushes before **sterilising** or **disinfecting** them.
- Use 70 per cent alcohol, or alcohol wipes, for cleaning tools.
- Keep floors and surfaces clear, tidy and clean.
- Maintain good personal and general hygiene – wash your hands regularly, and clean cups and mugs thoroughly.

Many clients are too embarrassed to complain, and are reluctant to do so, when they encounter problems with hygiene or hairdressing service. Ideally the need should not arise, but in case it does, always encourage clients to let the salon know what is wrong so that the problem can be dealt with.

HEALTH AND SAFETY
It is when the salon is busiest that the greatest care needs to be taken. Don't let your standards of cleanliness drop, however rushed you may be.

PREPARING CLIENTS

Once a client has arrived for an appointment and you have taken care of her coat and belongings, find out what services have been requested or booked in advance and prepare the client accordingly.

TIP
If a client's clothes are stained, make sure this is noted. Clothes may be returned to the salon for cleaning. Alternatively the client may have this done herself and send the bill for the salon to pay.

Gowning and protecting

- Remember to check that the chair is clean.
- Place tissue or a towel over the client's collar and shoulders.
- Place a suitably sized gown in position, and secure it.
- If shampooing, place a thicker towel over the shoulders.
- If cutting, use cottonwool, tissue or a cutting cape in place of a thicker towel.
- If tinting or bleaching, use dark towels, plastic capes and special tint coverings.
- Make sure all the client's clothes are covered and all materials are secured so that they remain in place.
- Do not tuck in absorbent materials – they act like sponges. Liquids can seep through and damage clothing.
- Make sure nothing falls between the client and the chair back.

WELLA

Gowning the client

Preparing the hair

Hair needs to be free from tangles, hairspray and other materials before it can be worked on. Prepare the client's hair as follows:

1. Loosen the hair by teasing it apart with your fingers.
2. Using a wide-toothed comb or **rake**, start combing the hair points and gradually work upwards to the scalp.
3. Proceed from the neck and sides to the top front.

HEALTH AND SAFETY
All towels, and ideally all gowns, should be freshly laundered. If a gown has to be re-used, make sure no part of it comes into contact with the client's skin.

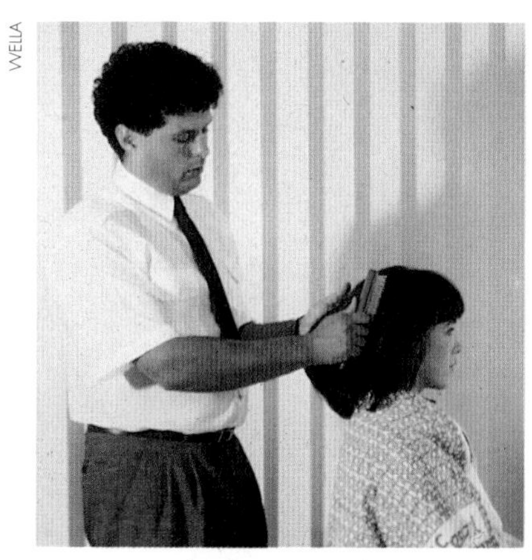

WELLA

Preparing the hair

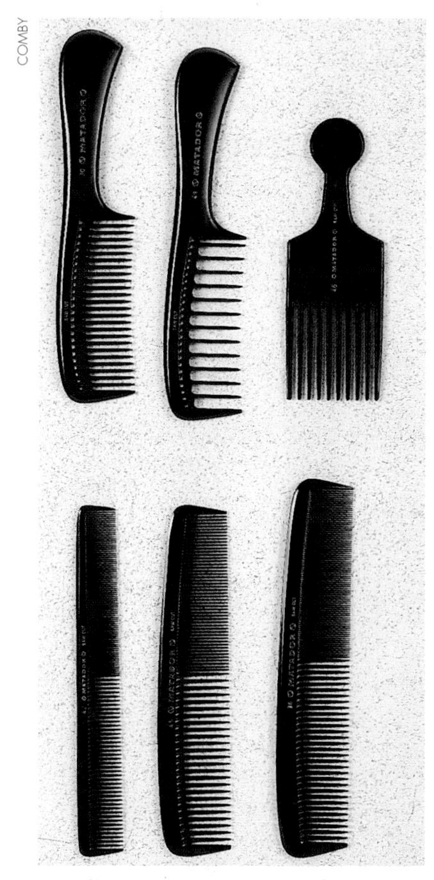

COMBY

Combs

TIP

Choose a comb that is unbroken, flexible, well balanced, non-inflammable, resistant to chemicals, and easy to clean. It should have widely spaced teeth, and have no mould marks or sharp edges.

4. Remove tangles and backcombing without pulling, scratching or breaking the comb.
5. Brush the hair smoothly and firmly, without jerking the client's head.
6. Start brushing at the hair points and gradually work upwards to the scalp.
7. Once the hair is free of tangles, brush in different directions to loosen it.

Combs and combing

Combs come in many shapes and sizes. They may be of vulcanised rubber, tortoise-shell, ivory, wood, metal, bone, horn or various types of plastic. Some combs are made of synthetic material, but these are apt to give rise to electric charges on the hair ('static') and make the hair 'flyaway'.

Always use good-quality combs. Poor-quality combs may break, tearing the hair and scalp. This could result in infection: a broken comb is difficult to clean and so may carry germs.

When using a comb, hold it correctly to avoid straining it or the hair:

- hold the comb firmly, with your middle fingers on one side and thumb and little finger on the other
- hold it so that your fingertips cannot slip to the teeth points
- hold it upright – do not flatten or drag it
- use a raking action, without tugging
- work from the points to the roots (if you start combing at the roots you will produce more knotting, and a painful few minutes for your client)
- support the client's head to prevent discomfort.

ACTIVITY

With your trainer, arrange a visit to a hairdressing supplier. Take note of the types of brushes and combs available. You may also be able to collect brochures of reception furniture: these would be helpful in designing the ideal salon.

Brushes and brushing

Brushes are made from a variety of materials. Good brushes are made from natural **bristles**, such as those of pigs. Others may be wire, plastic or rubber. They are designed for various purposes, such as dressing, or clearing loose hair, so choose the correct type of brush for the job in hand.

For preparing hair, use a firm, tufted brush which takes out tangles. For dressing hair, use a short, tufted brush. Generally, for thick, coarse hair a short natural-bristle or nylon tufted brush is suitable for salon use. For soft, thin hair a longer bristle may be kinder. The brushing action stimulates and distributes natural oil – this is best achieved with a soft bristle brush. Hair styling requires a variety of brushes, but the personal choice of a brush is finally determined by its weight, length, size and comfort in use.

Brushing should be a smoothing, stroking action – never harsh scrubbing. Two brushes may be used with a rolling wrist action, one following the other.

ACTIVITY
Use your practice blocks to develop the correct action in combing and brushing. First use one brush and your hand; then two brushes, one in each hand.

HEALTH AND SAFETY
Use only good-quality tools which are not likely to damage the hair, and apply them gently and correctly. If you accidentally tear the scalp with a broken brush or comb, report this at once to your trainer or senior. They will try to stop the bleeding, clean with water, apply a clean dressing and seek medical advice.

Cleaning tools

- Clean tools after use.
- Never use tools on another client without cleaning and sterilising them first.
- Remove loose material from combs and brushes, wash and disinfect them, then dry them. **Disinfectant cabinets** may be used after drying.
- Always rinse liquid disinfectants from tools with plenty of water, otherwise they may irritate the client's skin.
- Don't leave metal tools for hours in liquid disinfectants or disinfecting cabinets. They will spoil and become pitted.
- Always check the manufacturer's instructions before using liquid disinfectants or disinfecting cabinets.

LOOKING AFTER CLIENTS

Before and during services

- Check that all protective coverings – towels, cutting collar and so forth – are accurately placed.
- Collect together all tools, equipment and products to be used so that the client's services are not constantly interrupted.
- Reassure the client that her belongings are safe.
- Explain the processes that are taking place as you go along.
- Indicate how each process is progressing, what is to follow, and how long it may take.
- During any lengthy process, offer the client reading materials, access to the telephone or writing materials. This could be a good time to ask her to complete a salon questionnaire.

DENMAN

Brushes

TIPS
Nylon tufts can be harsh on hair if used too often. Natural bristle brushes are kinder to hair.

A good brush will penetrate and grip the hair, and allow you to place the hair where you want it.

After services

- Ensure that the client's clothes are not stained or covered with loose hairs.
- Complete record cards for the services completed. Include any comments made by the client regarding the services she has received.
- Make sure that all the client's belongings are returned to her before she leaves the salon.
- Offer to arrange the client's next appointment, and make sure that she has the salon's telephone number and address for her future use.

ANDREW COLLINGE PHOTO: JOHN SWANNELL

PROFESSIONALISM

Each client who walks through the salon door is different, with a unique combination of hair type and colour, skin and scalp condition, past history of hair care, and present requirements. It is your job as a professional responsible for giving good client care to examine the hair and scalp, to assess what state it is in, to ask questions and listen to your client's answers, to decide what treatment is necessary, and to agree with your client on a course of action.

Just as a doctor needs knowledge of medicine and a reassuring bedside manner, so you need knowledge of hair, the scalp and the skin, and the ability to discuss these with your clients clearly, confidently and tactfully. You also need to be able to recognise any problems, and know how to deal with them. For this, you need too a professional understanding of the bones and muscles that make up the structure of the head and neck.

This part of the chapter includes detailed information about these aspects of hairdressing. Take time to read it carefully, to learn about the 'raw materials' you will be working with daily.

ACTIVITY
With colleagues, practise asking different types of question. Ask your trainer to explain the difference between 'open' and 'closed' questions.

THE HEAD

The bones

The foundation of the head or **skull** consists of the bones of the **cranium** (the top, sides and back of the head) and the bones of the **face**.

- The **frontal**, **parietal**, **temporal** and **occipital bones** form the rounded part of the head. Together they enclose and protect the brain, and the organs of sight and hearing.
- The **maxillae**, the **mandible** and the **malar** and **nasal bones** form the face.

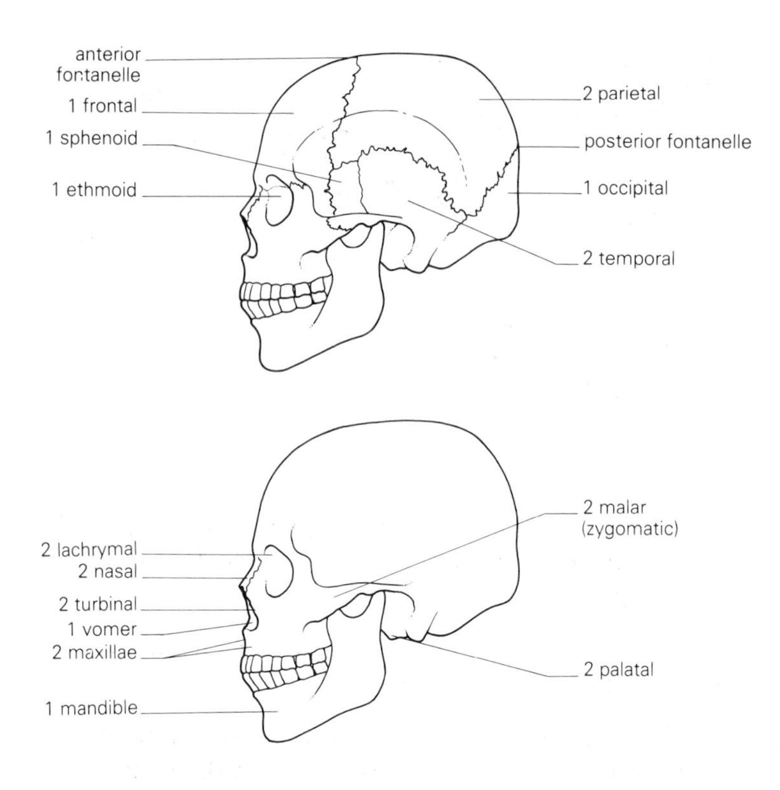

Bones of the cranium

Bones of the face

- The other bones are inside the skull and form the roof of the mouth, the back of the eye sockets, and structures at the back of the nose.

At birth, spaces between the bones of the cranium allow them to glide over each other. The largest spaces between the bones are called **fontanelles**. The two main ones are the **anterior** (front) and **posterior** (back) fontanelles. These are the 'soft spots' on a young baby's head. These soon close together, to form immovable joints called **sutures**.

ACTIVITY
List the bones of the head. Which of these are important in hair styling?

The muscles

- **Occipital-frontalis** A muscle that covers the upper cranium. It connects with the fibrous tendon sheet of the scalp. It lifts the eyebrows, as in frowning, surprise or horror.
- **Orbicularis oculi** Muscles surrounding the eyes. They form the eyelids and close the eyes. They wrinkle the eyes when contracted.
- **Orbicularis oris** A muscle surrounding the mouth. It forms the lips, closes the mouth, and helps in speaking.
- **Temporalis** A muscle that connects the temporal bone at the side of the head to the malar arch and the mandible. It closes the mouth and aids in chewing.
- **Masseter** A muscle situated between the malar arch and mandible. It closes the jaw during chewing.
- **Zygomaticus** A muscle that runs from the malar to the angle of the mouth. It elevates the lip muscles outwards.

Muscles of the head and face

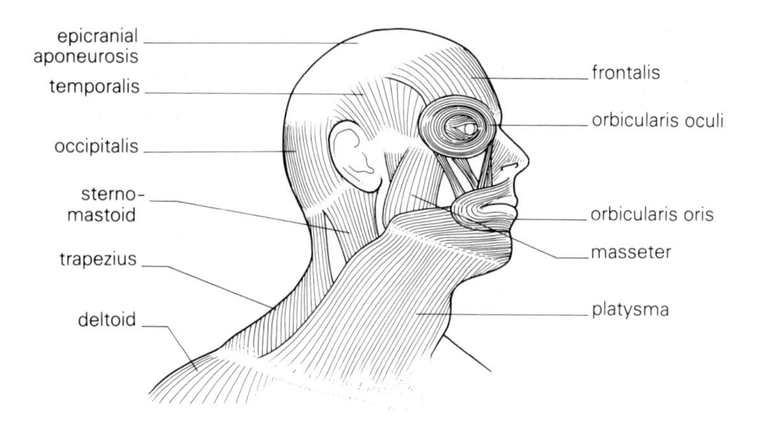

- **Sternomastoid** A muscle running from the sternum and clavicle to the temporal bone. It flexes the neck, and rotates and bows the head.
- **Platysma** A muscle within the neck. It wrinkles the skin and depresses the corners of the mouth.
- **Trapezius** A muscle that forms the upper part of the back, and the sides and back of the neck. It draws the head backwards.

The scalp

The **scalp** is the flexible, protective covering of the top of the head. It consists of the following:

- **skin**, with hair
- **connective tissue**, which firmly attaches the skin to the tendon
- the **epicranial aponeurosis**, a sheet of non-elastic fibrous tendon
- loose connective tissue between the tendon sheet and the skull bones
- the **occipito-frontalis** muscle, which lies between the occipital and frontal bones of the cranium.

The scalp

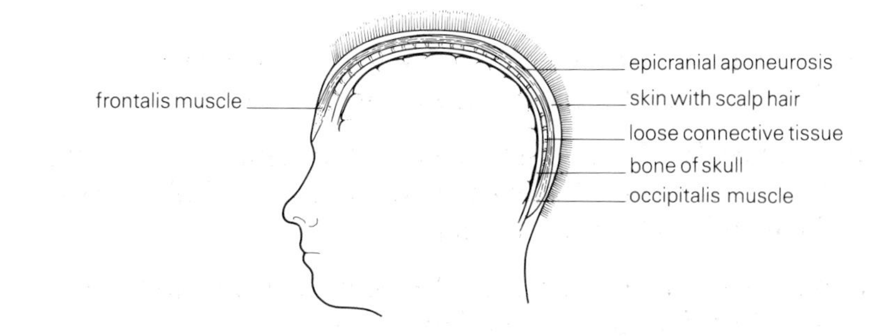

The nerves

The main **nerves** concerned with the muscles, skin and glands of the head and neck are as follows:

- the 5th cranial nerve (the **trigeminal**)
- the 7th cranial nerve (the **facial**)
- the 11th cranial nerve (the **spinal accessory**)
- the 2nd and 3rd **cervical** spinal nerves.

The 5th cranial nerve carries messages to the brain from the facial skin, teeth, nose and mouth. There are three branches:

- the **ophthalmic nerve** serves the tear glands, the skin of the forehead, and the upper cheeks
- the **maxillary nerve** serves the upper jaw and the mouth
- the **mandibular nerve** serves the lower jaw muscles, the teeth and the chewing muscles.

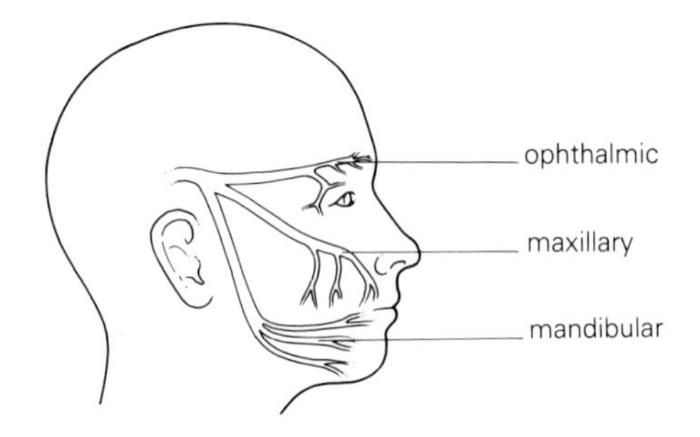

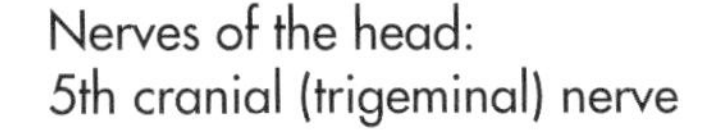
Nerves of the head:
5th cranial (trigeminal) nerve

The 7th cranial nerve passes through the temporal bone, behind the ear, and then divides. It serves the ear muscles, the occipitalis, the muscles of facial expression, the tongue and the palate. There are five main branches:

- the **temporal nerve,** behind the ear muscles, the orbicularis oculi and the frontalis muscle
- the **zygomatic nerve,** which serves the eye muscles of the orbits
- the **buccal nerve,** which serves the upper lip and the side of the nose
- the **mandibular nerve,** which serves the lower lip and the mentalis muscle of the chin
- the **cervical nerve,** which serves the platysma muscle of the chin.

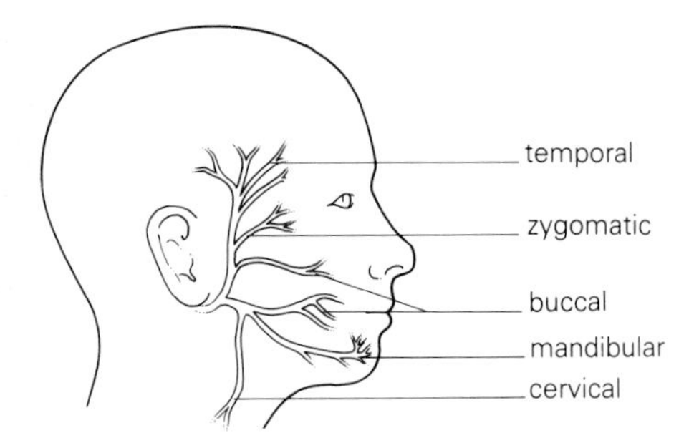

Nerves of the head:
7th cranial (facial) nerve

The 11th cranial nerve serves the sternomastoid and trapezius neck muscles, and the deeper structures of the head. It triggers the bending and turning of the head.

The 2nd and 3rd pairs of cervical nerves serve the back of the scalp, the sternomastoid, and the trapezius muscles.

The blood supply

The main blood vessels supplying blood to the head and face are the **carotid arteries**. These sub-divide into the internal and

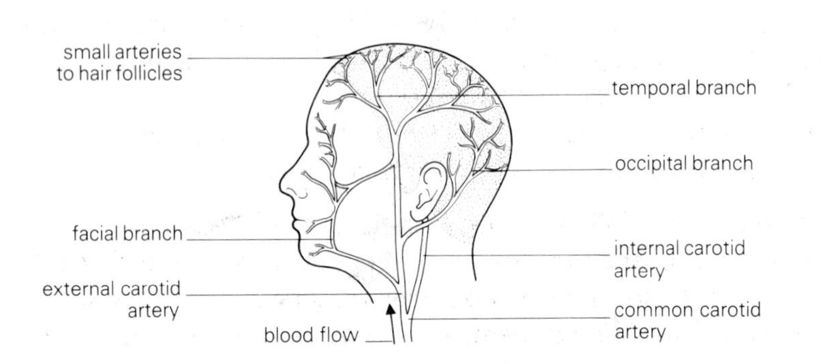

Blood supply to the head

external branches. The internal branch lies deep in the neck and supplies the brain and other parts of the head. The external branch divides into three further main branches:

- The **occipital** branch on each side of the head supplies the back and the vertex of the head and scalp.
- The **temporal** branch on each side passes up the side of the face, the side of the head and the scalp, supplying also the hair follicles and papillae.
- The **facial** branch on each side supplies the muscles and tissues of the face. It passes along the chin and up to the front of the head.

Note that **arteries carry blood** *from* the heart. They branch to form smaller **arterioles**, which in turn branch to form tiny vessels called **capillaries**. These carry blood through the tissues. The capillaries then join up to form the **venules**, which join to form the larger **veins**. In the head the main veins are the internal and external **jugular veins**. These are situated at the sides of the neck.

The internal jugular vein and its branch, the **facial vein**, carry blood from the face and deep within the head. The external jugular vein carries blood from the scalp, hair follicles and papillae. It has two branches: the **occipital** and the **temporal veins**. These carry blood from those areas supplied by the carotid artery branches. The jugular veins join with the **subclavian veins**, which lie 2–3 cm above the clavicle.

Note that **veins** carry blood *to* the heart.

Blood vessels from the head

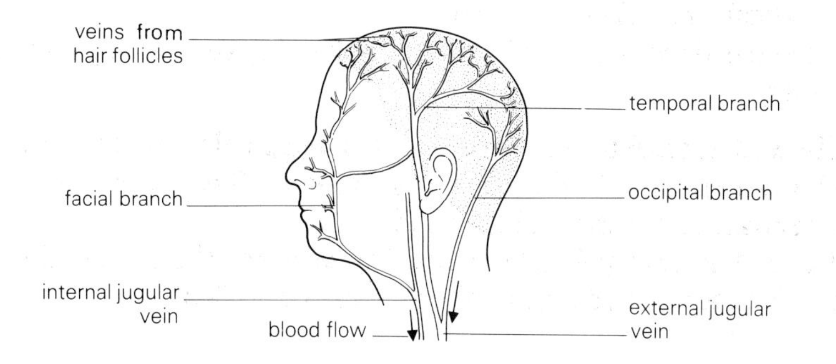

THE SKIN

The **skin** is the outer covering of the body. It is a complex and important organ, made up of different layers and containing many parts: oil and sweat glands, hair muscles, blood and lymph vessels, nerves and sensory organs.

The skin has four main functions: protection, temperature control, secretion and excretion, and sensation.

- **Protection** The skin forms a tough, flexible, physical barrier. It keeps excess water out, and body fluids in. The oil and sweat it produces are acid, helping to prevent bacterial growth. **Melanin** pigments in skin help to filter out harmful rays of the sun. Vitamin D is produced in the skin, in the presence of sunlight, which helps to maintain body health.

- **Temperature control** The hair, hair muscles and sweat glands help to maintain the normal body temperature of 37 °C. In cold weather, muscles make the hairs stand up, trapping an insulating layer of warm air over the surface of the skin. In hot weather the sweat glands excrete water which evaporates from the skin, cooling the body.
- **Secretion and excretion** Oil or sebum is used as a protective covering, waterproofing and lubricating the skin and hair. Waste products such as water and salt are passed out of the body via sweat.
- **Sensation** Beneath the top layer of the skin are nerves and sense organs. The many nerve endings are responsible for feelings of heat, cold, pain and touch. These sensations protect the body from harm.

The epidermis

The skin consists of several layers of different cell tissue. The outermost layer is called the **epidermis**. It has five distinct layers.

- The **horny layer** is the hard, cornified top layer of skin. It is constantly being worn away and replaced by underlying tissue.
- The **clear layer** is transparent and colourless, allowing colour from below to be seen. There is no melanin, but the cells contain **keratin**, the principal protein of hair.
- The **granular layer** lies between the softer living cells below and the hardened dead cells above. It contains granular tissues.

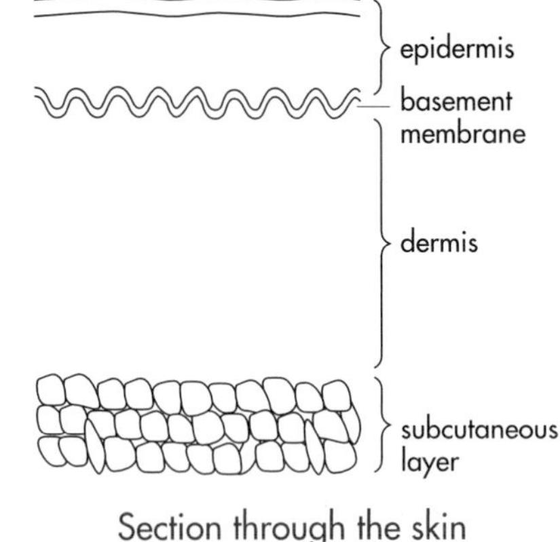

Section through the skin

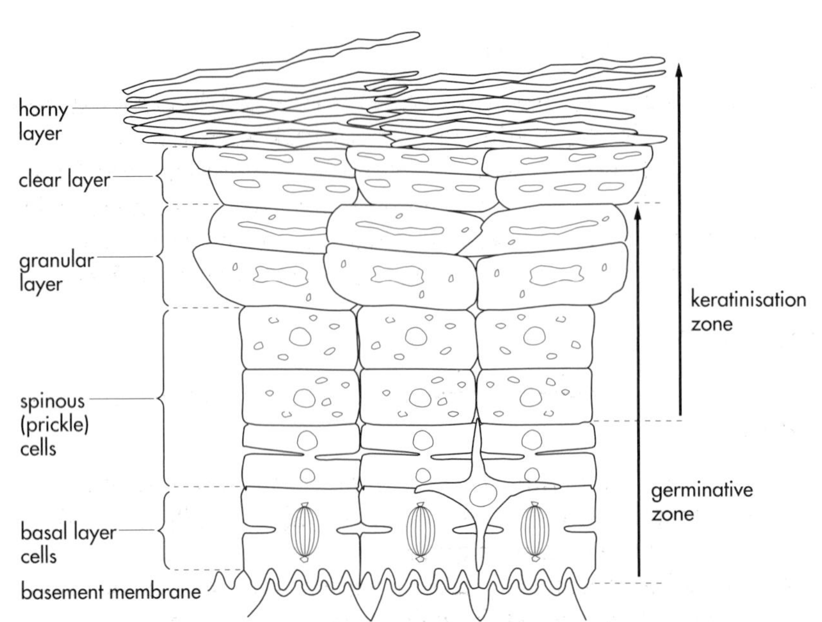

The layers of the epidermis

The hair in skin

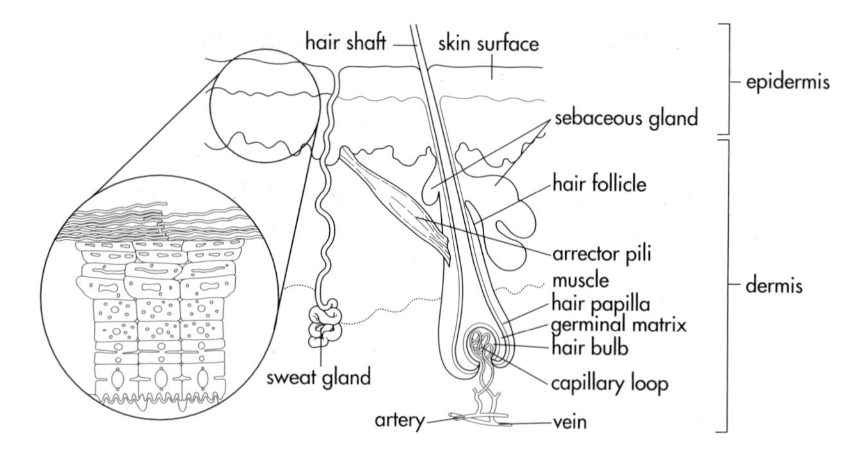

- The **mixed layer** consists of mixed cells. Immediately below the granular layer lie **prickle cells** (spinous cells) which are softer, alive and active. Below these lie the **Malpighian cells**, which contain **melanin**, the skin colour pigment. (The names **stratum aculeatum, stratum spinosum** and **stratum Malpighi** are also used for this mixed layer of cells.)
- The **germinating layer** is the lowest or base layer of the epidermis. It is the site of most active growth. The cells are softer and fuller than those above. The germinating layer connects with the underlying dermis.

The dermis

The **dermis** is the thickest layer of the skin. It is here that the hair follicle is formed. The dermis is made up of elastic and connective tissue, and is well supplied with blood and lymph vessels. The skin receives its nutrient supply from this area. The upper part of the dermis, the **papillary layer**, contains the organs of touch, heat and cold, and pain. The lower part of the dermis, the **reticular layer**, forms a looser network of cells.

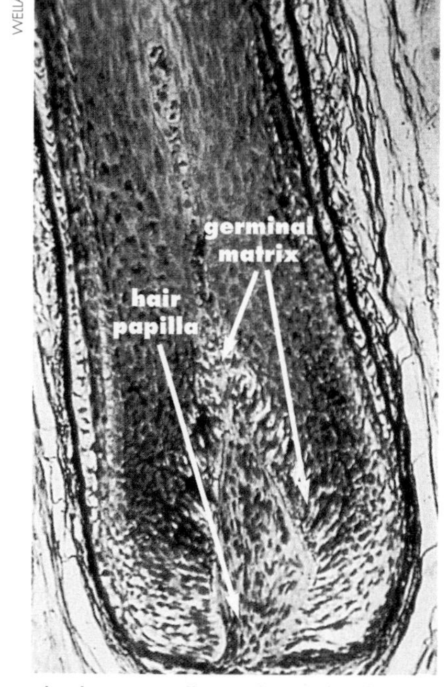

WELLA

The hair papilla and germinal matrix

The subcutaneous tissue

The **subcutaneous tissue** lies below the dermis. It is also known as the **subcutis**, or occasionally as the **hypodermis**. It is composed of loose cell tissue and contains stores of fat. The base of the hair follicle is situated just above this area, or sometimes in it. Subcutaneous tissue gives roundness to the body and fills the space between the dermis and muscle tissue that may lie below.

The hair follicle

Hair grows from a thin, tubelike space in the skin called a **hair follicle**.

- At the bottom of the follicles are areas well supplied with nerves and blood vessels, which nourish the cellular activity. These are called **hair papillae**.
- Immediately surrounding each papilla is the **germinal matrix** which consists of actively forming hair cells.

- As the new hair cells develop the lowest part of the hair is shaped into the **hair bulb**.
- The cells continue to shape the form as they push along the follicle until they appear at the skin surface as **hair fibres**.
- The cells gradually harden and die. The hair is formed of dead tissue. It retains its elasticity due to its chemical structure and keratin content.

ACTIVITY

Draw an outline of a hair, in its follicle, in the skin. Label the different parts.

Oil

The oil gland, or **sebaceous gland**, is situated in the skin and opens out into the upper third of the follicle. From it **oil**, or **sebum**, is secreted into the follicle and on to the hair and skin surface. Sebum helps to prevent the skin and hair from drying. By retaining moisture it helps the hair and skin to stay pliable. Sebum is slightly acid – about pH 5.6 – and forms a protective anti-bacterial covering for the skin.

Sweat

A **sweat gland**, or **sudoriferous gland**, lies beside each hair follicle. These are appendages of the skin. They secrete sweat which passes out through the sweat ducts. The ends of these ducts can be seen at the surface of the skin as sweat **pores**.

There are two types of sweat gland: the larger, associated closely with the hair follicles, are the **apocrine glands**; the smaller, found over most of the skin's surface, are the **eccrine glands**.

Sweat is mainly water with salt, and other minerals may be present. In abnormal conditions sweat contains larger amounts of waste material. Evaporation of sweat cools the skin. The function of sweat, and thus the sweat glands, is to protect the body by helping to maintain the normal temperature.

The hair muscle

The **hair muscle**, or **arrector pili**, is attached at one end to the hair follicle, and at the other to the underlying tissue of the epidermis. When it contracts it pulls the hair and follicle upright. Upright hairs trap a warm layer of air around the skin. The hairs also act as a warning system – for example, you soon notice if an insect crawls over your skin!

THE HAIR

Many hairdressing processes depend on certain properties of hair. This section introduces you to the structure and chemistry of hair.

The structure of hair

Hairs are fine strands of tissue which appear above the skin surface. They cover most of the body, with the exception of the

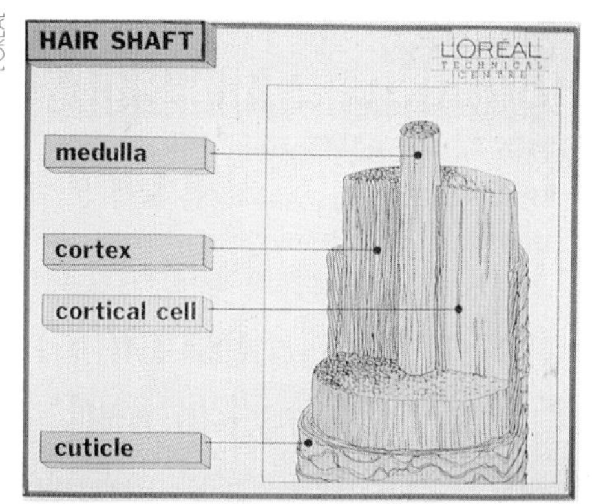

The hair shaft

L'OREAL

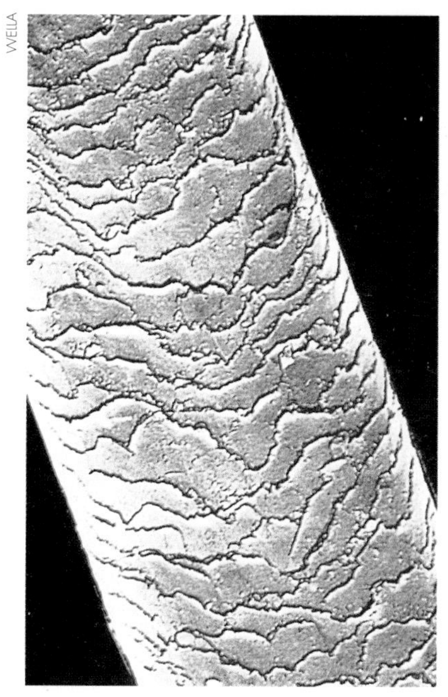
The hair cuticle

WELLA

eyelids, the palms of the hands and the soles of the feet. There are three different types of hair.

- **Lanugo hair** Fine, downy hair that covers the body of the unborn child: it is lost just before or around birth.
- **Vellus hair** Fine, short, fluffy hair which covers most parts of the body. It can be seen clearly on the faces of women.
- **Terminal hair** Longer, coarser hair, found on the head, on the faces of men, in ears and eyebrows, on the arms, legs and chest, and in the pubic region.

Each hair has the same basic structure. There are three layers.

- **Cuticle** The outer layer of colourless cells, which forms a protective surface to the hair. It regulates the chemicals entering and damaging the hair, and protects the hair from excessive heat and drying. The cells overlap, like rooftiles; if you rub a hair from base to tip it feels smooth, but if you rub it from tip to base it feels rough.
- **Cortex** The middle and largest layer, consisting of long spiral chains of cells like springs. Each cell is made of bundles of fibres. These are composed of small bundles of **macrofibrils** which in turn are formed from even smaller bundles of **microfibrils** which are made up of the smallest bundles of **protofibrils** – all long, spiralling, ladderlike chains. The way these fibres and cells are held together determines the strength of hair, its thickness, curl and elasticity. **Pigments** in the cortex give hair its natural colour.
- **Medulla** The central space of the hair. It serves no useful purpose, and is not always present.

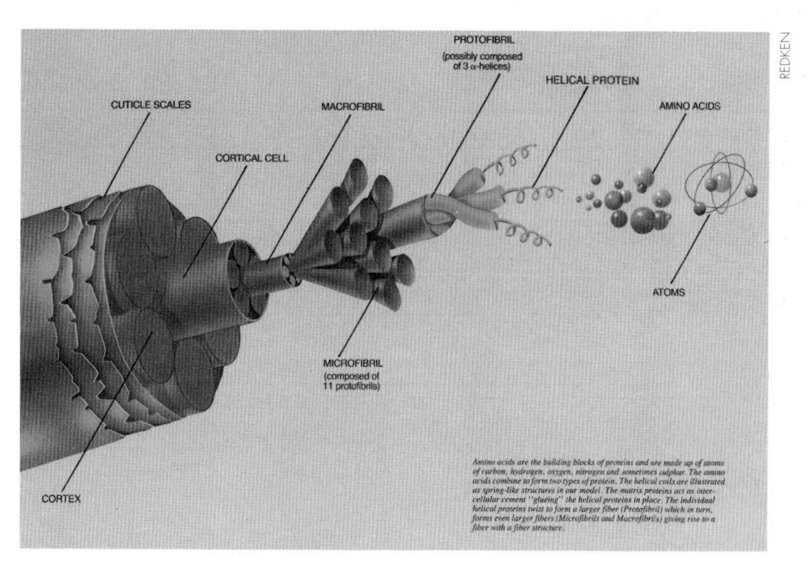

Inside the hair

REDKEN

Chemical properties of hair

The bundles of fibres found in the cortex are made from molecules of **amino acids**. There are about twenty-two amino acids in hair, and the molecules of each contain atoms of elements in different proportions. Overall, the elements in hair are in approximately these proportions:

carbon	50%
oxygen	21%
nitrogen	18%
hydrogen	7%
sulphur	4%

The amino acids combine to form larger molecules, long chains of amino acids called **polypeptides** or, if they are long enough, **proteins**. One of the most important of these is **keratin**. Keratin is an important component of nails, skin and hair: it is this protein that makes them flexible and elastic. Because of the keratin it contains, hair can be stretched and compressed, curled and waved.

ACTIVITY
List the functions of the hair and skin. How may these be affected by hairdressing processes, both physical and chemical?

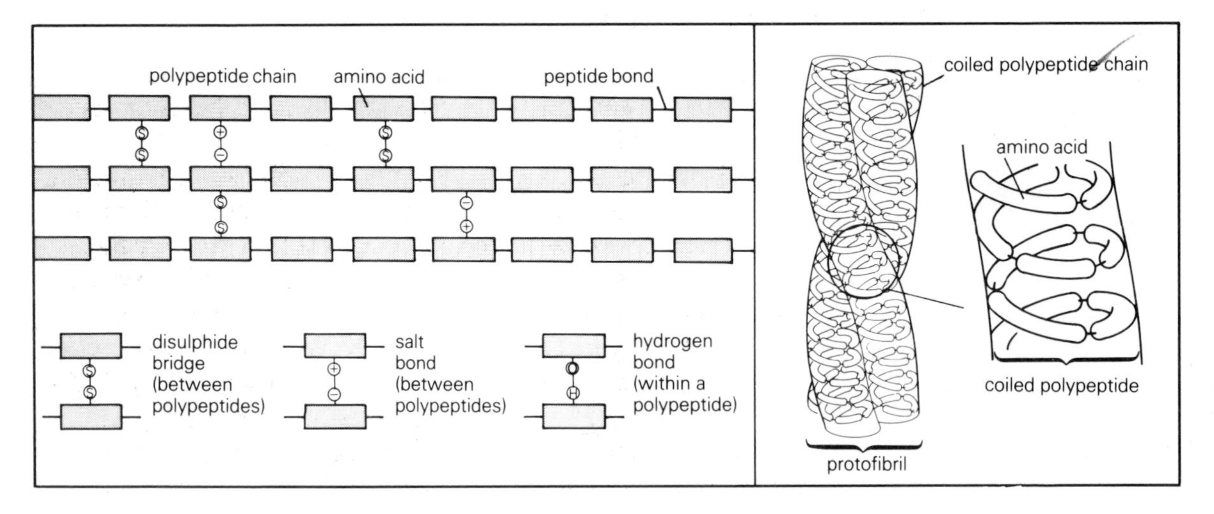

Cross-links within hair

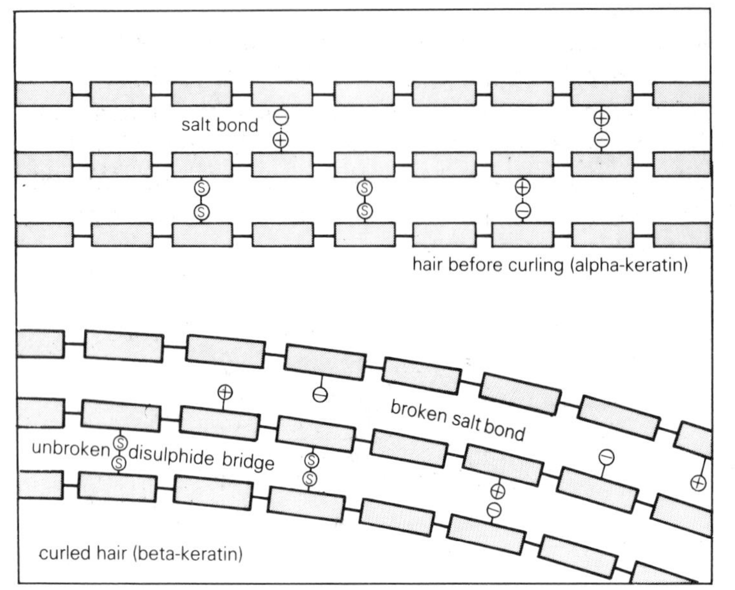

Hair in its 'alpha' and 'beta' forms, before and after curling

In hair, keratin forms long chains which coil up like springs. They are held in this shape by cross-links between chains. The three kinds of link are **disulphide bridges (sulphur bonds)**, **salt bonds** and **hydrogen bonds**. Salt bonds and hydrogen bonds are relatively weak and are easily broken, allowing the springs to be stretched out: this is what happens in curling. The normal, coiled form of keratin is called **alpha-keratin**; when it has been stretched, set and dried it is called **beta-keratin**. The change is only temporary. Once the hair has been made wet, or has gradually absorbed moisture from the air, it relaxes back to the alpha state. Disulphide bridges are much stronger, but these too can be altered, as in perming.

ACTIVITY
Examine a colleague's hair and scalp. Note the condition of the hair and the skin, the hair length and its colour, and whether the hair has been permed, tinted or given some other treatment.

Physical properties of hair

Hair naturally contains a certain amount of water, which lubricates it, allowing it to stretch and recoil. Hair that is dry and in poor condition is less elastic.

Hair is **hygroscopic**: it absorbs water from the surrounding air. How much water is taken up depends on the dryness of the hair and the moistness of the atmosphere. Hair is also **porous**: there are tiny tube-like spaces within the hair structure, and the water flows into these by **capillary action**, rather like blotting paper absorbing ink. Drying hair in the ordinary way evaporates only the surface moisture, but drying over long periods or at too high a temperature removes water from *within* the hair, leaving it brittle and in poor condition. Damaged hair is more porous than healthy hair, and easily loses any water: this makes it hard to stretch and mould.

Curled hair returns to its former shape as it takes up water, so the drier the atmosphere, the longer the curl or set lasts. Similarly, curling dry hair is most effective just after the hair has been washed, because although the surface is dry the hair will have absorbed water internally. Blow-styling and curling with hot irons, heated rollers, hot combs and hot brushes all have similar temporary effects.

Hair porosity

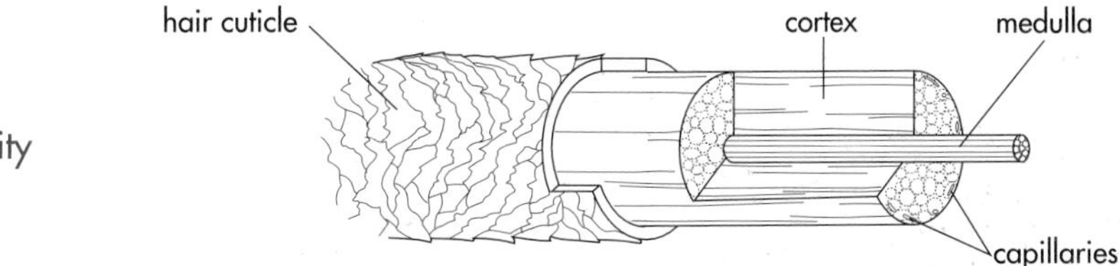

Hair growth

Hair is constantly growing. Over a period of between one and six years an individual hair actively grows, then stops, rests and degenerates, and finally falls out. Before the hair leaves the follicle the new hair is normally ready to replace it. If a hair is not replaced then a tiny area of baldness results.

The lives of individual hairs vary and are subject to variations in the body. Some are actively growing while others are resting. Hairs on the head are at different stages of growth.

Stages of growth

The life cycle of hair is as follows.

- **Anagen** The active growing stage of the hair, a period of activity of the papilla and germinal matrix. This stage may last from a few months to several years. It is at this stage of formation at the base of the follicle that the hair's thickness, shape and texture is determined. Hair colour, too, is formed in the early part of anagen.
- **Catagen** A period when the hair stops growing but cellular activity continues at the papilla. The hair bulb gradually separates from the papilla and moves further up the follicle.
- **Telogen** The final stage, when there is no further growth or activity at the papilla. The follicle begins to shrink, and completely separates from the papilla area. This resting stage does not last long: towards the end of the telogen stage, cells begin to activate in preparation for the new anagen stage of regrowth.

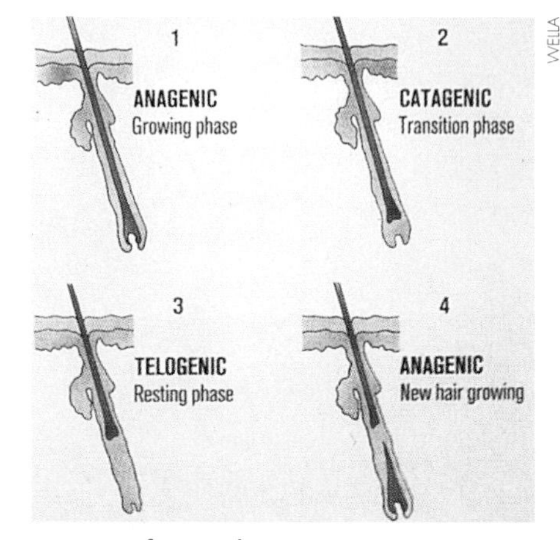

Stages of growth

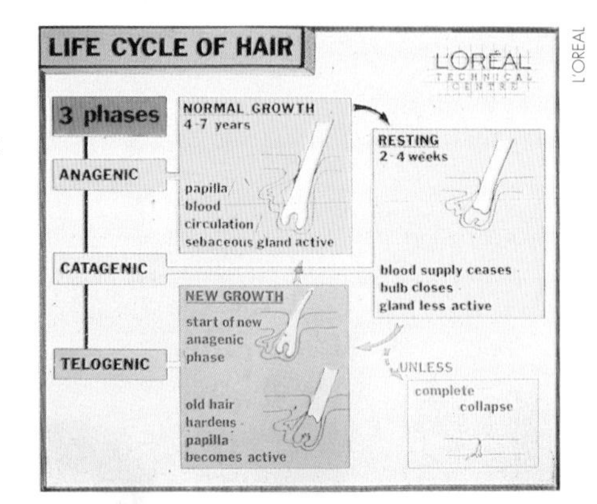

The new anagen period involves the hair follicle beginning to grow down again. Vigorous papilla activity generates a new hair at the germinal matrix. At the same time the old hair is slowly making its way up and out of the follicle. Often the old and new hair can be seen at the same time in the follicle.

In some animals most of the hairs follow their life cycle 'in step', passing through anagen, catagen and telogen together. This results in moulting. Human hair, however, develops at an uneven rate and few follicles are shedding their hair at the same time. (If all hairs fell at the same time we would have bald periods!)

Regeneration of the hair

The regeneration of hair is influenced by many factors:

- health
- diet
- age
- sex
- hormone balance
- hereditary factors
- climate
- physical condition
- chemical effects
- effects of disease.

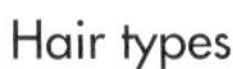
Hair types

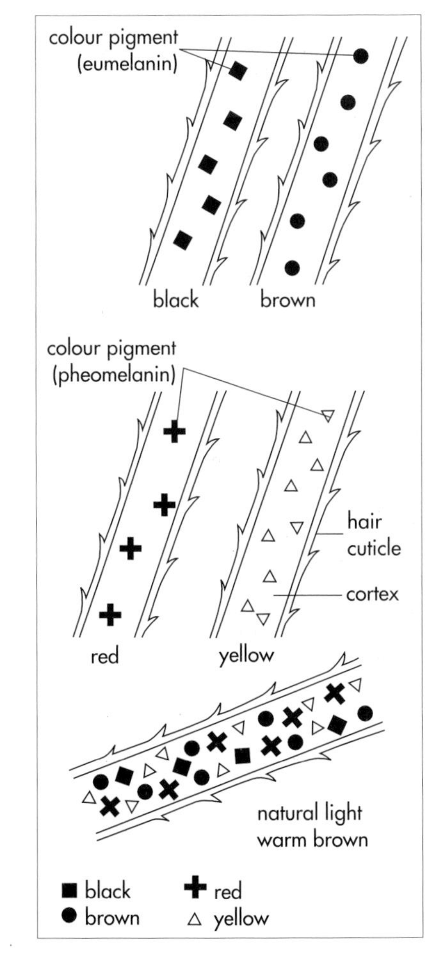

Hair pigments

Hair types

Human hair is grouped into the following types:

- **Caucasian** (European) Loosely waved or straight hair.
- **Black** (Afro-Caribbean) Tight, kinked, woolly, curled hair.
- **Mongoloid** (Asian) Coarse, straight, lank hair.

The differences between these groups are distinctive, and form an interesting study for forensic scientists.

Hair texture can be either fine, medium or coarse. Some very tightly curled hair varies in texture throughout its length. Afro-Caribbean hair follows this pattern. The fine points can break under harsh treatment, and need special care.

Hair colour

The **natural colour** of hair depends on the amounts and proportions of **pigment (melanin)** it contains. Two types of pigment are found in hair: eumelanin and pheomelanin.

- **Eumelanin** gives black and brown colours. Dark ash-brown hair contains a lot of eumelanin.
- **Pheomelanin** gives red and yellow colours. Blonde hair contains relatively little melanin.

White and albino hair contains little or no pigment.

Neutralising, tinting and bleaching are chemical processes that act on these pigments to change the hair colour.

DISEASES

Inside us, and on our skin and hair, we all carry large numbers of **micro-organisms**. These are very small living things; they include **bacteria, fungi** and **viruses**. Individual micro-organisms are so small that they cannot be seen with the naked eye: bacteria and fungi can be seen through a microscope, but viruses are too small even for that. However, we may be able to see large numbers, or **colonies**, of bacteria or fungi.

Many micro-organisms are quite harmless, but some can cause disease: these are called **pathogens** (or **germs**). Flu, for example, is caused by a virus, thrush by a fungus, and bronchitis often by bacteria. Those diseases that can be transmitted from one person to another are said to be **infectious**. The body is naturally resistant to infection: it fights pathogens using the **immune system**. So we may carry pathogenic organisms without necessarily having any disease. And there are many diseases that aren't caused by micro-organisms.

The skin may also provide a home for tiny **insects** such as lice, and these too can cause disease.

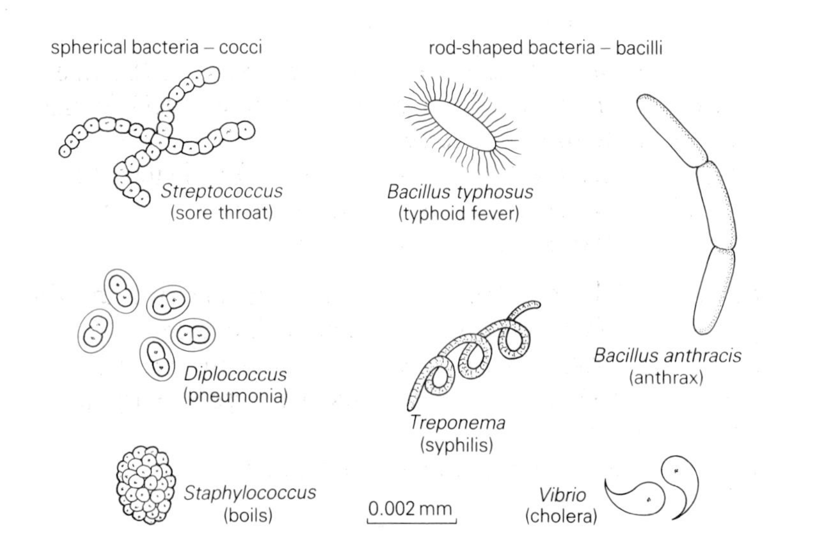

Examples of bacteria

ACTIVITY

Arrange with your trainer a visit to the library or a biology laboratory at your local college. Look at a range of pictures to help you recognise different hair and scalp diseases. Make notes of what you see.

Alternatively, you might be able to visit your local hospital or clinic and get first-hand information about consultation and diagnosis.

Treatment

When you have a disease, the **symptoms** are the signs that you can see or feel that tell you that something is wrong. They are produced by the infection and by the reactions of the body. Symptoms help you to recognise the disease.

> **HEALTH AND SAFETY**
> Find out more about hair and scalp diseases and disorders. There are other textbooks that give more details. When examining clients, make your observations carefully. Check your diagnosis with a trainer or senior.

Infectious diseases should always be treated by a general practitioner. Non-infectious conditions and defects can often be treated in the salon or with products available from chemists, or by a specialist such as a **trichologist**.

Salon hygiene

A warm, humid salon can be a perfect home for germs. Given nourishment in the form of dirt and dust, they may reproduce rapidly. This is why it is important to keep the salon clean at all times, including clothing, work surfaces, tools and other equipment. A tidy salon is easier to clean, so get into the habit of clearing up as you work.

Bacterial infectious diseases

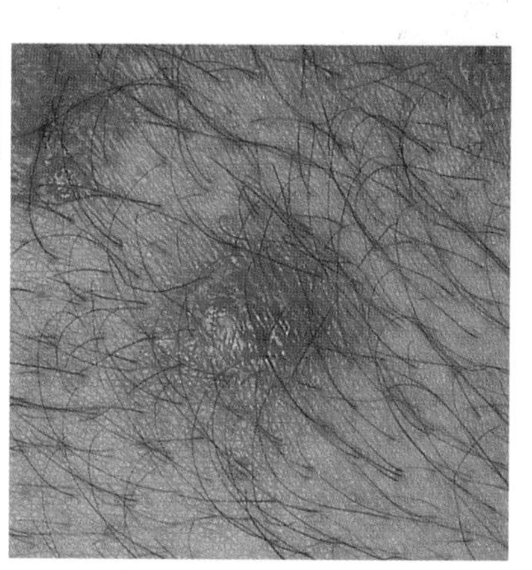
DR A L WRIGHT

Furunculosis

- **Furunculosis** Boils and abscesses.
  Cause An infection of the hair follicles by staphylococcal bacteria.
  Symptoms Raised, inflamed, pus-filled spots; there is irritation, swelling and pain.
  Treatment By a doctor.
- **Sycosis** A bacterial infection of the hairy parts of the face.
  Cause Bacteria attack the upper part of the hair follicle; this may spread to the lower follicle.
  Symptoms Small, yellow spots around the follicle mouth; burning, irritation and general inflammation.
  Treatment Antibiotics, given by a doctor.
- **Impetigo** A bacterial infection of the upper layers of the skin.
  Cause A staphylococcal or streptococcal infection.
  Symptoms First, a burning sensation; spots appear and become dry; honey-coloured crusts form; spots merge to form larger areas.
  Treatment Antibiotics, given by a doctor.

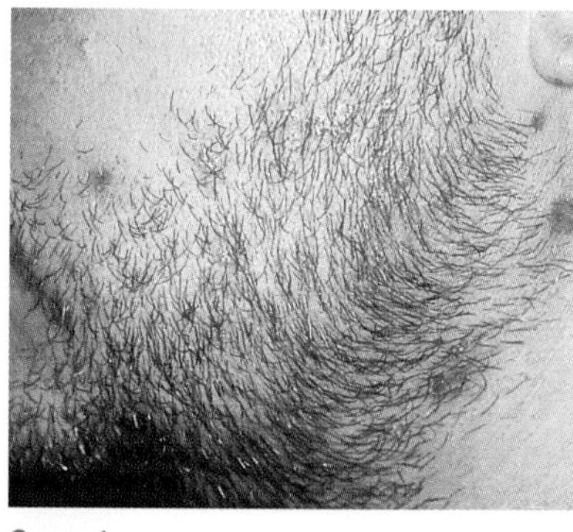
DR A L WRIGHT

Sycosis

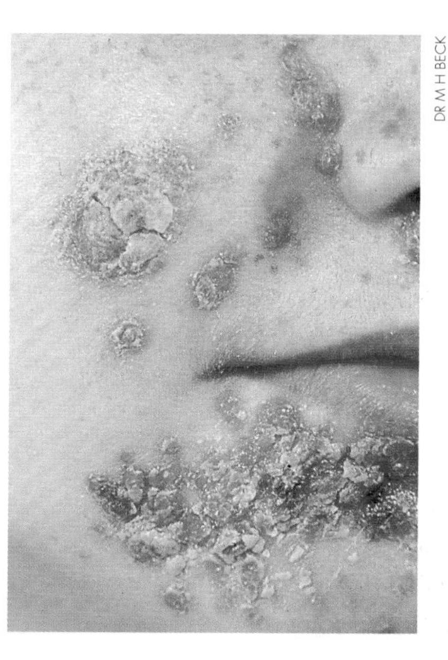
DR M H BECK

Impetigo

- **Folliculitis** Inflammation of the hair follicles.
  Cause A bacterial infection, or chemical or physical actions.
  Symptoms Inflamed follicles. These are a common symptom of certain skin diseases.
  Treatment By a doctor.

Viral infectious diseases

- **Herpes simplex (cold sore)** A viral infection of the skin.
  Cause Possibly exposure to extreme heat or cold, or reaction to food or drugs; skin may carry the virus for many years.
  Symptoms Burning, irritation, swelling and inflammation precedes the appearance of fluid-filled blisters, usually on the lips and the surrounding tissues.
  Treatment By a doctor.

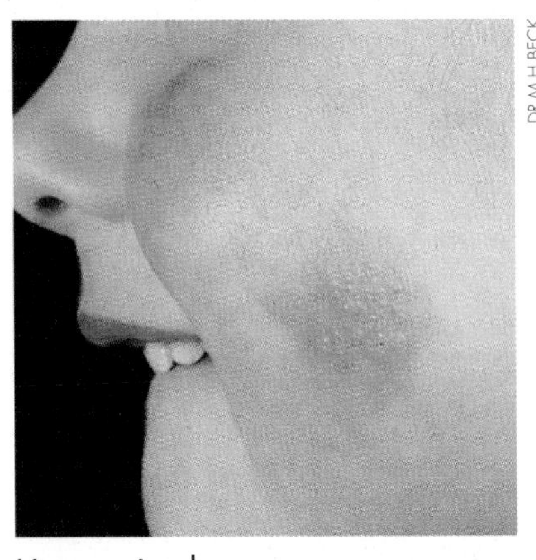

DR M H BECK

Herpes simplex

- **Herpes zoster (shingles)** A viral infection of the epidermis and nerve endings.
  Cause Perhaps from chickenpox in earlier years; the virus may have lain dormant in the skin before the shingles appears.
  Symptoms Painful blisters appear, often on one side only, of the head or body: sore, inflamed areas result. This may be preceded by a fever. Aching and pain may continue after the condition has cleared.
  Treatment By a doctor.

- **Influenza** and the **common cold** Viral infections of the body.
  Cause Viruses, which attack cells of the body.
  Symptoms Fever, sneezing, aching and the other all-too-familiar symptoms.
  Treatment By a doctor, if serious, or with cold-relief treatments from a chemist.

- **Warts (verrucae)** A viral infection of the skin.
  Cause The lower epidermis is attacked by the virus, which causes the skin to harden and the skin cells to multiply.
  Symptoms Raised, roughened skin, often brown or discoloured. There may be irritation and soreness. Warts are common on exposed areas such as the hands or face.
  Treatment By a doctor.

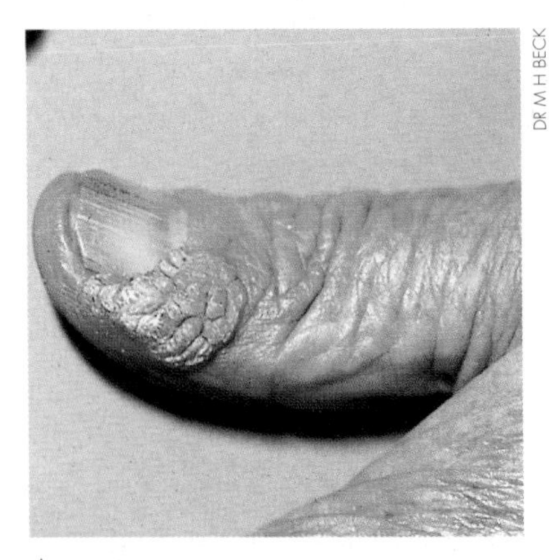

DR M H BECK

A wart

Fungal infectious diseases

- **Tinea capitis** Ringworm of the head.
  Cause Fungal infection of the skin or hair.
  Symptoms Circular areas of grey or white skin, surrounded by red, active rings; hairs broken close to the skin, which looks dull and rough. It is common in children.
  Treatment By a doctor.

- **Tinea pedis (athlete's foot)** Ringworm of the feet.
  Cause A fungus attacks the skin between the toes, which becomes soft and soggy. The disease is common among those using swimming pools and not drying their feet

DR A L WRIGHT

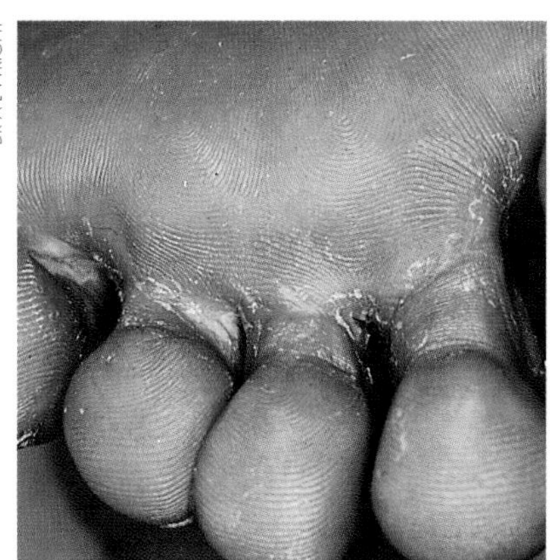

Tinea pedis

S LEWIS

The head louse

BLM HEALTH

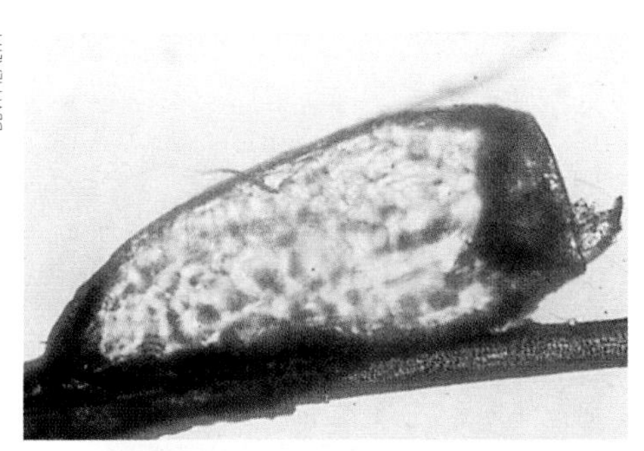

A nit (egg of a louse)

DR M H BECK

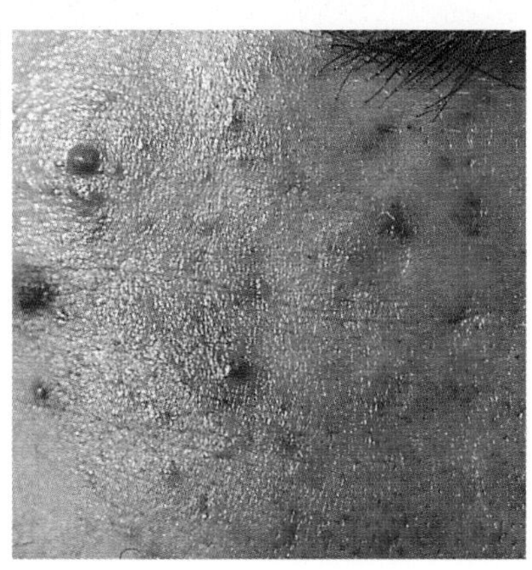

Acne

thoroughly, and those standing for long periods (including hairdressers).
Symptoms Soft, sore skin; sometimes bleeding; a bad odour; some irritation.
Treatment By a doctor, or with products from a chemist.

Diseases caused by animal parasites

- **Scabies** An allergic skin reaction to the itch mite.
  Cause A tiny animal mite, *Sarcoptes scabiei*, which burrows through the skin, where it lays its eggs.
  Symptoms A rash in the skin folds, around the midriff and on the insides of the thighs. It becomes extremely itchy at night. there are reddish spots and burrows (greyish lines) under the skin. Scabies is not found on the head or scalp except in children under two years.
  Treatment By a doctor.
- **Pediculosis capitis** Infestation of the head by lice.
  Cause *Pediculus humanus capitis*, the head louse, attacks the skin and feeds by puncturing the skin to suck the blood; it lays eggs (**ova**) on the hair, close to the skin.
  Symptoms An itchy reaction like a mosquito bite. Some people develop an allergic reaction, with itchy red marks. Lice can be seen by parting the hair; more commonly the eggs (**nits**) or hatched eggs can be seen stuck to the hairs. Live eggs are found close to the scalp. Lice are passed only by actual contact between an infected head and another head.
  Treatment By a doctor, or with products from a chemist.

Non-infectious conditions of skin and hair

- **Acne** A disorder of the hair follicles and sebaceous glands.
  Cause This is not fully understood, but increased sebum and other matter blocks the follicle: the skin reacts to this blockage as though it were a foreign body such as a splinter.
  Symptoms Raised spots or bumps in the skin, commonly on the face and forehead; soreness, irritation and inflammation; severe cases produce cysts and scarring.
  Treatment By a doctor.
- **Alopecia** Baldness or thinning of hair. **Alopecia areata** is the name given to baldness in circular areas; it is common on the scalp. If the condition continues, these areas join to form **alopecia totalis**, complete hair loss from the scalp. **Alopecia universalis** is complete baldness of the body.
  Causes The hair follicles are unable to produce new hairs to replace the old ones. **Male-pattern alopecia** is baldness found in the teenage years of men and the later years of women; its cause is hereditary, and treatment can be given by the salon, a trichologist or a doctor. **Cicatrical alopecia** is baldness due to scarring of the skin arising from chemical or physical injury. The hair follicles are damaged and permanent baldness results.

Symptoms Areas of thinning or diffuse hair; in alopecia areata there are small hairs in a pale pink smooth area. These hairs are thinner near the scalp.
Treatment By a doctor or a trichologist.

- **Canities** Grey or white hair.
  Cause Colour pigment not forming in the new hair.
  Symptoms The presence of white hairs.
  Treatment Tinting.

- **Eczema; dermatitis** At its simplest, red, inflamed skin.
  Causes There are several, with either internal or external factors: it may be due to physical irritation or to an allergic response.
  Symptoms These range from slightly inflamed areas of skin, to severe splitting and weeping areas; there may be irritation, soreness and pain; in advanced stages the underlying skin may become infected.
  Treatment By a doctor.

- **Dandruff (pityriasis capitis)** Dry, scaling scalp.
  Cause Fungal infection, or physical or chemical irritants.
  Symptoms Dry, small, irritating flakes (or scales) of skin; if the scale becomes moist and greasy it sticks to the skin and the condition known as **scurf** results. Dandruff can be accompanied by **conjunctivitis** (inflammation of the eye) or **blepharitis** (inflammation of the eyelid)
  Treatment By various anti-dandruff medicines and shampoos (see Chapter 3).

- **Seborrhoea** Excessive greasiness of the skin and hair.
  Cause Over-production of sebum, which may be due to physical or chemical irritants.
  Symptoms Very greasy, lank hair, and greasy skin, which makes grooming and dressing of the hair difficult.
  Treatment Regular washing, with a minimum of physical or chemical stimulation; in extreme cases it is best treated by a trichologist or a doctor.

- **Psoriasis** An inflamed, abnormal thickening of the skin.
  Cause Unknown.
  Symptoms Areas of thickened skin, which may be raised and circular; silvery or yellow scales may be present; the skin may be sore, itchy or painful.
  Treatment By a doctor or a dermatologist.

Defects of the hair

- **Fragilitas crinium (split ends)** Fragile, poorly conditioned hair.
  Cause Harsh physical or chemical treatments.
  Symptoms Dry, splitting hair-ends.
  Treatment Cutting hair-ends and using conditioners.

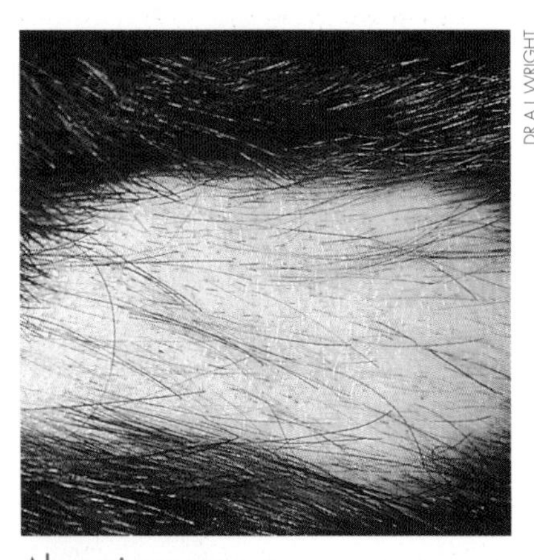
DR A L WRIGHT
Alopecia areata

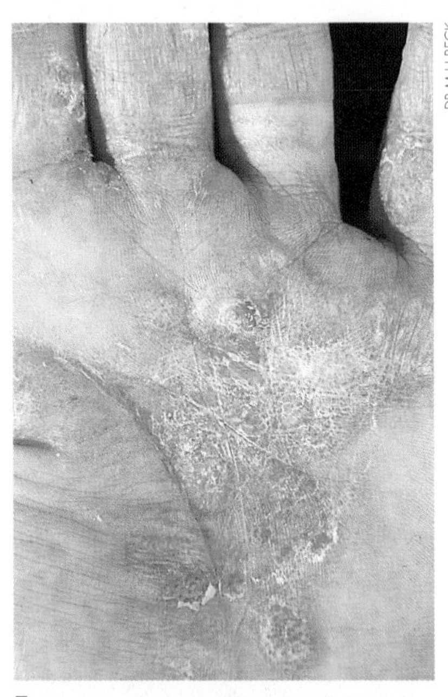
DR M H BECK
Eczema

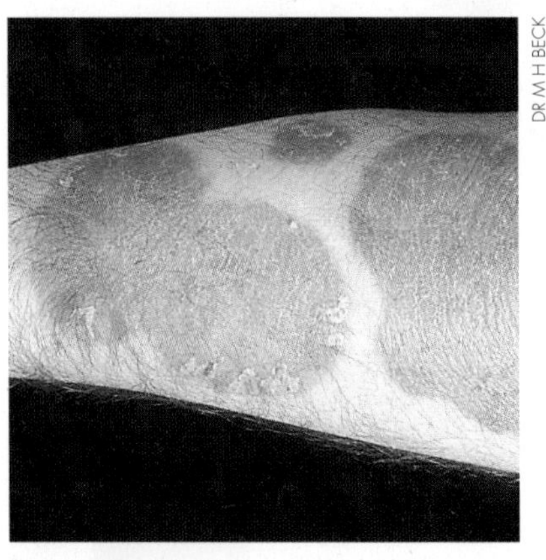
DR M H BECK
Psoriasis

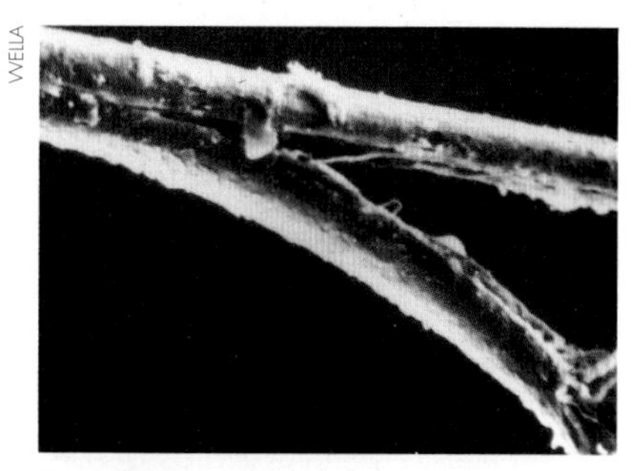

WELLA

Fragilitas crinium

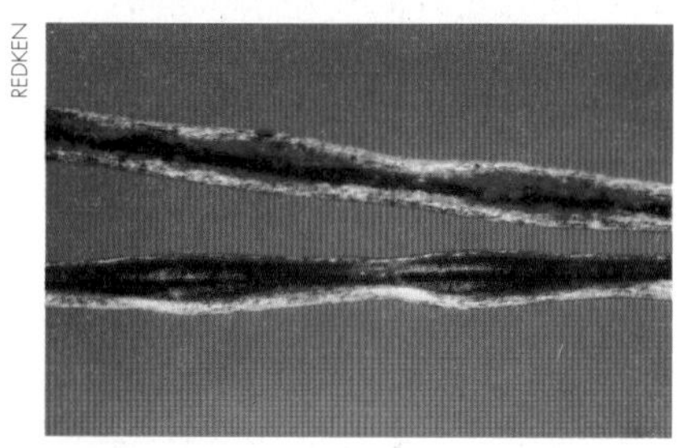

REDKEN

Monilethrix

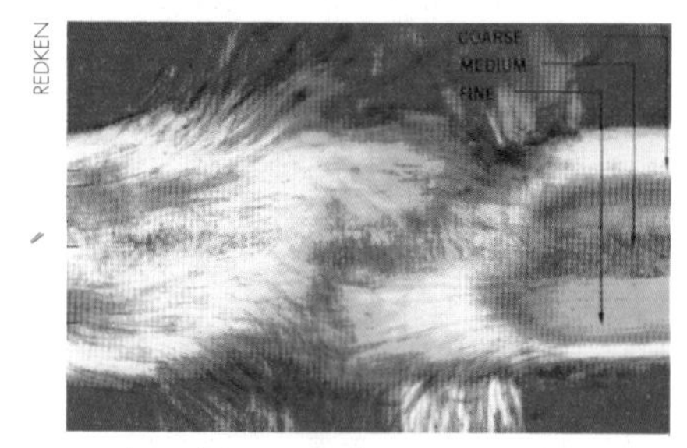

REDKEN

Trichorrhexis nodosa

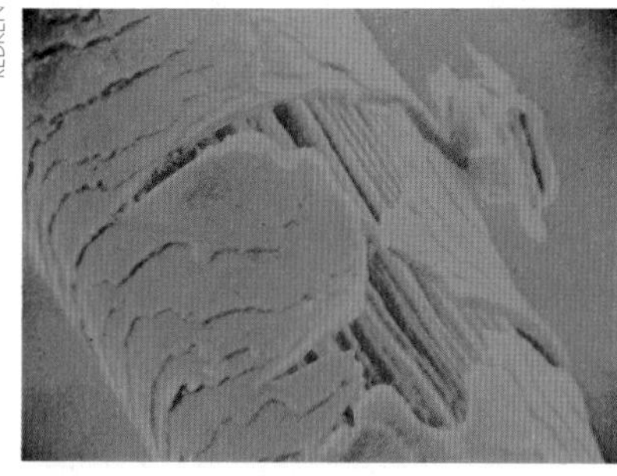

REDKEN

A damaged hair cuticle

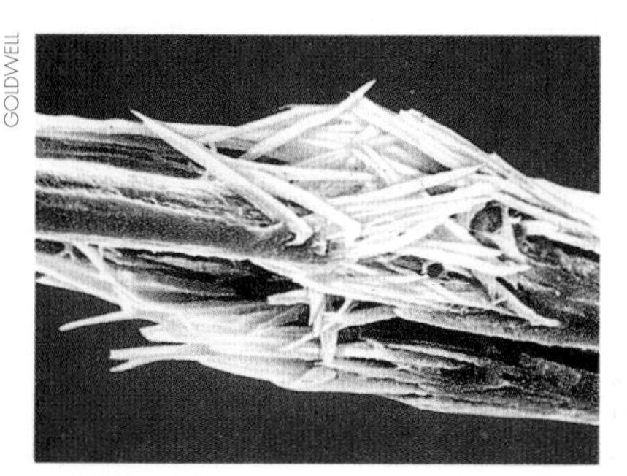

GOLDWELL

Damaged hair

- **Monilethrix** Beaded hair.
  Cause Irregular development of the hair when forming in the follicle.
  Symptoms Beadlike swellings and constructions of the hair shafts; hair often breaks close to the skin.
  Treatment By a doctor; conditioning may help.
- **Ringed hair** Alternating white and coloured rings of the hair shaft.
  Cause Irregular distribution of pigment during hair formation or regeneration.
  Symptoms Distinct bands of coloured and colourless hair – there may be few or many.
  Treatment There are few effective treatments other than hair colouring.
- **Trichorrhexis nodosa** Nodules on the hair shaft, containing splitting sections of hair.
  Cause Harsh physical or chemical treatments.
  Symptoms Areas of swelling nodules and lengthwise splitting of the hair.
  Treatment Cutting at the ends may help, as may conditioning with products such as hair thickeners.
- **Sebaceous cyst** Swelling of a sebaceous or oil gland.
  Cause The sebaceous gland becomes blocked, possibly due to a growth of cells arising from the gland wall.
  Symptoms Bumps, lumps or swellings, 12–50 mm across, on the scalp, soft to the touch owing to fluid content.
  Treatment Removal of the contents, by a doctor.
- **Damaged cuticle** Broken, split, torn hair.
  Cause Harsh physical or chemical treatments.
  Symptoms: Rough, raised, missing areas of cuticle; hair loses its moisture and becomes dry and porous.
  Treatment By conditioners, thickeners, restructurants and similar products.

Hair conditions and defects

Diseases are not the only kinds of disorder you will meet. There are various **conditions** of hair that are caused by reactions to physical and chemical processes like backcombing and bleaching. These are non-infectious: they cannot be passed to another person.

There are also **defects**, caused by irregular hair growth. Some are hereditary, and may be shared by members of the same family; others are due to the abnormal structure of hair follicles or to harsh treatment.

Health risks

You need to be able to recognise skin and hair diseases, and be hygienic in your work. This will help you to avoid catching diseases yourself, or passing them from one client to another.

Two other health risks are also important to hairdressers: you should know about these as well.

AIDS

The **acquired immune-deficiency syndrome (AIDS)** is not itself a disease – it's a condition that makes the body *vulnerable* to diseases. It is these other diseases that may actually lead to death. Because AIDS is often fatal and because there is as yet no known cure, it may seem very frightening. Nevertheless, some fears about AIDS result simply from misunderstanding. To protect yourself and your clients, you need to understand the condition.

AIDS is caused by a virus known as the **human immunodeficiency virus (HIV)**. This virus attacks the body's immune system and may make it less effective, leaving the body vulnerable to other infections. But some people carry the HIV virus – they are **HIV-positive** – *without* having AIDS. Anyone who is HIV-positive is potentially able to pass the virus to someone else.

You can become infected only if your body fluids, such as your blood, come into contact with body fluids of someone who is HIV-positive. This most commonly occurs during unprotected sex: condoms help to protect both partners. But this is not the only way – drug addicts who share needles are at risk, and the virus can be transferred through a cut or through broken skin. Remember that infection only occurs through the exchange of body fluids. The virus is sensitive to its surroundings, and cannot live long outside the body (so you can't catch it from a toilet seat, for example). Blood for transfusions is now specially checked to make sure that it does not contain HIV.

HEALTH AND SAFETY

If a tool infected with the blood of an AIDS carrier, such as a razor used for shaving or lining a hairstyle, is used on another client without being sterilised, there is the possibility of cross-infection.

ACTIVITY

Some people are unnecessarily frightened about AIDS. Others take unnecessary risks. Find out more about this condition. Discuss your feelings about it, and how it should affect your work.

Hepatitis B

This infection of the liver is another disease caused by a virus. The **hepatitis B virus (HBV)** is transmitted through infected blood, body tissue fluids and infected water.

The disease is long-lasting and weakening, and can be fatal. Successful treatments are available, but the virus is very resistant and is said to last a long time outside the human body. Good hygiene is therefore essential. Disinfection, sterilisation and the use of detergents and bleach for washing surfaces is thought to help.

Inoculation is available to protect against HBV. It should be seriously considered by all those who may be at risk, including hairdressers, beauty therapists, electrolysists and manicurists.

General hygiene

In the salon, so long as you take sensible precautions there should be no risk to you or your clients. It is essential that you are thorough in sterilising all equipment, particularly that used for electrolysis, ear piercing and tattooing. Good hygiene, correct disinfection, and protection of any cut or open skin will reduce the dangers not just of HIV/AIDS and hepatitis B but of all infectious diseases.

- Keep any cuts and open skin wounds covered.
- Wash your hands regularly.
- Clear away spilt blood from all surfaces, and apply bleach, detergent or a disinfectant. Wear rubber gloves.
- Always clean and sterilise tools before using them on clients.
- Use only sterile, disposable razors or needles on, or in, the skin.
- Wrap any blood-soaked materials carefully and place them in a special covered bin.
- Arrange removal and disposal of suspect materials by the local health authority.

CONSULTING AND DIAGNOSING TECHNIQUE

Examining the hair

MAHOGANY

In every consultation with a client (page 14), there are certain things you must attend to.

- Listen to what the client tells you.
- Find out what the client wants – her desires or requests.
- Question her, courteously, so that you get useful information on which you can base accurate decisions.
- Observe the client carefully and thoroughly during the examination.
- Ensure that she is comfortable and at ease throughout the consultation.

Here are some of the questions you can ask yourself:

- Is the hair dry, brittle or breaking?
- Is it extremely greasy?
- Is the hair too short or uneven?
- Is there too much frizz or perm from previous treatment?
- Is there variation in synthetic colouring?
- What have been the effects of physical processes, such as crimping or tonging?
- What have been the effects of chemical processes, such as perming or colouring?
- Have incompatible chemicals been used, such as home hair treatments that leave metallic salts which might react with hydrogen peroxide during bleaching?

Diagnosis like this may tell you whether hair will stand up to processes such as perming. (Further aspects of hair, such as hair growth patterns, are considered in Chapter 5.)

ACTIVITY

Bleach some samples of hair to varying degrees of lightness. Rinse, clear, and dry them. Then wind and perm them all, using the same size of curlers, the same length of time (5 or 10 minutes), and the same perm lotions. Compare the results.

You should also be able now to recognise infections and diseases of the hair and scalp. It's important to avoid **cross-infection** – carrying an infection from one person to another – so remember these points:

- Make sure you are free of infection yourself, and that your hands are clean.
- Examine the client's hair and scalp before beginning any hairdressing treatment. Divide the hair so that you can see the scalp. Feel the hair for roughness.
- If you find signs of disease or infection, do not carry out any hairdressing but ask a senior hairdresser to give a second opinion. If she agrees with you, the senior will then tell the client tactfully, and suggest a visit to the doctor as soon as possible.
- If you notice the infection when you have already started hairdressing, finish what you are doing and then consult with a senior. Allow the client to leave as soon as possible, without coming into contact with others.
- Sterilise all equipment and disinfect the area where you were working.
- Stay quiet and unflustered, so as not to cause anxiety to other clients.

HEALTH AND SAFETY

When dealing with a child, examine the hair and scalp for signs of infestation.

TIP

Agreement between the client and senior staff is necessary before a client is referred to a doctor.

ACTIVITY

With a colleague, take turns at being the client or hairdresser in the consultation process. Notice the kinds of remark or question that gain most information, and note how one question may lead to another.

Testing the hair and skin

There are various tests you can make to help you diagnose the condition of your client's hair. These tests will help you decide what actions to take before applying hairdressing processes. Results of tests should be noted on the client's record card. Skin allergies are considered in Chapter 8.

- **Skin test** (also known as the **pre-disposition test, patch test** or **Sabouraud–Rousseau test**) A test to assess the reaction of the skin to a chemical product. It is used particularly before tinting (see Chapter 8).
- **Strand test** A test used to assess the resultant colour on a strand or section of hair while colour is processing and developing (see Chapter 8).

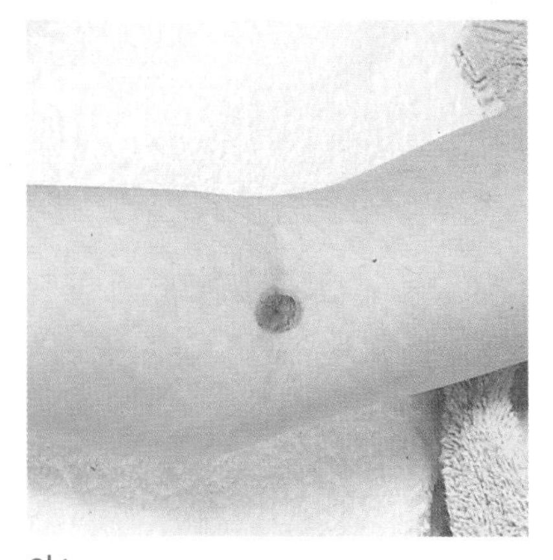

Skin test

ACTIVITY

Collect samples of hair from your salon – these can be used for various hair-testing procedures. Longer pieces will be the most useful, but lengths of 5 cm or more can be used. Collect and store the hair carefully, preferably in envelopes.

TIP

If you don't consult with your client correctly and communicate with her effectively – and treat everything she tells you as confidential – you are likely to end up with a dissatisfied client. She may even decide not to come back to the salon.

- **Test cutting** A test in which a piece of hair cut from the head is processed to check its suitability, the amount of processing required and the timing, before the process is carried out. This test is used for colouring, straightening, relaxing, reducing synthetic colouring, bleaching and incompatibility (see Chapter 8).
- **Test curl** A test made on the hair to determine the lotion suitability, the strength, the curler size, the timing of processing and the development. It is used before perming (see Chapter 7).
- **Curl check or test** A test used to assess development of curl in the perming process. This test is used periodically throughout a perm and for final assessment (see Chapter 7).
- **'Peroxide' test** A test made on hair that has been stripped of its synthetic colour. This test is used to assess the effectiveness of the process (see Chapter 8).
- **Incompatibility test** A test to detect chemicals already on the hair which could react adversely with the chemicals used in hairdressing processes such as colouring and perming (see Chapters 7 and 8).
- **Elasticity test** A test to determine how much the hair will stretch and then return to its original position. By taking a hair or hairs between the fingers and extending it or them, you can assess the amount of spring or elasticity. If the hair breaks easily then further tests are required – a test curl, for example (see Chapter 7).
- **Porosity test** A test to assess the ability of the hair to absorb moisture or liquids. If the cuticle is torn or broken then absorption may be quick. If the cuticle is smooth, unbroken and tightly packed, it may resist the passage of moisture or liquids. By running the fingertips through the hair, from points to roots, you can assess the degree of roughness (see Chapter 8).

ACTIVITY

Carry out each of the tests listed in this section. Take careful notes of each result. Make sure that you list exactly what is done, the time taken, and the materials used. Use part of the hair sample as a 'before' example, to be compared with the 'after' result. Keep these carefully in your notebook or folder.

Negative results of tests may indicate that care is needed when giving the service as planned, or even that it should not be given at all.

Other factors that may limit or affect the services given include adverse conditions of the skin, hair or scalp, incompatibility of a product, the presence of a hairpiece (or the consequences of wearing one), a condition that justifies referral, such as a suspected infection or infestation, or a condition of which the diagnosis is doubtful.

CLIENT AFTER-CARE

REGIS

After-care and subsequent salon services include

- advising clients on how to manage new styles
- passing product knowledge on to the client, together with manufacturers' recommendations for after-care
- discussing the possible effects that salon services might have on the client and her hair in the future, particularly those involving treatment with chemicals
- prompting and encouraging clients to ask about salon services about which they are unsure
- guiding clients to adopt safe practices, such as combing and brushing hair correctly, or avoiding swimming without hair protection (which can affect coloured and bleached hair)
- promoting the client to use products and practices that will benefit her and keep her hair in good condition
- recording carefully all the services the client receives in the salon, so that they can be readily identified if she asks for a repeat treatment.

ACTIVITY
Collect individual manufacturer's product and technical services information. This can form the basis for giving useful advice to your clients.

MAINTAINING CLIENT GOODWILL

A client's trust and goodwill are enhanced by clear communication, and the manner in which you communicate with her. Leaving misunderstandings to run riot can undermine a great deal of careful, thoughtful work. The following points may be of help.

- Telling the client the reasons for delays or disruptions in services can be reassuring; leaving her to wonder what is happening is the last thing to create goodwill!
- Learn to recognise the cultural differences and needs of your clients. Different races and religious creeds have different requirements, and you must be able to understand them. Ask your seniors for help and advice about this.

- Your client will feel more comfortable if she is confident that you are looking after her personal belongings carefully and reliably. Simply putting her possessions on a chair in reception and leaving them there is not acceptable – she is sure to feel anxious about them.
- Discussing with the client how the services she is receiving are progressing reduces tension and uneasiness.
- You can also help to maintain her confidence by being prepared to enlist the aid of other competent staff if necessary.

ACTIVITY

Look up the words 'goodwill' and 'trust' in a dictionary. Make a note of the meanings given there, and keep it in your folder.

ACTIVITY

Describe ways in which you would ensure the client's confidence while dealing with her and giving the services she requests.

ASSIGNMENTS: CLIENT CARE

A practical activity

With the help of your colleagues, practise the different processes of client care, such as consultation, preparing the client and her hair, questioning a client, examining hair and scalp, testing hair and skin, and so on. Keep notes of any problems and difficulties you come across. The use of audio and video recorders is invaluable; keep copies of your tapes if you can. Then answer the following questions. Record your answers for your folder.

1. What is client consultation? Why is it necessary?.
2. List the questions that need to be asked during a consultation. How do you record the consultation process?
3. Make a list of your salon's services and the prices charged for them. List any other sales or services you know of.
4. List the hair and skin tests that you can use. State when and why each test should be applied and how you record the results of them.
5. What are the processes of client and hair preparation? Why are they necessary?
6. Why are anatomy and physiology included in your studies?
7. Make a list of the body systems.
8. What is meant by the words 'goodwill', 'trust' and 'confidentiality'?

For you to find out

Investigate the process of analysis and diagnosis of diseases and defects of the hair and skin. Exercises can be simulated by working with your colleagues. Use your textbooks, drawings, sketches, photographs and other means of illustration. Both audio and video recorders can be helpful. Then answer the following questions. Record all your answers for your folder.

1. What do the words 'analysis' and 'diagnosis' mean?
2. Outline the stages of examining the hair and scalp. What are you looking for? How do you record the results?
3. List the symptoms of the various conditions. List the causes of each disease. How does this information affect the work to be done?
4. List the hair and skin tests that can help you decide what can be done for your client. How do you compile the results? What do you do with them?
5. What are the different hair types, hair textures and hair conditions? Describe these, and try to illustrate them. How do they affect hairdressing services?
6. Draw a hair and the skin in cross-section. Label the different parts. List the effects that hairdressing services (chemical and physical) may have on the hair and skin.

A case study

Your salon has decided to take on a new range of products, which can be used for most of the services offered to clients. Outline what you need to do

- to understand what the products can do and what they have to offer – their advantages and disadvantages
- to satisfy yourself of their suitability for your different clients
- to best present these new products to your clients
- to begin to understand how the different services and products are finally priced.

What might you do if the clients began to complain of the results of these new products?

PREPARING FOR ASSESSMENT

In preparing for your assessment on client care the following checklist may be useful. Check that you have covered and now fully understand these items:

- consulting with clients before any services are applied
- identifying clients' wishes and requirements
- recognising the differences between hair types, states and conditions
- considering the effects of chemicals on 'virgin' (untreated) and treated hair
- differentiating between diseases, conditions and defects of the hair and scalp
- referring clients to others
- testing hair and skin for suitability for the different chemical treatments
- identifying factors that limit services and choices of product
- dealing with a client when test results indicate that her request for service cannot be carried out safely
- preparing clients for an agreed service – the time the service takes, the price charged and the after-care required
- communicating effectively, reassuring the client that goodwill, trust and confidentiality are maintained in your salon
- maintaining accurate records of information – and understanding how it should be used.

When you feel that you are ready to be assessed, talk to your trainer and arrange a suitable time.

CHAPTER 3

Shampooing and conditioning hair

CAROL HAYES & ASSOCIATES

INTRODUCTION

Shampoos and shampooing, conditioners and conditioning, are important parts of good hair care, and indeed the basis of it. Whether shampoos and conditioners are sold for you to use in the salon or for clients to use at home, their application requires thought and care. They affect most of the physical and chemical applications in hairdressing.

There is a wide range of shampoos and conditioners, especially designed for use on the hair and skin. The chemistry involved is not simple. Much time, effort, money and research is spent on designing and making professional products so that they can benefit the user's hair and be safe to use. Always follow the manufacturer's guidance for their use, since only the maker can be fully aware of their composition and effects.

The following are some of the topics that are covered in this chapter:

- understanding shampoos and shampooing
- selection of products
- chemistry of shampoos
- how shampoos work
- shampooing techniques
- acidity and alkalinity
- hair condition, conditioners and conditioning
- hair treatments.

SHAMPOOING – PRINCIPLES

Shampooing is the important procedure of cleaning both the hair and the scalp. Shampooing removes dirt, grease and any other matter that coats the hair and scalp. This is essential in preparing the hair for other processes: if any deposits remain in the hair after shampooing, they may interfere with these processes – for example, they could block perm chemicals or leave the hair too greasy to blow-style.

cuticle
deposits
cortex

Dirt on the hair cuticle

Good shampooing can be both physically and psychologically soothing, relaxing and enjoyable. Make sure your client is comfortable throughout. Poor shampooing technique may irritate your client, and lead to general dissatisfaction.

SALON AMBIENCE

Equipment

Preparing to shampoo

- Discuss with the client what you are going to do.
- Select suitable protective clothing – gowns and towels.
- Analyse the state of hair and scalp, examining it carefully. Consider what processes to follow. Ask questions, such as 'What products do you use at home?', 'How often do you shampoo your hair?', 'How do you style your hair?'
- Report immediately to a senior member of staff any signs of abnormality (disease or injury). Serious injury and some infectious diseases indicate that no hairdressing service should be carried out (see Chapter 2).
- Consult with the client throughout. Make sure the client knows the price to be paid for any special treatments used, and agrees to your choice of shampoo.
- Indicate how long shampooing will take – about five minutes – and what is to follow.

Choosing a shampoo

Shampoos come in various forms, including creams, semi-liquids and gels. There are different shampoo bases (the substances that form the bulk of the shampoo), and some are kinder and gentler on hair and skin than others. The detergent content in shampoos for greasy hair is higher than in those for normal or dry hair. The balance of the various shampoo ingredients is important. So too is their ability to deal with different hair types and conditions.

Shampoos may be named after the ingredients contained in them, such as 'lemon shampoo' for its lemon essence or citric acid content. Herbal, vegetable and other natural products are popular.

Increasingly, hairdressers are using one basic, general-purpose shampoo for all types of hair. Such a shampoo does not contain special ingredients to deal with particular problems; instead these are treated afterwards with creams, lotions or other products. The method is thought to be more effective.

Popular shampoos

- **Johoba** For dry hair: contains a light non-greasy oil, which has good moisturising effects.

TRESemmé

Shampoos

- **Coconut** For dry hair: contains an emollient, which helps to regain smooth and elastic hair.
- **Camomile** For greasy hair: brightens, shines, soothes; the dry powder is effective.
- **Rosemary** For normal hair: reduces scale, is antiseptic and stimulating.
- **Soya** For normal hair: contains a useful moisturiser.
- **Oil** For dry hair: contains pine, palm, almond and other oils; softens and conditions.
- **Egg** The egg white for greasy hair (it emulsifies grease and is easily rinsed), the egg yolk for dry hair.
- **Medicated** Helps to maintain the normal state of hair and skin; juniper is helpful if the scalp is scaly.
- **Treatment** Various shampoos, each designed to deal with a specific problem, such as dandruff or excessive greasiness: they usually contain cetrimide, selenium sulphide or zinc pyrithione.
- **Pre-perm** Intended to be used before the application of a perm process: contain chemicals that ensure that the hair surface is clear of chemicals that could interfere with the perm's action on the hair, and that the porosity of the hair is even throughout its length; follow the manufacturer's instructions for use.

ACTIVITY

Try making your own conditioning rinses. Try a teaspoonful of lemon juice in half a litre of water.

As a setting lotion, try using three teaspoonfuls of beer. Use light beer for fine hair, dark beer for coarse hair. You will find that the smell of beer disappears while the hair is drying.

Making the right choice – the needs of the hair

The right choice of shampoo depends on several factors.

WELLA

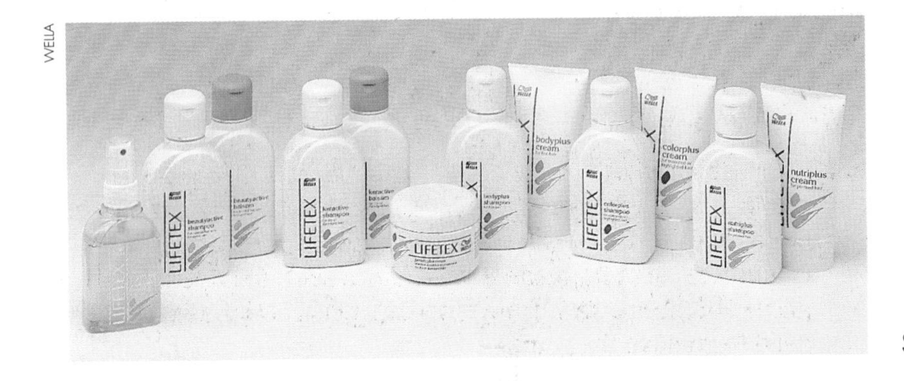

Shampoos

- **Type, texture and condition of hair** Fine hair requires a shampoo that will not degrease it or make it too fluffy. Choose a shampoo that will add body, or consider using a hair thickener. Coarse hair requires a shampoo that will tend to soften it and make it more pliable. Thick hair requires a shampoo that will penetrate and make good contact with all of the hair and the whole scalp. (See page 58 for a discussion of products designed to deal with hair in poor condition.)
- **Frequency of shampooing** If hair is washed once or more daily, choose a shampoo specially designed for frequent use.
- **Water quality** If the water used in the salon is hard (see page 54), soap-based shampoos will tend to form scum. Use soap-free shampoos. In soft-water areas most types of shampoo can be used.
- **The function of the shampoo** Is it intended to colour, tone, condition or just cleanse the hair?
- **Hair treatments planned** What are you going to do with the hair later? Some shampoo ingredients (lanolin is an example) coat the hair shaft. This would prevent cold perm lotions from working, for instance. In this case you would need to use a pre-perm shampoo.

ACTIVITY

When visiting a chemist or hairdressing wholesaler, note the shampoos that are recommended for frequent use (once or more daily).

Which types of shampoo does your salon use? Which does it sell for home use?

TIP

Regular brushing helps to remove dirt from hair.

How shampoos work

The object of shampooing is to clean the hair by removing dirt, grease, skin scale and sweat, plus any hairspray, gel, mousse, dressing cream, etc. Water alone cannot dissolve and rinse out all these substances so as to leave the hair in a suitable condition for processes such as blow-styling, setting, perming or bleaching.

Shampooing involves rubbing the head with shampoo and water to enable the cleaners to surround the hair and dirt particles. Using large amounts of shampoo is unnecessary and wasteful. A small amount, thoroughly spread and massaged into the scalp, is just as effective.

Types of shampoo

- **Soap shampoos** These are not generally used in salons nowadays. They cleaned the hair, but formed scum deposits on the hair and skin when used with hard water. These coated the hair and made it lank. Citric acid (from lemon juice) and acetic acid (from vinegar), made into rinses, were used to remove the scum.

ACTIVITY

Use a shampoo containing soap with hard water. Note the scum that forms.

Then use an acid rinse. Notice how the scum is cleared from the scalp and hair.

- **Soapless shampoos** These are now popular in most salons. They are effective in both hard and soft water, and do not leave scum deposits. The early soapless shampoos were very harsh and removed too much grease from the hair and skin. They also produced static electricity, which made the hair flyaway. These faults have now been largely overcome.
- **Synthetic detergents (surface-active agents, surfactants)** The bases from which soapless shampoos are made. An example is **triethanolamine lauryl sulphate**, commonly known as **TLS**.

Detergents

By itself, water does not spread thoroughly over the hair and scalp. This is because water molecules are attracted together by weak electrical forces. These have their greatest effect at the water surface, creating what is known as **surface tension**. On hair, water by itself tends to form droplets. The **detergent** in shampoo reduces surface tension, allowing the water to spread over the hair and scalp, wetting them. Detergents are, in other words, **wetting agents**.

Each detergent molecule has two ends. One end (the **hydrophilic** one) attracts water molecules; the other (the **hydrophobic** one) repels them, and instead attracts grease. Detergent molecules lift the grease off the hair surface and suspend it in the water. The suspension is called an **emulsion**. The dirt is held by the grease, so as the grease is removed, the dirt loosens too. The emulsion and loose dirt can be rinsed away with water, leaving the hair clean.

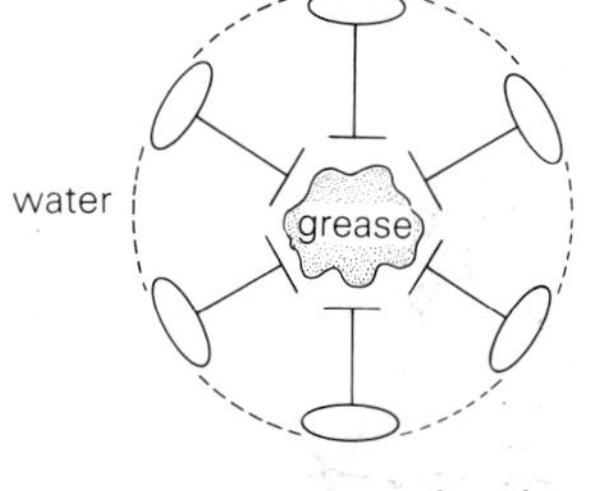

Detergent molecules surrounding grease

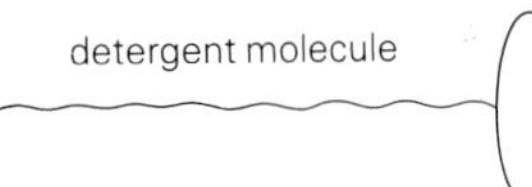

A detergent molecole

SHAMPOOING TECHNIQUE

Apart from cleaning the hair, shampooing can affect the client's mood. Hands and fingers used too lightly or too harshly may irritate, as may missing out parts of the head. Be thorough in all your hand and finger movements.

> **HEALTH AND SAFETY**
> Remove rings, wrist watches or bangles when shampooing to avoid moisture or shampoo building up on your skin, which could become sensitised.

Shampooing method

1. Protect and care for the client throughout the process.
2. First prepare the hair by combing and disentangling it. Ensure that long hair is off the face and neck. Do not let it become tangled.
3. Check that the client is comfortable, especially the position of the head.
4. Run the cold water first, then mix hot water into the cold. Test the water mixture and temperature on the back of your hand. After lifting the spray, and before applying it to the client, test the water temperature again.
5. Check the water flow and pressure. Do not allow water to flow down the neck or on to the face.
6. Keep one hand between the head and the water spray – you will then be aware of any temperature changes.
7. Thoroughly wet the hair: avoid wetting the client.
8. Ensure that the hair, particularly if it is long, is controlled and directed into the water stream.
9. Apply shampoo, first into the palm of your hand. Distribute it evenly over the hair and scalp. Use as little shampoo as is necessary, or most of it will be wasted.
10. With clawed fingers, massage the scalp in a circular manner. Cover the whole scalp – be sure to avoid missing any part.
11. Rinse the hair thoroughly, again checking the water temperature and pressure.
12. If necessary, apply more shampoo and repeat the process.
13. Finally rinse all traces of lather from the skin and hair.

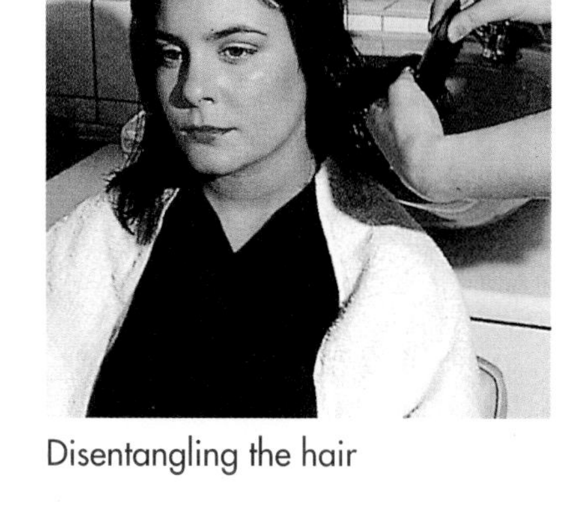

Disentangling the hair

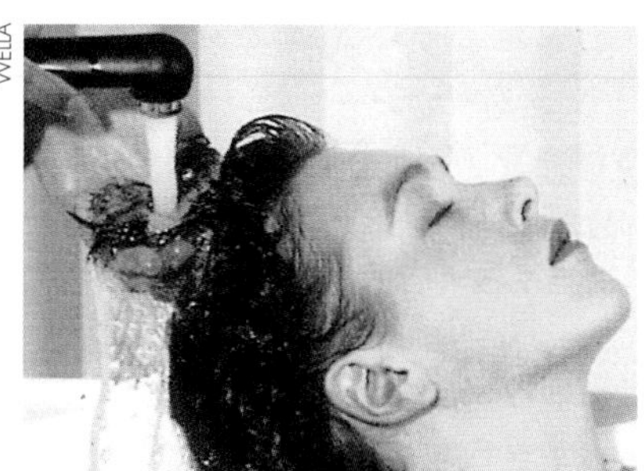

WELLA

Shampooing: water flow

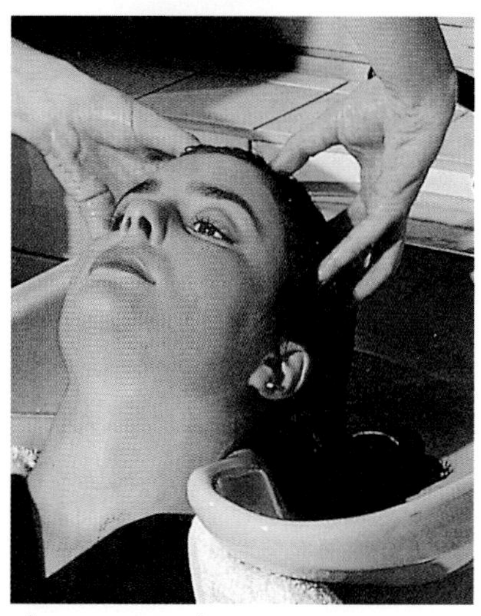

Shampooing: finger positions

> **HEALTH AND SAFETY**
> Sharp fingernails can scratch or tear the skin, causing discomfort and even infection. Keep your nails smoothly filed.

Massage techniques

There are three types of massage movements you can use when shampooing: **effleurage** (stroking), **pétrissage** (rotary), and **friction** (rubbing).

1. Begin shampooing with smooth effleurage movements.
2. Continue with firm but gentle rotary pétrissage movement:
    - Let your fingertips glide over the scalp. Lift your hands periodically to avoid tangling the hair.
    - Move your hands towards each other – up from the sides to the top and down across the nape area.

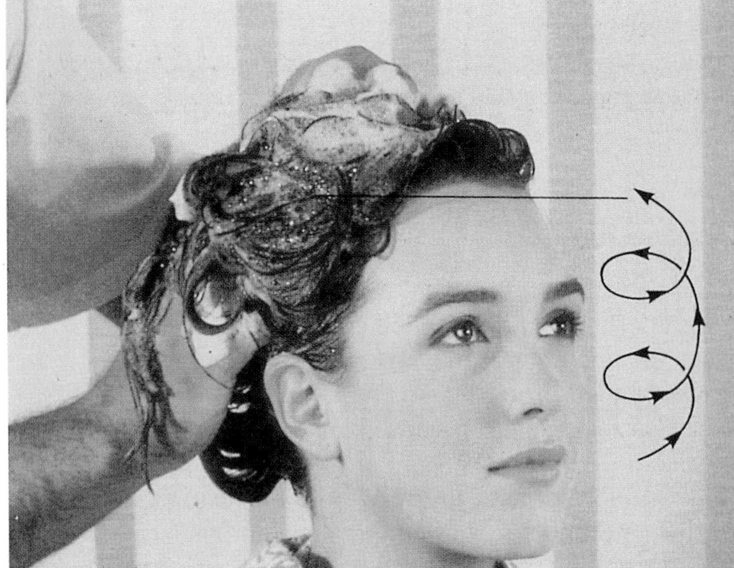

Shampooing: finger movements

- Move your hands in decreasing circles around the head to make sure you cover the scalp fully.

3. Use lighter, plucking, friction movements to stimulate the scalp gently.
4. Finally, use soothing effleurage movements to complete the shampooing process.

While shampooing

- Make sure the client is comfortable at all times.
- Check massage movements, water temperatures, water flow and pressure, and the client's position.
- Work hygienically. This is good practice at all times; it also reassures your client who can then relax and enjoy the hairdressing processes.

HEALTH AND SAFETY
Remove any shampoo from the eyes with plenty of cool, clean water.

After shampooing

1. Turn off the water flow. Return the spray head to its place.
2. Lift the hair from the face. Wrap it with a towel, and gently remove any surplus water remaining in the hair.
3. Reposition the client comfortably.
4. Check that all shampoo, dirt and grease has been removed and that the skin and hair are clean. (Your assessor or trainer will be specially looking to see whether the hair and skin *are* clean after shampooing.)
5. At this stage you may apply conditioner if this is required.

The hair should now be ready for combing and the processes that follow.

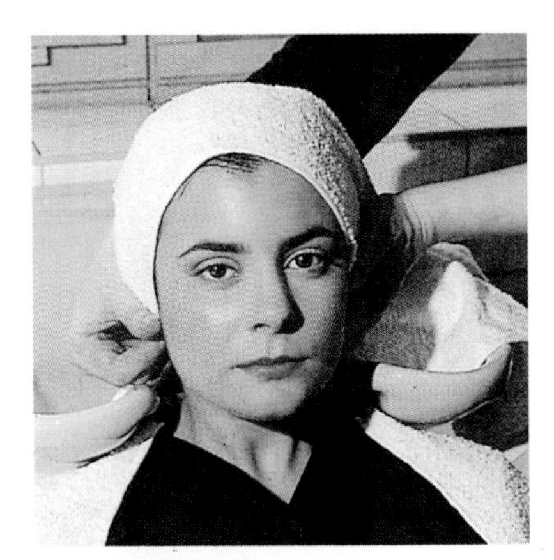

After shampooing

Do's and don'ts

- Give your complete attention to the client.

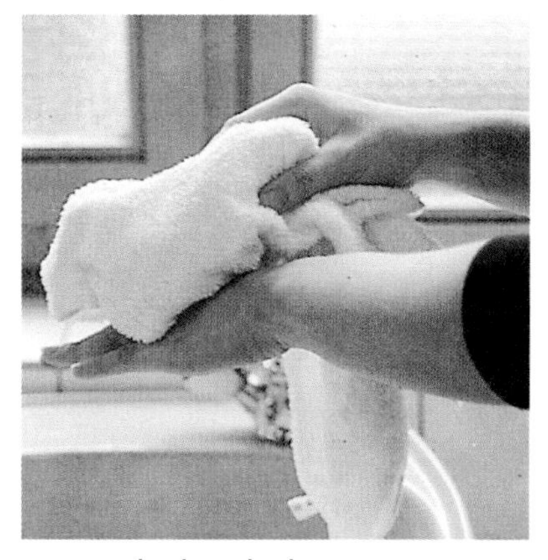
Patting the hands dry

HEALTH AND SAFETY

Raising a client from a forward washing position too quickly can make her feel dizzy. Allow a little time before moving her to another position.

Do not let the hair fall over the client's eyes when moving.

Remember that, apart from chilling and scalding your client, water that is too hot or cold can cause shock. Always check the water temperature before applying the water.

- Never use unwashed linen on another client.
- Ensure that towels and gowns are clean, in place, and not too tightly secured.
- Use sensible hygiene to prevent cross-infection and to safeguard health generally.
- Do not allow shampoo to come into contact with the client's eyes.
- Direct the water flow away from the client to avoid wetting her clothes and face.
- Comb the hair after shampooing, without tugging or pulling it.
- As soon as you have finished, clean the part of the salon where the shampooing was carried out. Remove dirty, used towels. Replace shampoo containers. Make sure the chair is left clean.
- Always turn off the water – do not allow water to run continuously between washes. This soon empties the hot water tank. By turning water off when it is not in use you avoid delay, waste and higher costs.
- Always rinse your hands after shampooing. Do not allow shampoo to remain: it might cause dryness and soreness (dermatitis). Gently pat your hands dry – never 'scrub' them with a towel.

ACTIVITY

With colleagues, shampoo each other's hair. Compare the shampoo actions used with long and short hair.

Massage the scalp. When the hair is long, notice the position of your hands. How often do you lift the hands from the head to avoid tangling the hair?

WATER FOR SHAMPOOING

Salons use a lot of water – about 10–20 litres for each wash. It is therefore important that there is a constant supply of both hot and cold water. Anything that interferes with the salon's plumbing and drainage systems may cause delay and financial loss. Don't leave hot taps running longer than necessary, or you could soon empty the hot water tank.

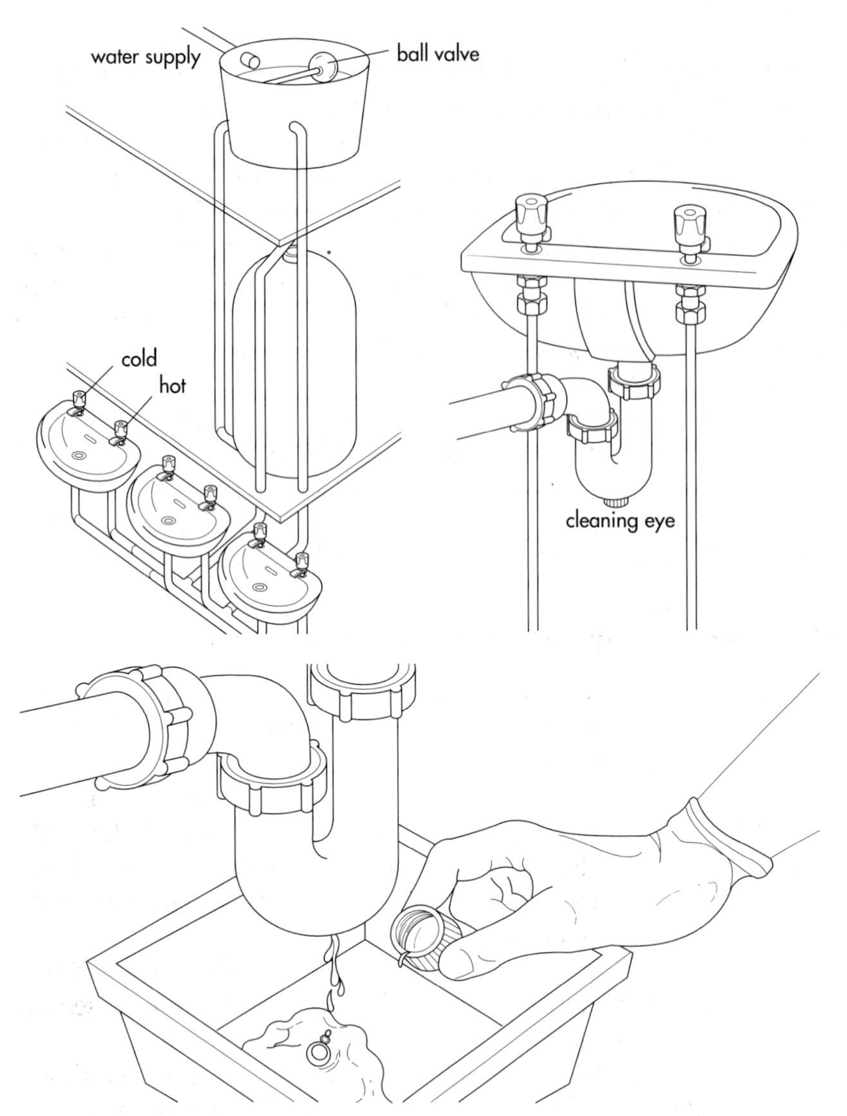

Hot water storage and supply (*far left*)
Plumbing and drainage (*left*)

Retrieving an earring from a bottle trap

Cold water reaches the salon via a main supply pipe from the road: if necessary this can be disconnected using a **stopcock**. Cold water is stored in a tank. Some is heated (using gas, electricity or oil) and this hot water is stored in a second tank.

Waste water leaves the salon via outlet pipes to the drains. Beneath each basin is a **waste trap**. This has two functions. First, it holds water and stops gases and smells from the drains reaching the salon. Second, it collects hair and debris, making the pipes less likely to block. If an earring, for example, falls through the plughole, you can retrieve it by undoing the trap.

HEALTH AND SAFETY
Always wear gloves when handling chemicals.

HEALTH AND SAFETY
Always report blocked pipes or basins immediately. Standing waste water smells, encourages bacterial growth, and may spread disease.

Hard and soft water

Hard water is water that contains calcium and/or magnesium salts. If these are not removed, they react with chemicals in soap (sodium stearate) to form an insoluble **scum** (calcium or magnesium stearate). So soap shampoos should not be used with hard water, without using special rinses afterwards. Soapless shampoos are now almost always used, and these do not form scum in hard water.

TIP
Prolong the life of your equipment by keeping it free from limescale.

The chemicals in water determine whether it is 'permanently'

ACTIVITY
Find out if the water in your salon is hard or soft. If it is hard, is it permanently or temporarily hard?

HEALTH AND SAFETY
Find out where the main electricity switch and the water stopcock are, and how to turn them off.

If a tank or pipe bursts, turn off *both* the electricity *and* the water. Until you have done so, don't touch light switches or electrical devices – you might be electrocuted.

or 'temporarily' hard. This affects the products and equipment used. **Permanently hard water** contains calcium and magnesium sulphates. These cannot be removed from the water by boiling. **Temporarily hard water** contains calcium and magnesium hydrogencarbonates (bicarbonates). Boiling temporarily hard water changes these into the carbonates, which are insoluble and so separate out of the water. These form a hard deposit of 'fur', or **limescale**, in steamers, kettles, hot water pipes, shower heads and sprays. Limescale can be removed using special descaling solutions.

Soft water is water that is free from calcium and magnesium salts. Soft water may be supplied direct by the local water authority, or it may be hard water that has been softened by a special softening process. Soft water does not form scum when used with soap, nor does it form limescale when it is heated.

Acidity and alkalinity: the pH scale

Shampooing, like other chemical actions, can affect the surface of the skin. You should consider how acid or alkaline the skin surface will be left after shampooing.

The **pH scale** measures acidity or alkalinity. It ranges from pH 1 to pH 14. **Acids** have pH numbers below 7. **Alkalis** have pH numbers above 7. **Neutral** substances have a pH close to 7. The *higher* the pH number, the more *alkaline* the substance; the *lower* the pH number, the more *acid* the substance.

The normal pH of the skin's surface is 5–6. This is referred to as the skin's **acid mantle**. The acidity is due in part to the sebum, the natural oil produced by the skin.

An important skin function is the protection of the underlying tissue (Chapter 2). The skin does this by acting as a barrier, preventing liquid loss from inside, and keeping excess liquid outside the body. It also protects the body from infection. An acid skin surface inhibits (slows down) the growth of bacteria, and makes them less likely to enter the skin. If the acidity of the skin is reduced – if the pH rises above 5–6 – infections are more likely. This may happen if the pH is not adjusted after chemical hairdressing processes such as perming.

The pH can be measured using **pH papers** or **Universal indicator papers**. **Litmus papers** will tell you whether something is acid, alkaline or neutral.

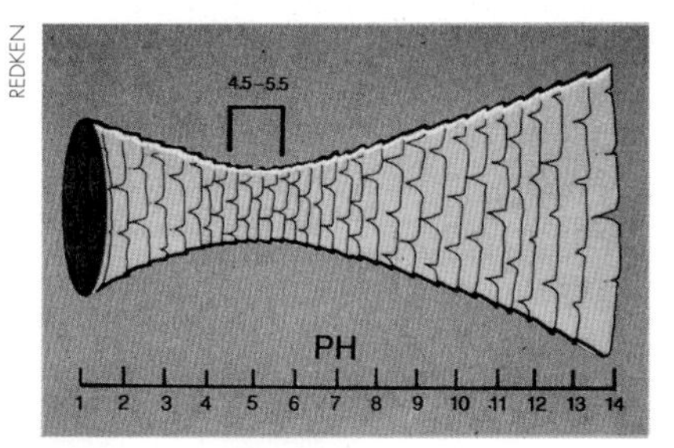

REDKEN

How pH affects the hair

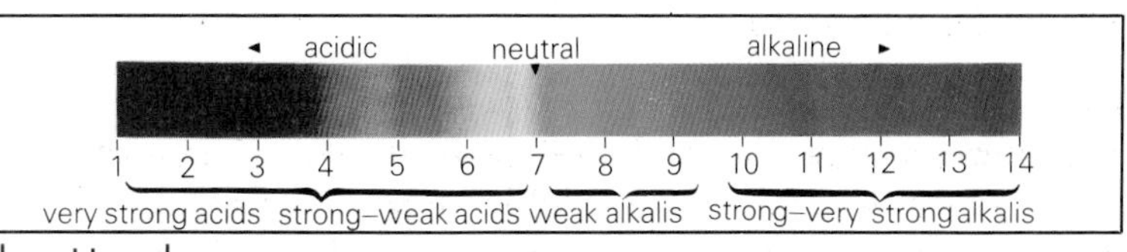

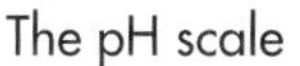

The pH scale

If hairs are placed in alkaline solution they swell, and the cuticle lifts. In slightly acid solution the cuticle is smooth and the hair is soft; in strong acid, however, it begins to break down.

ACTIVITY

Keep a 'product knowledge' book. Record the shampoos and conditioners you use. What are their active ingredients? What pH does each have? (You can use indicator papers to find out.) What are the effects on your clients' or your own hair?

How would you advise your clients about choosing a shampoo?

CONDITIONING – PRINCIPLES

Conditioned hair

Caring for your client's hair and keeping it in good condition is the basis of good hairdressing. If the hair is torn and breaking, or the surface cuticle rough and splitting, the appearance will be dull and uninteresting. It may lose elasticity, and shape and curl will be difficult to hold. Control too becomes difficult. If you ignore poor condition and apply further harsh treatments, you may cause more serious damage.

The client

- As a first step, consult the client. Ask what has been done and what has been used on it to. If this is a regular client, check the record card for past history.
- Examine and analyse the hair and scalp closely. Assess the condition and extent of any damage to the hair.
- From what you can see, diagnose any problems – porous hair, loss of elasticity, cuticle peeling, split ends, dryness, greasiness and so on. Try to find the reasons for these faults.
- Advise the client – what can be done, what treatments are available, which products to use, and the possible benefits.
- Agree with the client the course of action to be taken. Make sure that the cost of services you agree is understood, and is acceptable.
- Make sure that the client is aware of the need for more than one treatment, application or process of conditioning.
- Emphasise the need for correct home care. Offer advice and suggest ways in which the client can deal with the problem.

Hair condition – possible problems

Hair condition is affected by many factors, including not just the external impact of chemicals, physical treatment and the weather, but also the internal effects of the client's health and lifestyle.

ACTIVITY

Visit your local chemist and list the different hair products that are available. You may be surprised at how many there are. Take note of the prices, the quantities and the names of the manufacturers. Compare this range with your salon's own range of hair products.

External factors

These include all physical treatments, such as:

- combing, brushing, backdressing
- shampooing
- blow-drying/styling
- hot rolling and brushing, crimping or tonging
- all hairdressing processes
- wearing postiche, dreadlocks, etc.

Careful examination of the hair and scalp is always necessary to check its state and condition. Look at the hair closely. Feel the hair's surface. Examine the skin of the scalp. Talk to the client, and listen to what is said. Ask if the client has had any problems.

Hair is subjected to many 'normal' treatments, such as shampooing. If badly carried out these can be the main cause of poor hair condition. If necessary, advise your clients on how to care for their hair at home.

ACTIVITY
Try drying several hair samples using a hand-held hairdryer, at 15 cm and 30 cm away from the hair. Compare the effects on the hair cuticle and appearance.

Effects of the weather

These include:

- sun, wind, sand, sea and salt
- extremes of climate – hot or cold, dry or humid
- moisture effects on the hair's elasticity or flexibility.

If the effects of the weather are not guarded against, hair condition will inevitably become poor. In extreme weather it is best to keep the hair covered and protected.

ACTIVITY
Expose one of your hair samples to the sun, another to salty water, and another to chlorinated water collected from a local swimming pool. (First ask the attendant if you may take a sample.) Compare their effects. Then use the samples for conditioning, and again record your results.

Chemical effects

These result from:

- all hairdressing processes, including perming, tinting and bleaching, and overprocessing generally
- swimming in the sea or in pools, if salt or chlorine is left on the hair and the hair is not rinsed thoroughly afterwards
- the use of cosmetics, particularly where manufacturers' guidance is not followed.

If correct procedures are not followed, and the effects are not dealt with, further damage may result.

L'OREAL

Healthy hair

General health and lifestyle

The normal or abnormal working of the body has a direct effect on the hair and scalp.

- Good health is reflected in good hair and skin. A balanced diet with plenty of fresh foods contributes to good health.
- Disease, and drugs used in the treatment of disease, take their toll on the hair and skin.
- Genetic factors affecting hair growth determine hair strength and texture.
- The hair of women in pregnancy is usually at its best. Deterioration of the hair and skin *after* giving birth is usually due to stress and tiredness.
- If hair becomes a focus of attention it may be pulled, twisted and in general handled too much.

Assessment

Close examination of the hair and skin may reveal the following states or conditions:

- dry/very dry, splitting hair, ends or shafts breaking, dull/very dull appearance
- hair normal, smooth cuticle, shiny, easy to manage
- greasy/very greasy, lank, difficult to control
- dry, splitting ends with greasy roots
- hair forming tight curls
- straight or wavy hair
- chemically processed hair
- lack of elasticity, breaks easily (poor tensile strength)
- poor porosity (absorbs quickly but cannot retain)
- externally coated with chemical deposits from products such as hairsprays.

When you have assessed the hair condition, consider the treatments available to correct it. These are described in the rest of this chapter.

ACTIVITY

Using some hair samples, apply different shampoos or conditioners and carefully note their effect on the cuticle, its elasticity and its appearance.

CONDITIONERS

The best **conditioners** protect hair so that it does not lose its natural condition, or help treated hair to return to a healthy condition. They have the following general effects:

TRESemmé

Conditioners

ACTIVITY
Use some samples of hair in poor condition to try out various hair conditioners. Note the effectiveness of each.

- the hair cuticle is smoothed
- hair tangling is reduced
- broken areas of the cuticle or cortex may be repaired
- the hair surface reflects more light, producing a gloss or sheen
- surface acidity/alkalinity is balanced.

Conditioners may also be used to deal with particular problems:

- some allow the cortex to attract water – these are called **humectants** and **moisturisers**
- others allow the cortex to retain moisture – these are called **emollients**
- some counteract the effects of oxidation (chemical reactions which take place during processes like tinting or bleaching) – these are called **antioxidants**.

The following are some of the conditioners used:

- control creams, dressings, oils, hairsprays, gels
- reconditioning rinses, emulsions, humectants
- acid and alkaline rinses
- restructurants and protein builders
- antioxidants
- pH balancers (after shampooing, tinting, etc.)
- gels, mousses (foams for setting, dressing, etc.)
- hair thickeners (for conditioning and building fine hair).

Types of conditioner

There are several different types of conditioner. Some remain on the surface of the hair, others penetrate the cortex. Some may be both surface *and* penetrating in their action. Both surface and penetrating conditioners may be combined with **bactericides** and **fungicides** to help stop the growth of bacteria and fungi on hair and skin.

Surface conditioners

Surface conditioners add gloss and help to make the hair manageable. They do not enter the hair but remain on the surface. They smooth the surface by coating it. Some also neutralise the effects of chemical processes such as tinting and bleaching.

Commonly used surface conditioners include:

- dressing creams and oils
- reconditioning creams and lotions
- acid or rehabilitating rinses.

These may be applied before, during or after treatments. They may contain some of the following ingredients:

- lanolin
- cholesterol
- vegetable and mineral oils

- fats and waxes
- lecithin
- citric, acetic and lactic acids.

Penetrating conditioners

Penetrating conditioners enter the hair shaft by capillary action – the passage of materials through the tiny cellular spaces within the hair. Penetrating conditioners are designed to repair the chemical structure of fibres within the cortex which have been damaged or affected by previous hairdressing processes. These types of conditioner can also smooth the hair cuticle and make the whole hair structure much stronger. They may contain the following ingredients:

- quaternary ammonium compounds
- sulphur compounds
- protein hydrolysates (individual amino acids and very short lengths of polypeptide, see below), which strengthen the hair
- humectants, which hold water in the hair
- emollients, which soften tissue and hair
- moisturisers, which help to retain moisture.

How conditioners work

Modern conditioners achieve their effects by chemically balancing the hair structure. They also counteract the effects that chemical and physical processes have on the hair. This applies particularly to the alkalinity or acidity of the hair's surface.

The electrical and chemical properties of substances in conditioners help them to adhere to or combine with the hair.

Materials which are chemically attracted to the hair structure are called **substantive conditioners**. The newer **hair**

ACTIVITY
With colleagues, examine and assess each other's hair condition before and after conditioning. Compare the effectiveness of different products and methods, and record your results.

MAHOGANY

Conditioned hair

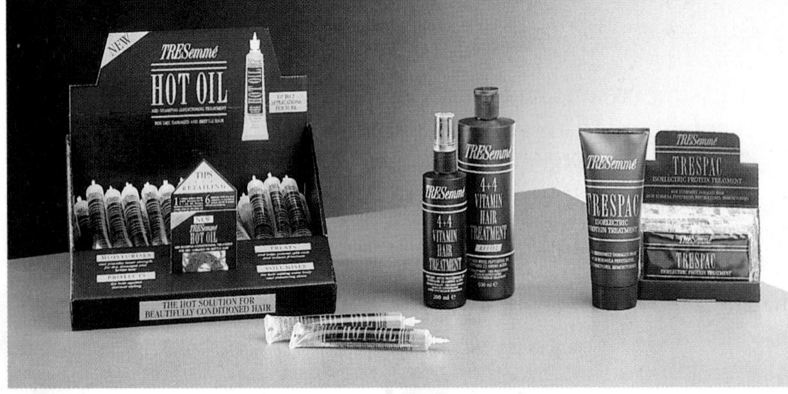

TRESemmé

Conditioning treatments

thickeners, **hair builders**, **restructurants** and **protein hydrolysates** combine with the polypeptide chains within the hair, and create extra crosslinks. This builds up the hair, and in some cases actually thickens it.

Protein hydrolysates are produced by a chemical reaction involving protein breakdown and the addition of water. They may be obtained from animal and other proteins. They are used in conditioners which strengthen and moisturise the hair.

CONDITIONING TREATMENTS

Conditioning treatments may be applied:

- to correct some hair states – dryness or greasiness, for example
- to counteract the effect of hairdressing processes
- as 'before' or 'after' treatments
- to soften and smooth tight curly hair or coarse hair
- to maintain healthy hair.

Dandruff

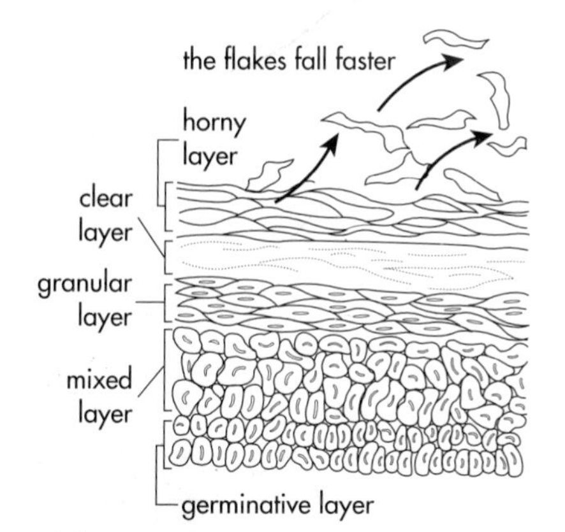

Flaking scalp

Dandruff, or **pityriasis capitis**, is caused by the overproduction of skin cells. It appears as small, very fine, white, loose scales. These may irritate the scalp to varying degrees; they are also unsightly when they fall on to the shoulders, and may cause the sufferer anxiety. If the scales stick to the skin small patches of dry skin may result: these can cause inflammation.

Treatment

Dandruff is commonly treated at home. Treatment may include special shampoos, lotions or creams derived from tar, sulphur or zinc pyrithione. Recent reports suggest that fungicides may be helpful.

Special shampoos are usually sufficient, but particularly serious cases may require daily applications of anti-dandruff lotions or creams. If these are not effective, advise your client to see a doctor or trichologist.

It is important that you do not handle the hair roughly, and that you reduce scaling that might irritate your client's eyes. Although dandruff is not thought to be infectious, you should still take all the usual measures for hygiene to prevent any possible cross-infection.

Greasy hair

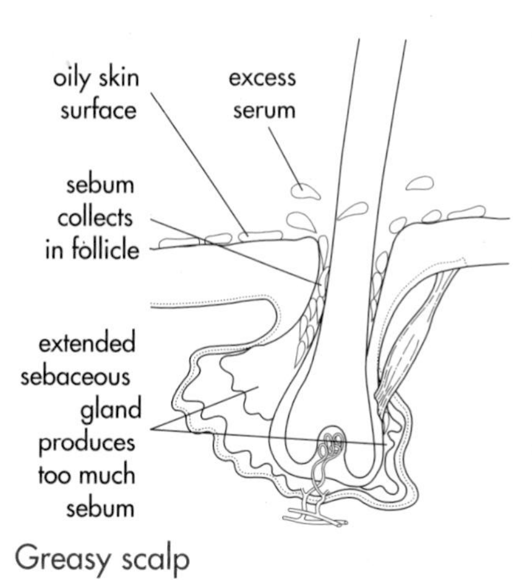

Greasy scalp

Greasy hair, or **seborrhoea**, is caused by grease from the sebaceous glands. These may be overstimulated by too much combing or brushing, or by too much hand or vibration massage. The use of greasy or oily products adds to the problem.

Treatment

Excessive grease must be removed by regular washing with balanced shampoos. Ammonium hydroxide, borax and astringent lotions may be used to correct excessively greasy conditions. **Astringent lotions** cause the skin to contract slightly, temporarily reducing the output of grease. If fungi or bacteria are irritating or stimulating the skin and causing the grease to be produced, fungicides and bactericides may be helpful, as may **alkaline rinses**.

These deal with the grease that is present: as with other problems, it is important also to identify the causes and deal with those too if possible.

HEALTH AND SAFETY
When treating dandruff or greasy hair, try one product at a time. Give it time to work before trying something else.

Other hair conditions

- **Fragilitas crinium (split ends)** Treat with substantive conditioners or restructurants, and by cutting.
- **Damaged cuticle** Treat with products such as restructurants or rehabilitating creams.
- **Trichorrhexis nodosa** Treat with protein hydrolysates or substantive conditioners.
- **Dry, brittle, broken, overprocessed hair** Treat with rehabilitating creams, moisturisers, restructurants or protein hydrolysates.

These conditions (also discussed in Chapter 2) may be caused by bad grooming, sleeping in rollers and curlers, wearing postiche too long, using poorly made combs and brushes, bad perm winding, chemical overprocessing, and overexposure to sun, wind and the like. Encourage your client to deal with the causes of the problem.

Where possible, cutting should be used to remove the worst areas of hair splitting.

Before and after processing

Where the cuticle has been damaged, the hair cortex becomes too porous, like a sponge, soaking up any chemicals applied to the hair. Older hair is more likely to be damaged than newer growth. The porosity must be reduced before hair will successfully take a perm or colouring.

Pre-perm treatments consist of lotions or creams that make porosity uniform throughout the hair, so that perm lotion will be taken up evenly. Pre-colouring treatments have a similar function, 'filling' or repairing areas of the cuticle. Use only conditioners that have been specially designed for use before chemical hairdressing processes, because these allow other materials to pass through to the hair – they are **permeable**. Conditioners that have not been designed to do this may form a barrier and make a process such as perming ineffective. Before using any

TIP
Before using any product, make sure you know what its action is. Record the effects of each product on each client. Did it do any good? Did it cause any problems?

conditioner, always check the manufacturer's instructions.

After processing, hair may need further treatment. For example, its normal state is slightly acid: many processes use alkaline solutions, so an acid conditioner may be needed at the end to correct the pH. Acid balancers and antioxidants help to remove surplus chemicals such as hydrogen peroxide, and to smooth the hair and keep it manageable.

MARK HILL FOR TRESemmé

Healthy hair

Maintaining a healthy condition

Keeping hair in good condition requires the regular use of conditioners to reduce the effects of harsh chemical and physical treatments.

Many poor hair states are caused by ignoring the basic principles of good hairdressing and grooming – cleaning and rinsing the hair correctly, carrying out processes as recommended, and handling the hair gently will all help to ensure good hair condition. Conditioners will keep healthy hair looking good and help in styling.

ACTIVITY

In your 'product knowledge' book, keep records of the different conditioners and treatments you use, and their effects on the different heads of hair. Don't forget those you use on your own hair!

OTHER TREATMENTS

The following treatments (with or without conditioners) may usefully be applied to the hair and scalp:

- massage
- steamers
- accelerators
- rollerballs
- radiant heat
- oil treatments, shampoos and applications.

Massage

Massage is a method of manipulating the skin and muscles. It may be applied by hand or machine. In the salon you will apply massage to the scalp, neck and face only.

Effects of massage

These include the following:

- improved blood flow to the skin – the redness this produces is called **hyperaemia**
- stimulation and soothing of nerve endings
- improved muscle tone, assisting normal contraction and relaxation

- removal of congestions or fatty lumps or adhesions in the skin
- improved removal of waste matter from the skin surface
- stimulation of the skin and of appendages such as hair follicles
- improved functioning of cells in the skin, including their nutrition, diffusion within them, and their ability to secrete substances.

There are several hand massage movements. Those of special interest to hairdressers are effleurage, pétrissage, tapotement, vibration and friction.

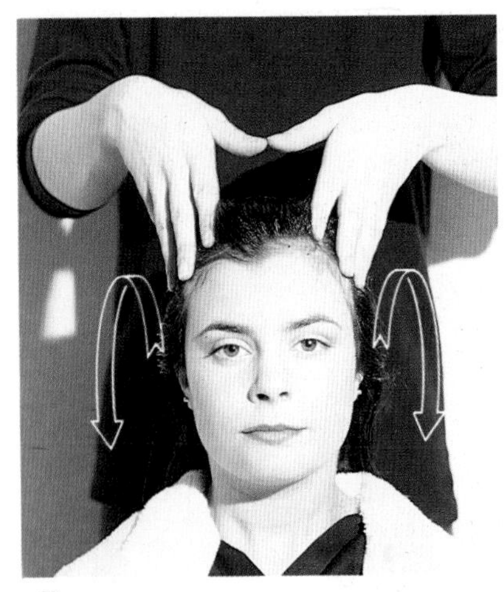

Effleurage

- **Effleurage** A smoothing, soothing, stroking action, performed with firm but gentle movements of the hands and fingertips. You use it before and after the most vigorous movements. It improves skin functions, soothes and stimulates nerves, and relaxes tensed muscles.
- **Pétrissage** A deeper, kneading movement, used to break down adhesions or fatty congestions in the skin. It assists the elimination of waste products and the flow of nutrients to the tissues of skin and muscles. Gentle pétrissage rotary movements are used on the scalp.

Pétrissage

- **Tapotement** A stimulating tapping or patting movement – a rapid, gentle beating applied with the hands and fingertips. Tapotement is used to stimulate nerves, restore muscle tone, and free the skin of fatty deposits. It is *not* recommended for scalp massage – it is mainly used on the body, on the hands and, lightly, on the face.
- **Friction** A rubbing movement applied with the fingertips in a light, flicking, gently plucking action. It is used on the scalp when applying lotions or during shampooing.
- **Vibration** A shaking movement, similar to friction but deeper. Light vibrations are soothing, heavier ones are more stimulating. These movements may be imitated by vibratory machines, commonly called 'vibros' and mainly used on the body. They *may* be used on the scalp, but only gently and carefully.

Friction

Points to remember

- Massage is only beneficial when applied in a quiet atmosphere. Keep noise and discussion to a minimum.
- Avoid hard, jerky, heavy movements to the scalp or head – these can only cause your client discomfort.
- Complete massage should not take longer than 15 minutes. Overstimulation might cause a headache, muscle fatigue or other problems.
- Do *not* give massage if there are any **contra-indications** – inflammation, breaks in the skin, spots, rashes or signs of disease, or if the client is undergoing medical treatment.

TIP

Use a timer for accuracy when you are giving massage.

TIP

Rotary movements of lightly applied pétrissage and friction are used throughout the shampooing process. Effleurage is used to distribute shampoos and conditioners.

- Do *not* give massage if the client has recently had a perm or colour.

Applying scalp massage

Scalp massage stimulates grease production and loosens skin, scale and dirt from the pores, so it is best given before shampooing. If the scalp or hair is very dirty, shampoo before *and* after massage. The duration of the massage depends on the client. Some people can stand more stimulation than others; older clients, for example, may be more sensitive.

A spirit-based massage lotion may help your hands and fingers to grip the skin surface. Remember that discussion between you and the client during massage will cause muscle tension to return, destroying the benefit of the massage.

1. Seat your client comfortably, with suitable protective garments.
2. Use effleurage first. Draw your fingertips firmly, but not too hard, over the head. Your hands should move from the front hairline down to the nape and shoulder tops.

   Repeat this several times. Make sure that the whole scalp is covered in this way. This soothes the skin surface and the underlying structures, relaxing the client.
3. Next use pétrissage. Apply this lightly but firmly: hard, fierce movements may rupture small blood vessels and cause discomfort.

   With the fingertips, feel through the hair to the scalp, and gently rotate the scalp over the skull. To achieve and maintain the correct balance, pressure and movement, claw the fingers and move them towards the thumbs. Slowly and gently cover the whole scalp, without exerting too much pressure. Use the small fingers, particularly on the temples.
4. Finally, use effleurage again: this removes excess blood brought to the scalp.
5. Allow your client to sit quietly for a while, to enjoy the effects of the massage.

ACTIVITY

Place a dry hair practice block (or samples of very dry hair in poor condition) under a steamer, and steam for several minutes. Note how much more resilient, or elastic, the hair becomes.

Steamers

Steamers are commonly used to apply moist heat to the skin and hair. They may be used before or during conditioning, and when tinting.

When you place the steamer over the client's head, steam is able to flow around the hair, which expands and softens. This helps conditioners to pass through the cuticle and enter the

TIP

Use distilled or deionised water in steamer kettles to prevent limescale build-up.

cortex of the hair. Conditioning products may be placed in the water reservoir and applied, with steam, to the hair. Steamers are beneficial when colouring and bleaching as they halve the normal processing time.

To achieve satisfactory results, always check the manufacturer's instructions before using the steamer.

WELLA

A steamer

Accelerators

Accelerators use radiated light and dry heat. They are useful for deep penetration of conditioning products. Like steamers, they help the hair to absorb conditioners and so reduce the processing time.

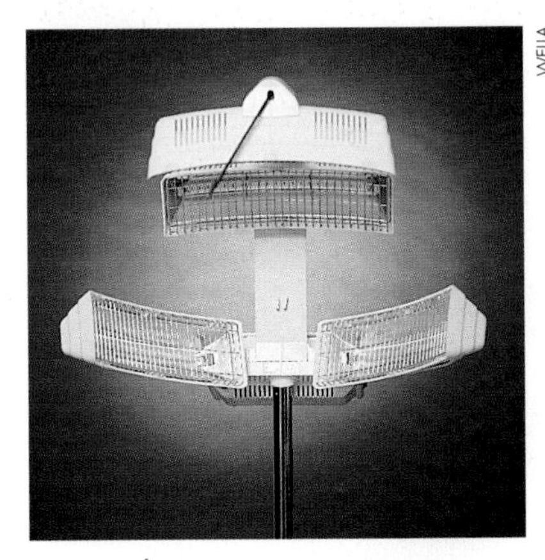
WELLA

An accelerator

Rollerballs

The **rollerball** is a new kind of accelerator, using infra-red heat and also offering a fan. The source of the heat moves continually, preventing 'hotspots'. Hairdressing processes can be carried out while it is in use. The rollerball can be used while perming, colouring or treating the hair, or simply to dry it.

Radiant heat and infra-red lamps

Like accelerators, **radiant heat** and **infra-red radiation** are used to irradiate the head and hair. The shorter rays of infra-red and radiant heat penetrate deep into the skin. Accelerators are used to activate certain chemical processes or to heat the hair before conditioning.

L'OREAL

A rollerball

Oils

Oils are useful for conditioning very dry, overbleached or overprocessed hair.

Oil applications or treatments

These consist in the use of a vegetable oil (such as olive or almond oil) directly on the hair and scalp. Use a brush or cottonwool to apply the oil.

1. Pre-heat the oil to a comfortable temperature. Never use hot oil, as this is dangerous and could burn. Alternatively, apply heat to the hair using hot towels, heat lamps, a steamer or an accelerator, before or after applying the oil.
2. Allow the oil to remain on the hair for 5–15 minutes. During this time you could apply a vibro massage.
3. Remove the oil from the head, first applying soapless shampoo: the shampoo combines with (emulsifies) the oil, and can then be rinsed off with water. Do not apply water first – it would prevent the shampoo from combining with the oil, so that after rinsing there would still be oil coating the hair and skin.

Oil shampoos

Oil shampoos contain conditioning agents and emollients or tissue softeners. They are pH-adjusted; they regulate the acid balance of the hair (see page 55).

1. Use oil shampoos similarly to oil applications, heated as described above. You may apply hand or vibro massage while shampooing.
2. Remove the shampoo by rinsing with water, lathering, and finally rinsing the hair.

CAROL HAYES & ASSOCIATES

CONDITIONING AND HAIR CARE PRODUCTS

- After conditioning, the hair should be smooth and shiny, and the cuticle should have been repaired. It should look and feel better.
- The hair should be more pliable, more elastic and more resilient. Setting and styling should hold longer.
- The hair should be tangle-free.
- Apply chemical processes only after careful testing – assess the condition thoroughly first.
- Read manufacturers' instructions carefully before applying conditioners or using equipment.
- Make sure the hair is towel-dry before applying conditioners. Excess water could dilute them and reduce their effectiveness.
- Help your client to improve the home management of her hair – advise on home treatments that will help to maintain the improved condition, and when to return to the salon.
- For future reference, note on the client's record card details of conditioning treatments given.
- Make sure that the client is satisfied with the condition of her hair, and so will feel encouraged to return to the salon again.

ACTIVITY
Look through the salon's client records. Note those of any clients who have been ill. Have these clients experienced any ill effects after having hair processes such as perms and tints?

Product summary

- **Shampoos** Many types are available – choose one to suit the hair's state.
  Johoba For dry hair.
  Soya For normal hair.
  Orange For greasy hair.
  Medicated For various hair types.
- **Setting and shaping agents**
  Setting lotions, gels, mousses, glitz, glaze, gloss, wax, other products Used to hold or coat the hair when it is wet.

Plastics, PVP, other products Leave a film on hair; help to wet the hair thoroughly; resist the effects of moisture; reduce static electricity; help hair to hold its style longer.
Cationic detergents, cetrimide, other products Keep hair pliable; repair damaged hair; reduce static; add shine.
Plasticisers, emollients, moisturisers Combine the features of other styling and shaping agents.

REGIS

WELLA

- **Hair thickeners and builders**
  Cationic detergents Give 'body' to the hair.
  Protein hydrolysates Attach to the hair and thicken it.
- **Conditioning rinses and agents**
  Lemon juice (*citric acid*) Removes soap scum.
  Humectants Ease combing; smooth the cuticle; counteract alkaline effects.
  Vinegar (*acetic acid*) Removes soap scum; reduces alkaline effects; smooths the hair surface; eases combing.
  Beer or champagne Add 'body'; smooth the cuticle; aid dressing.
  Cream rinses or mousses Ease combing and brushing.
  Cetrimide and other products Used after chemical processing – aid damaged cuticle; smooth the hair surface; act as anti-oxidants and pH balancers.
- **Restructurants**
  Rinses, creams, gels or mousses, quaternary ammonium compounds, protein hydrolysates, proteins from soya and keratinous products Penetrate and aid damaged hair; soften hair; smooth the cuticle; add shine; make hair pliable and able to hold shape; repair and fill hair structure; thicken fine hair.
- **Antioxidants**
  Rinses, lotions, creams Used after bleach and tints – stop oxidation; neutralise alkalis.
- **pH balancers**
  Rinses, lotions, creams Used after chemical processing – counteract oxidation.
- **Dressings**
  Control creams, vegetable and mineral oils, gels and gloss Smooth the hair surface; soften the cuticle; retain moisture; add shine; aid dressing.
- **Lacquers**
  Shellac (*hard coating*), *plastic* (*pliable coating*) Resist moisture, retain style/curl/shape, smooth the cuticle.

HEALTH AND SAFETY
Dipping your fingers into containers is unhygienic. Use a spatula or a tissue, once, then discard it.

- **Two-in-one technology**
  Products that combine both a shampoo and a conditioner – '2 in 1' – are effective and popular.
  A chemical in the shampoo forms a molecular lattice, on which a conditioner is suspended. The hair is washed; when it is rinsed, the water breaks down the lattice and releases the conditioner. Further washing removes the conditioner. These are excellent home hair care retail products enhancing salon treatments.

ASSIGNMENTS: SHAMPOOING AND CONDITIONING HAIR

A practical activity

The process of selecting suitable shampoos and conditioners is important. In the beginning it helps to work with your colleagues to establish a procedure which will elicit all the facts on which to base choice. Work through the following sequence:

1. Examine each other's hair and scalp. Note down what you see.
2. List the questions you might ask, such as: 'What has the client been using? What have been the results? Why is she not satisfied? What problems has she had?', and so on.
3. Determine the state of hair and skin.
4. Note down carefully the different conditions present.
5. Consider the range of products available. What are their advantages and disadvantages?
6. What hairdressing services have been previously carried out for the individual? What is intended to be carried out next?

When you have established a reliable process of selection, extend it to meet the requirements of your clients. Be methodical and compile your notes so that further information can be added or changes made.

For you to find out

Investigate all the sources of information you can find that deal with shampoos, shampooing, conditioners and conditioning. Use your libraries, local stores and chemists' shops to find out what is available, particularly for home use. Product knowledge sessions with your wholesalers and manufacturers can be very helpful for studying products for salon use. Don't forget trade publications. Then answer these questions:

1. What shampoos are there available? What are the differences? List the ranges. Note their contents and prices.
2. What conditioners are there available? What are the differences? List the ranges. Note the contents and prices.
3. How are they applied? Is any special equipment required?
4. How do the different shampoos and conditioners work?

5. What is 'detergency'?
6. Outline a shampooing method. Name the massage movements used.
7. How does water affect shampooing?
8. What is the pH scale? How does it affect shampooing?

A case study

A client of yours has extremely dry hair, breaking at the points. It is unruly and unmanageable. Describe how you would proceed to deal with this client. Work through the following sequence, writing down the outcome of each step.

1. Find out what has been used on the hair. (Use your question list.)
2. Find out what physical or chemical hairdressing processes have been applied.
3. Determine the type, texture and condition of the hair throughout its length.
4. Decide which products to use, and explain to the client why you are proposing to use them. Agree on what is to be done, how long it will take and how much it will cost.
5. Note the results and effects produced. Keep notes for your folder and record card.
6. Ensure that treatment is continued by advising the client what to use, and how to use it, at home.
7. Examine hair and scalp carefully on subsequent visits and amend the treatment if necessary.
8. Add any further information that you think is necessary and discuss with your senior or tutor.

PREPARING FOR ASSESSMENT

In preparing for assessments on shampooing and conditioning hair, the following checklist may be useful. Check that you have covered and now fully understand these items:

- analysing different hair conditions
- applying suitable examination and consultative techniques
- selecting from a range of suitable shampoos, conditioners and treatments
- applying good shampooing and conditioning techniques
- understanding the massage movements and when they should or should not be applied
- compiling and applying product knowledge
- maintaining accurate and careful records of information
- applying any further information you think necessary.

When you feel that you are ready, talk to your trainer and arrange a suitable time for your assessment.

Drying hair

INTRODUCTION

After shampooing your client, you need to consider how the hair is to be finished. Does the hair require positioning or placing? Should it be left to dry naturally? Other options that could be taken are:

- setting the hair into shape and drying under a hood dryer using a variety of techniques, such as pin-curling, rollering or fingerwaving; techniques of this kind are described in Chapter 6
- blow-styling, using a variety of techniques
- heat-moulding, using a variety of techniques and tools to dry and shape the hair
- towel-drying or blow-drying the hair and then applying a heat-moulding technique to shape it

Whichever method you use to dry the hair, the following points also require consideration:

- applying the different forms of drying and shaping to a variety of hair lengths and shapes – above or below the shoulders, layered lengths and so on
- determining the important factors influencing the finished shape, such as the client's hair cut or style, her hair growth patterns, and her hair texture and structure, and whether it is curly, wavy or straight
- application of hair cosmetics and aids to drying and shaping, such as setting/finishing sprays, gels or mousses.

Study this chapter together with Chapter 5 ('Cutting and styling hair') and Chapter 6 ('Setting and dressing hair').

WELLA

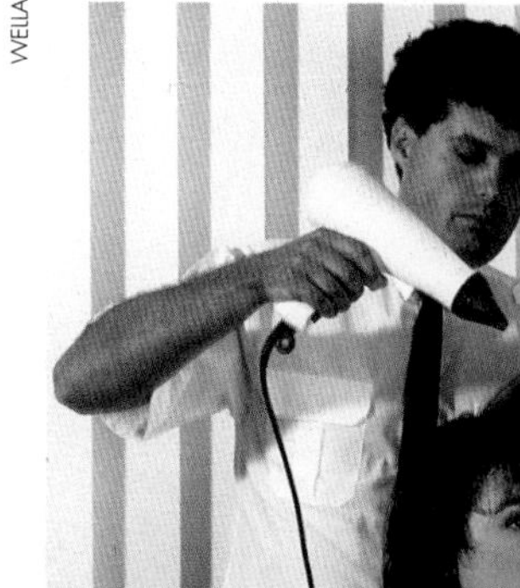

Drying hair

DRYING HAIR TO SHAPE AND CREATING A FINISHED LOOK

Drying hair – principles

Drying hair is the process of styling wet hair while blow-drying it. Using a hand-held dryer, you use a variety of techniques to create different effects. While directing heated air on to the wet hair, you mould the hair with brushes, combs or your fingers, positioning it to fit the style for which you have cut it.

Like other methods of setting wet hair (see Chapter 6), blow-styling works by changing the hair's structure. Wet hair can stretch, adding up to 50 per cent to its length. Heat softens it: the weaker links between the polypeptide chains (the hydrogen bonds and salt bridges) are broken, allowing the keratin to stretch and change from its alpha to its beta form. While hair is wet, and heat is applied, it can be moulded into a chosen shape.

The styled shape is only temporary, though – as the hair gradually absorbs moisture from the atmosphere, it returns to its original state. Combing styled hair with hot water returns the hair to its natural form straight away.

Heat moulding techniques

Heat can be applied to hair in other ways: to wave it, using irons; to curl it, using tongs; to crimp it, using heated crimpers; or to straighten it, using hot combs or hot brushes.

Like other methods, these techniques depend on the softening effect of heat. The moulded hair must be allowed to cool before it will hold its shape – if you comb through it while it is still warm you will lose or distort the shape. Hair moulded in this way returns to its natural state if combed with hot water.

ACTIVITY

On your collected hair samples or the practice block, try out the effects of different setting lotions, mousses, gels and creams, using fine, medium and coarse hair. Note the appearance and the feel of the hair, and how long the styles hold before drooping.

The client

- Prepare your client by removing wet towels and making sure that she is comfortable (see page 18).
- Before you begin work, communicate with your client about her requirements and wishes.
- Diagnose what can and should be done.
- With the client, discuss what should be done and why. Explain why certain techniques have been selected for her. The client, especially if new, will find this reassuring.
- Make sure the client understands and agrees with the final effect you are trying to achieve.
- Analyse the technical requirements at this stage, in the light of your overall plan.
- Indicate how long the process will take – generally about 20–30 minutes for blow-styling.
- Monitor and evaluate your work as it progresses. Make sure your client is satisfied and reassured throughout.
- Explain to your client how to achieve a similar style at home.

For other important considerations, see Chapter 5 ('Cutting and styling hair').

TIP

If the hair is left to dry naturally it takes the shape of natural growth patterns (see page 88), which need to be fully considered.

BLOW-STYLING TECHNIQUE

The technique you choose will be determined by the hair texture, the quality and quantity of hair, the style to be produced, and the cut. The most suitable hair for blow-styling is firm, thick, coarse hair. There are now a number of styling aids – thickeners, setting mousses and gels – which are designed to give direction to the

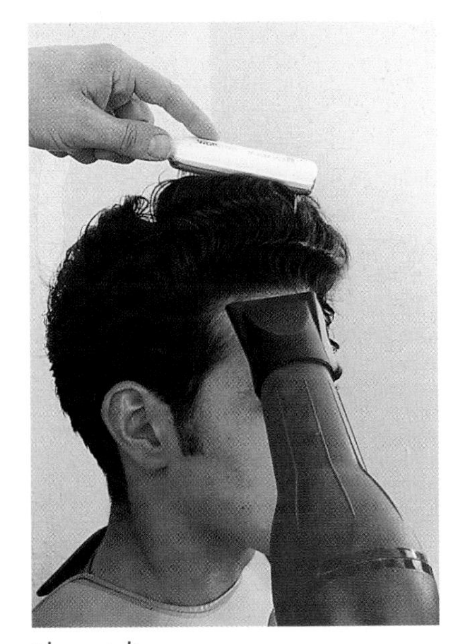

Blow-styling

MICOL GROUP (PHOTO *DAILY EXPRESS*)

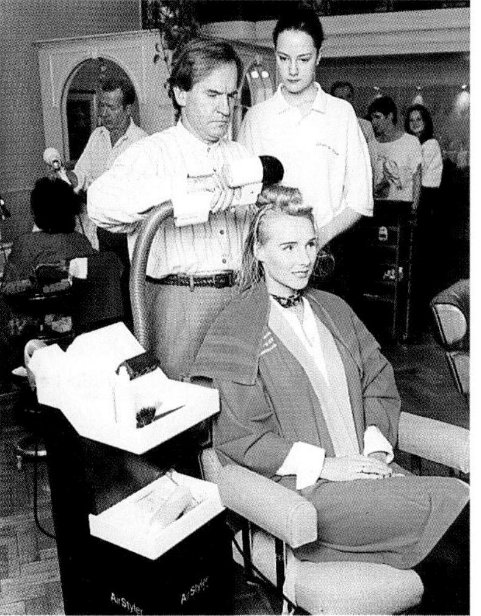

An Airstyler – dries, smooths and shapes the hair in a single process

GOLDWELL

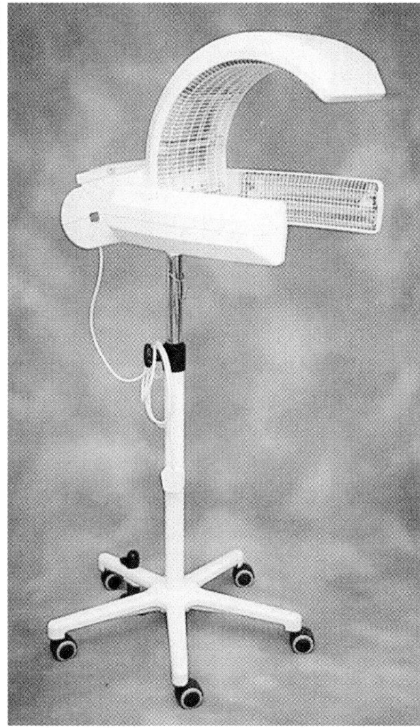

A heat lamp

FORFEX/GOLDWELL

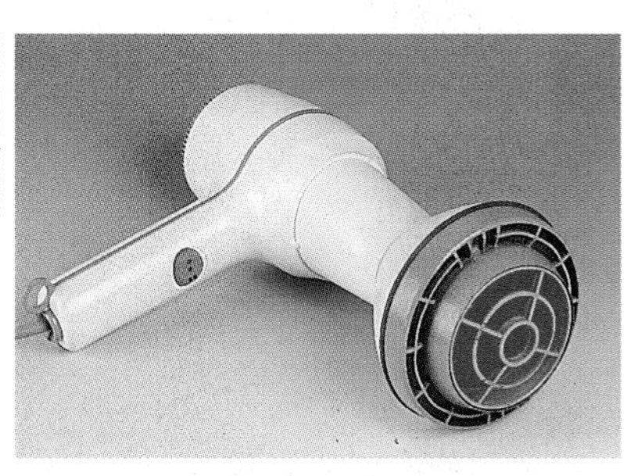

A hand-held/infra-red dryer

hair. Fine, fluffy hair requires the help of one of these if you are to obtain successful results.

Whether the client's hair is curly, wavy or straight, whether the length is above or below the shoulder, whether it is layered or is cut to give a one-length look, the techniques in the following list can be adapted to suit:

- **Blow-waving** Shaping the hair into waves, using directed heated air from a dryer, and combs, brushes or your hands. It achieves natural, soft fullness (see page 78).
- **Blow-drying** Simply drying the hair with the hand-held dryer. It is usual to blow-dry hair into a chosen shape, or in a required direction (see page 76).
- **Scrunch drying** Gripping and squeezing clumps of hair, while directing heated air into the hand. The process yields a casual, ruffled, moulded shape (see page 77).
- **Finger or hand drying** Lifting, teasing, pulling and directing hair with the fingers or hands. Casual, soft and full shapes can be achieved. Billowing fullness is perhaps the chief effect.
- **Blow-combing** Drying and shaping using a comb, or a comb attachment fixed to the hairdryer. It is a kind of blow-drying, and achieves shape and direction.
- **Blow-stretching or straightening** A means of smoothing, unkinking or straightening the hair. A variety of brush shapes and sizes may be used (see page 79).

A **blow-style** consists of first shampooing the hair, then softening it with a dryer or heated lamp, and finally moulding it into shape using a blow-dryer. It may be dressed, if required, when the hair has cooled.

Natural drying – leaving the hair to dry naturally – may be chosen, depending on whether the cut and the style are suitable. Natural drying may be assisted by the heat of the sun, infra-red lamps, accelerators, rollerballs or other equipment.

Equipment/tools/products

- The **hand-held dryer** is the most important piece of equipment you need. There is a wide range of models to choose from. The dryer should have adjustable speeds and temperatures, and be designed for long periods of use. It needs to be light and easy to hold, and to have controls positioned where they are easy to reach when in use. There should be a means of attaching it safely to the bench when not in use.
- **Hand dryer attachments** – such as nozzles and diffusers – are available (see page 79). Using the dryer without a nozzle or diffuser allows for a wider directed air flow.

Hand-held dryer (*far left*)
Hand-held dryer and styling brushes (*left*)

ACTIVITY
At your wholesaler's, look at the different types of hand-held hairdryer. Professional models are designed to be used continuously in the salon. Compare these with the hairdryers in the shops, which are designed for home use. Clients often ask which is the best dryer for home use: what would you say?

HEALTH AND SAFETY
All tools and equipment should be tested periodically.The tests should be recorded (with dates) and the equipment should be clearly labelled.

Blow-drying and shaping: a summary

Length/texture	*Tools*	*Techniques*	*Effects/results*
Short; tight/very curly fine/medium/coarse	Small round brushes to form roller shapes to grip/smooth/ straighten	Blow-drying	Smoother, looser, more wavy
Short; curly/wavy, medium/coarse	Small/curved round brushes with/without diffuser	Finger drying, scrunch and blow-waving	Fashion, natural, casual
Short, one-length looks	Small, curved, vent brushes	Blow-combing/ scrunch/natural/ finger drying, blow waving	Casual, spiky, flat or lifted
Medium-length/below-nape, above-shoulder; loose curl/wave, medium/coarse (most versatile)	Curved/half-round/ vent/flat/circular/ small/medium brushes	Blow/finger drying scrunch	Tight, loose, curled, wavy, straight, ruffled, casual or set
Long, below-shoulder, one-length bobs; wavy/straight, medium/coarse	Large/flat/circular brushes	Finger/natural drying, blow drying (beware of snagging long hair)	Lifted, or flowing, smooth or straighter
Layered looks, varied lengths; slightly wavy, medium/coarse	Variety: round, curved, vent/circular etc.	Finger/hand/ scrunch drying	A variety of tousled natural, casual, ruffled looks

Notes

1 Short and medium-length hair that is slightly wavy and of medium-to-coarse texture is probably ideal for blow-drying techniques.
2 Varying the dryer speed gives you better control of the hair, particularly longer hair.

- **Brushes** are probably the most important items after blow-dryers. A firm, stiff, bristle or plastic brush is required. This will help you to grip, direct and control the hair. (Soft brushes are suitable only for finishing.) Half-round plastic brushes are used for general shaping. Larger types are best used on long hair, smaller for short-to-medium hair. A range of smaller roller brushes on which to form shapes is also required. Different brushes are necessary for particular shapes.
- **Combs** should be professional and heat-resistant. The comb you will use most will have both widely spaced and narrowly spaced teeth.

HEALTH AND SAFETY

Metal combs retain heat and can burn the skin.

ACTIVITY

Various different attachments for hairdryers are made. What are they, and what do they do? Check the manufacturers' instructions, and practise handling these attachments.

Styling aids

TIP

Always dry the roots first, before the middle and end lengths of the hair. If you don't do this, the hair won't lie in the direction of the style you intend.

Blow-styling, setting, styling and dressing can be usefully aided by using some of a large variety of products. Most hair cosmetic manufacturers feature them. Some are physically designed to give added support to the hair shapes, so as to retain style as long as possible. Others have a chemically bonding action with the internal hair structure, which both retains moisture and resists the effects of excess moisture of new shaped hair styles. Yet others combine both physical and chemical attributes that enhance hair shaping and styling.

There are aids available to meet most needs. Product knowledge will help you select the correct one for your client. The aids in the following list may contain **plasticisers** to enfold and support the hair, **moisturisers** to retain or resist moisture (see page 59), protective **screeners**, silicone **shiners**, **sun carers** and so on.

- **Blow-styling aids** protect the hair from excessive heat, augment the length of time for which the hair shape is held, and give body to the hair. There are different strengths – firm hold, extra hold, medium hold, ultra, ultimate and so forth –

TRESemmé

L'OREAL

WELLA

Styling products

for different hair conditions and texture types. Different products are sold for use before, during and after blow-styling.

- **Dressing aids** give sheen, shine, gloss or glitz to the hair. Gels, oils, silicones, mousses, foams and waxes may be used to reflect light and to enhance a healthy-looking shape.
- **Setting aids** enhance the hair's elasticity, help the hair to keep its spring and bounce, and allow it to stretch easily. Volume/styling/body-building mousses, soft-shaping gels, sprays and styling creams, cetrimide conditioners and finishing hairstyle sprays are all commonly used.
- **Protectors** shield the hair from the harsh effects of exposure to the sun – for example, sunscreeners, sun care sprays and ultra-violet filters and gels.
- **Curl enhancers** enable the hair to retain curl or wave formation longer and include perm enhancers, maximum-curl retainers and volume, movement and shape revitalisers.

TIP

There are so many recent developments of these style aids that you will need to visit manufacturers and wholesalers regularly to maintain and update your product knowledge.

ACTIVITY

When cutting long hair to short, collect the lengths of hair and tie them at the root-ends. These make excellent switches for practising the blow-styling of long hair.

Collect cuttings of hair of different textures, and apply the various blow-styling aids. Make notes of the different effects.

HEALTH AND SAFETY

Always check tools and equipment before use to make sure that they are safe to use.

Preparing hair for blow-styling

1. Shampoo and towel the hair dry, then comb out any tangles.
2. Cut the hair into style.
3. Apply a suitable blow-styling aid, such as mousse, gel or lotion, if required.
4. Section the hair – the longer the hair, the more sections you will need.
5. Clip long hair out of the way and re-section it as required.
6. Position and grip the hair with a brush, a comb or your fingers to control it.

Blow-drying

You can start blow-drying at any part of the head. On long hair it is best to dry the lower, underneath sections first. With practice you will achieve a continually moving brush technique, with the lift and control required. Do not allow the top sections, which are still wet, to fall on to the lower, previously dried ones: this spoils work done and wastes time. Clip wet hair well out of the way.

Blow-styling works best on coarse hair. Fine hair may quickly become overheated and overdried. When dealing with short hair, take care not to blow it out of line. The air stream should be

CHARLES WORTHINGTON FOR L'OREAL

> **TIP**
> As with other techniques, blow-styling may seem difficult at first. Keep practising! The brushes will become easier to use, the handling of the hair will become more controlled, and you will achieve the desired shape more quickly.

> **TIP**
> Remember that dryers blow out and suck in air. Ensure that the client's hair, your clothes or towels are not sucked into the dryer, which could get blocked.

directed the way the hair is intended to lie. Short hair may be best rolled on to a circular brush, allowed to cool, and combed or dressed into position.

Which tool or technique you use depends on the style effects required. For full, soft effects use large, round brushes. For more bounce and curl, use smaller brushes. Fluffy effects may be achieved with open bristle brushes. A general method is as follows:

1. Towel-dry the hair. With hands and fingers loosely stroking and lifting the hair, remove any excess moisture. Apply mousse or blow-drying aids, if required.
2. Cleanly divide small sections of hair. The angle to lift the hair is determined by the fullness required. Lift the hair to allow the heated air to penetrate the section. For one-length, bobbed shapes, take sections horizontally or diagonally. For swept-back shapes, use vertical sections.
3. It is important to work methodically and cleanly. Make sure that the hair *not* being dried is clipped up, so that it doesn't get in the way.
4. Place the sectioned hair on to the brush with the thumb or fingers. When the hair is firmly in position on the brush, begin directing heated air on to it – first on one side of the section, then on the other. With the brush, direct the hair section away from the head so that the root ends are thoroughly dried. Do not wind the brush right down – allow space for the hair to be dried. Keep the brush moving as the heated air is passed repeatedly over the section, winding the hair up and down to allow the warm air to penetrate the hair fully. Make sure each section is fully dry before passing on to the next.
5. Allow the hair to cool before removing the brush – when warm, it is still soft.
6. For maximum lift, hold the hair section well up from the scalp. Keep the dryer close to the hair but moving, and directed away from the scalp. This action should be for short periods of time. Generally, hold the dryer about 30 cm from the hair. For wedge shapes, blow air through the hair section as the hair is allowed to flick from the brush in a combing, lifting action.

Scrunch drying

1. Prepare the hair for blow-drying by removing excess moisture with a towel, or hood drying the loose hair.
2. Run the fingers through the hair and lift it from the scalp. As you lift it, grip it firmly. Direct the heated air into your hand just before closing your grip. Hold the hair firmly and continue drying.
3. To see the effect produced, tousle the hair by shaking it. It is important to follow the shaping process in the mirror.
4. Continue to direct the hot air into the palm of the hand, to

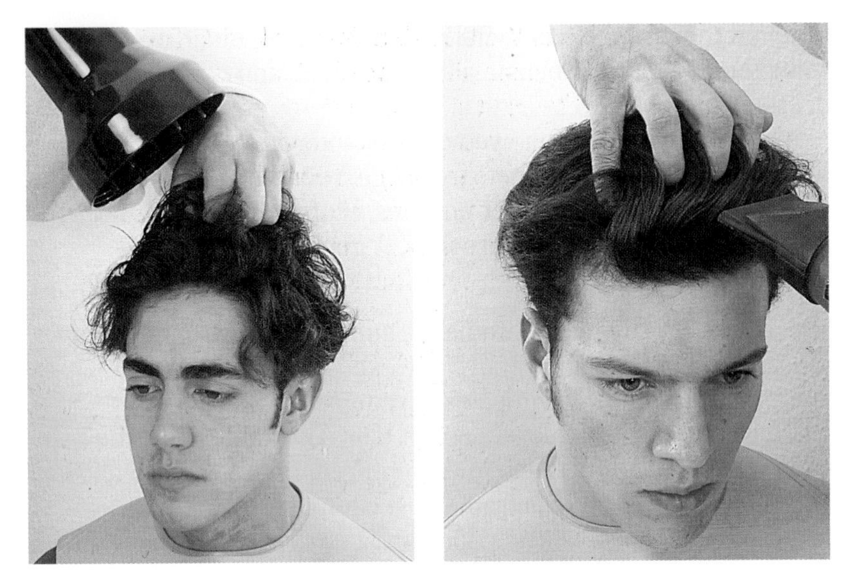

Scrunch drying (*far left*)
Finger drying (*left*)

prevent discomfort. Repeat the process of blow-drying, gripping the hair, and lifting hair sections, to increase volume and shape.

5. Work from side to side. Make sure each section is dry before proceeding to the next.

Providing the shape is carefully studied, a full, lightly tousled effect can be produced by this method.

Hand or finger drying

This is similar to scrunch drying, but uses hands and fingers to lift, mould and shape the hair. It gives a wider, looser, billowing fullness.

ACTIVITY
Select three textured practice blocks of different hair and blow-style each in a very full style. Leave them in the salon where they can absorb atmospheric moisture. Note how long the different textures of hair hold their shape and position.

Blow-waving

A method of waving using a comb or brush, carefully directed heated air, and a series of shaping movements. Position the hair into a crest formation and direct heated air through a nozzle attachment. Control the waves by comb or brush movements in relation to the hair position. Repeated combing or brushing is required to shape the hair.

1. Begin at the front hairline and follow the hair's natural movements.
2. With the wide-toothed end of the comb, make a backward, slightly turning movement, gripping the hair and holding it in a wave-crest shape.

HEALTH AND SAFETY
Do not try to blow-wave when the hair is too dry or wet. Keep the airstream moving, to prevent discomfort.

ANDREW COLLINGE (PHOTO: JOHN SWANNELL)

3 Direct warm air on to the trough below the crest. The airstream should be opposite to the direction of the comb holding the hair. The airstream should be at half strength, or the hair will be blown away from the comb.
4 Movements of both hands must be co-ordinated and repeated. Continually move the dryer along the hair. This directs the heat evenly and avoids burning the scalp.
5 The second crest is formed similarly to the first. Direct the airflow along the line the hair is intended to lie. This produces the required line and shape. When you reach the hair ends, position them in line with the waves formed.
6 Use of the coarse end of the comb allows air penetration and speeds the process. For finishing, use the fine end. A smooth finish can be obtained by lightly blowing through a net stretched over a frame.

Blow-drying tools

WELLA

Hand-held dryer with a diffuser and nozzle

Apart from the variety of brushes and hand-held dryers, the diffuser and nozzle are particularly useful.

The **diffuser** fits over the end of the hair dryer and distributes an even flow of warm air. It reduces a strong air flow to a gentle one, and is used for finishing styles. It is ideal for producing soft, casual, ruffled, natural curl looks. It can be used on various hair lengths.

The **nozzle** is intended to concentrate the hot air flow on to a specific area. It is ideal for blow-waving, as it allows the air to be directed at the troughs and crests of the wave shapes.

Electrically heated **styling irons** or **tongs** are often used to finalise a dried hair shape. The hair is rolled and held in place long enough for the heat to soften the hair. The irons are then slid out to leave a smooth rolled shape, similar to that produced by rollers. The various angles and directions into which the hair is placed determines the final style.

Electrically heated **hot brushes** and **heated rollers** are available in several sizes. They are applied to the dried hair in a similar manner to styling tongs. They are popular in many salons, and a great many clients use them at home.

FORFEX/GOLDWELL

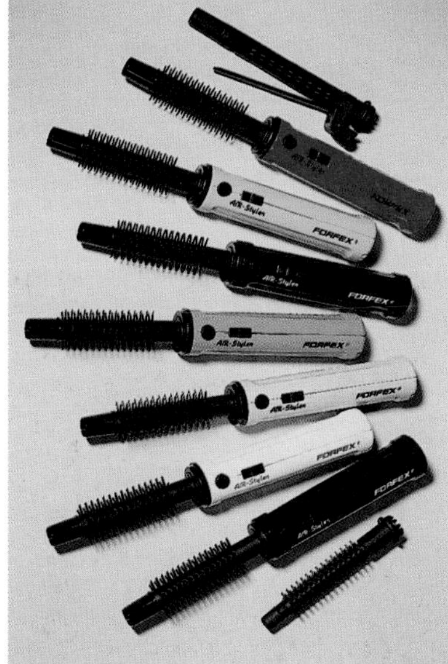

Heated brushes and tongs

ACTIVITY

Collect three types of hairspray and try them out on fine and coarse hair. Position the hair on a practice block or sample so that the hair is sprayed in an upright position. Over the next few days, note which is quickest in absorbing moisture from the atmosphere.

Blow-stretching or straightening

This involves the technique of stretching the hair rather than waving it. The aim is to straighten and smooth the hair lengths. Use larger, round brushes under or on sections of hair, and turn them to grip and slightly stretch the hair. This technique produces soft, slightly lifted shapes on very short hair, and sleek straightness on long hair. The brush size must be varied to suit different lengths of hair. Use a hand-held dryer, as in blow-drying, and direct the heated air on to the stretched hair. This technique is equally suitable for women's and men's hairstyles. You may also use heated combs for straightening hair.

Blow-stretching

HEALTH AND SAFETY

Precautions when blow-styling

Use only professional tools.

Ensure that all electrical equipment is in good order.

Never use electrical equipment with wet hands – you might be electrocuted.

Never use faulty equipment.

Work comfortably. Avoid continually twisting or stretching your body.

Maintain high standards of hygiene.

Test the heat of the dryer before applying it to the hair – you may cause discomfort to your client or damage to the hair. If the air is too hot for the skin, it is too hot for the hair.

Direct hot air away from the scalp.

Do not keep the dryer in one place too long.

When straightening, never overstretch the hair.

Do not attempt to shape hair when it is too wet.

Tugging and pulling the hair may cause breakage.

Use suitable blow-styling aids, such as lotions and creams, to protect the hair from overheating.

Do not blow-style hair that is in poor condition.

TIPS

Make sure the filter on the hairdryer is cleaned regularly – if blocked it could damage the dryer.

Don't hold the dryer too close to your body. If you do it will pick up fluff from your clothes, which may block the filter.

Don't rev the dryer motor – this eventually causes it to overheat and fuse.

DEALING WITH COMPLAINTS

If your client does not like the style you have produced, the following may help:

- Take steps to rectify the complaint as soon as possible.
- Try to see the client's point of view and be sympathetic in your response.
- Explain that the new style requires time to adapt to.
- Honestly justify what you believe is correct and suitable.
- Do not talk the client into something that you do *not* believe is suitable.
- Do not allow the client to leave with a poor shape or style.
- It is relatively simple to rectify a blow-style by re-dressing, re-setting, wetting the hair and blow-drying it again.
- Exercise tact, understanding and courtesy throughout.

CHARLES WORTHINGTON FOR L'OREAL

- Most clients do not like to express displeasure and may become distressed. Be aware of this, and make sure your client really is satisfied.

ACTIVITY

Compile case histories of the different situations that you have met. Briefly outline the outcomes. Keep your notes in your folder.

ASSIGNMENTS: DRYING HAIR

A practical activity

Using your practice blocks, hair switches or models, experiment by applying the different blow-styling and heat-moulding techniques. Note the differences produced on the different hair textures and densities. Use photographs, sketches and video taping to capture the 'before' and 'after' effects. Then answer these quesitons.

1. What happens to the hair structure during blow-styling? Make sketches where possible.
2. What effects do the different hair-drying techniques produce? List these.
3. List the best drying techniques to use on hair of different lengths. Consider, for example, below-shoulder-length hair, layered lengths, one-length styles and as many others as you can. Keep your list in your folder.
4. How do you choose which products to use on the different hair types? How do you know that they will be suitable? What questions would you ask? List these.
5. Your client is considering changing from setting to blow-styling. What advice would you give? List the points that you would put to your client.

For you to find out

Investigate the variety of hair cosmetics that are available for blow-styling, heat-moulding and setting. Check in your local stores and chemists' shops for information on home use products. Check how these compare with products used in your salon: compare prices, effects, package sizes and so forth. Then answer these questions. Keep your answers in your folder.

1. How could you present a new hair cosmetic to your clients? How could you prove its suitability.
2. How would you explain the effects of the different hair cosmetics used for blow-styling and shaping? List these, and keep your list for reference.
3. List the differences between the various hair cosmetics.
4. What after-care advice do you give your clients regarding hair-drying to shape and the use of hair cosmetics? List the points that you can make.

A case study

Your client has fine hair which has previously been set. She feels that this is old-fashioned and would like to change to blow-styling.

1. How do you deal with this? Briefly outline and list the points that you would make.
2. If blow-styling would not suit your client, how could you explain and justify the alternatives you propose?
3. How would you deal with the after-care required? What do you propose?
4. List the products, equipment and tools that you would require to meet your client's wishes.
5. What problems might arise? List the precautions to be taken.

PREPARING FOR ASSESSMENT

In preparing for assessment on drying hair the following checklist may be useful. Check that you have covered and now fully understand these items:

- checking a client's previous hairdressing history
- discussing the possible limitations of hair type, condition and so on
- determining a suitable blow-style, and agreeing it with the client
- explaining the techniques and movement sequences
- ensuring that the equipment used is safe
- applying suitable hair cosmetics
- anticipating problems that might arise
- being familiar with the precautions that need to be taken
- ensuring cleanliness of all tools
- completing short or long hair styles in an acceptable time.

When you feel that you are ready, talk to your trainer and arrange a suitable time for your assessment.

CHAPTER 5

Cutting and styling hair

INTRODUCTION

Professional and competent hair cutting is the basis of good hairdressing. Cutting hair is styling hair. Designing a cut style needs care, precision, artistic appreciation, technique combination and control. It includes the elements of balance, rhythm, line and movement, and other factors as well. It is reflected in all hairdressing services – setting, blow-styling, dressing and more. Good cutting design leads to hair arrangements which become suitable, pleasing and acceptable styles.

The following are some of the topics we will cover in this chapter.

- hair styling – design and choice
- important factors influencing style
- style suitability
- aesthetic appreciation
- cutting tools and equipment
- cutting techniques
- cutting procedures.

This chapter needs to be studied together with Chapter 4 ('Drying hair') and Chapter 6 ('Setting and dressing hair').

TIP

Your first attempts at cutting may not produce the results you had hoped for, but with continued practice you will acquire the skill.

CHEYNES TRAINING FOR PAUL MITCHELL LUXURY HAIRCARE

HAIR STYLING – PRINCIPLES

Hair styling is the creating or designing of attractive hair shapes or arrangements. It involves competent cutting, setting, blow-drying and dressing.

A **hairstyle** is an expression of form and shape. It is achieved by arranging the hair into suitable, balanced lines, which complement the shape of the head and the facial features.

The aim of the style is to enhance your client's appearance. This helps to boost her confidence and make her feel good. There are styles for work, play, special occasions, business meetings, parties and so on. The hairstyle should be considered a part of the complete **ensemble**, including the clothes, make-up and accessories.

The client

- Make sure you have protected your client's clothes adequately.
- Before attempting a new style, talk it over with your client to be sure that you are in agreement.
- Discuss what is required and make sure that you consider all your client's needs, including her general lifestyle.
- Examine the hair type, texture, length, colour, quality and quantity – all can influence the hairstyle. Look at how the hair has been cut previously, and decide whether there is enough hair for a change of style.
- Analyse the client's requirements and requests. Beware of requests for named styles: the name a client uses for a certain style may mean something completely different to you! Make sure you interpret your client's wishes correctly.
- Assess the limitations. Do not make the mistake of being persuaded to cut hair into a style you are sure would not suit your client.
- With your client, select the style. Many clients are swayed in their choice of style by pictures of attractive young models in magazines. If you think the style favoured by the client is unsuitable, tactfully suggest an alternative. Not giving the client exactly what she has requested should not be the result of your whim, bias or incompetence, nor a wish on your part to dominate the situation. Your professional initiative is required.
- Advise the client how long cutting will take – anything from 15 minutes for a trim to one hour for a complete restyle.
- Agree with the client how much hair should be taken off.
- Help your client by advising her how to manage the hairstyle at home successfully.
- Reassure the client afterwards – the resulting style, if new, may need getting used to. If your client is not immediately pleased with the result, don't be disappointed but keep your comments positive. Others will soon compliment her on her hairstyle, and boost her confidence.

TIP

Ask your client the reason why she has decided to have a new style.

MAHOGANY

ANDREW COLLINGE (PHOTO: JOHN SWANNELL)

Choosing a hairstyle

The hairstyle you choose with your client must be designed to suit these important factors

- the shape of the face and head
- the features of the face, head and body
- the dress and occasion for the style
- the quality and quantity of the hair
- the weight, shape and distribution of the hair
- the age of the client
- the way the hair grows, its position, proportion and form in relation to other styling requirements.

TIP

Creative interpretation of your client's wishes may be necessary, but always consult your client first.

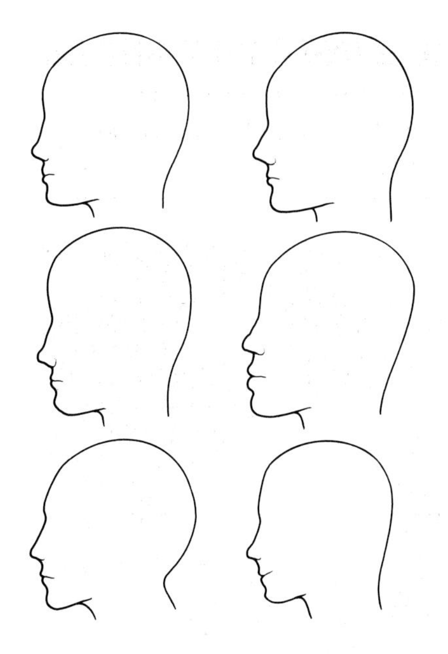

Profiles

The shape of the face and head

This is the base on which the hairstyle will rest. The proportions, balance and distribution of hair should relate to the underlying structure and **features**. Use features such as the eyes, nose and chin as a guide to the finished style.

If you look at the outline of your client's face, you will see that its outline is quite individual – round, oval, oblong, heart-shaped, square, and so on. An oval shape is considered ideal, as most hairstyles fit it.

- The apparent length of square and oblong faces may be increased by sleek, flat styles, or reduced by full sides.
- A large, round face looks even rounder when the hair is full and foaming around it; it looks longer when dressed high at the front and less full at the sides.
- Hard-looking shapes – resulting, for example, from prominent jaw bones – appear harder still when hair is dressed back, but softer with forward hair movements.
- The roundness or flatness of the head shape and the profile – the side view of the chin, mouth, nose and forehead – affect the look of the style.
- The neck – its length, fullness and width – directly affects the fall of the back and nape hair.

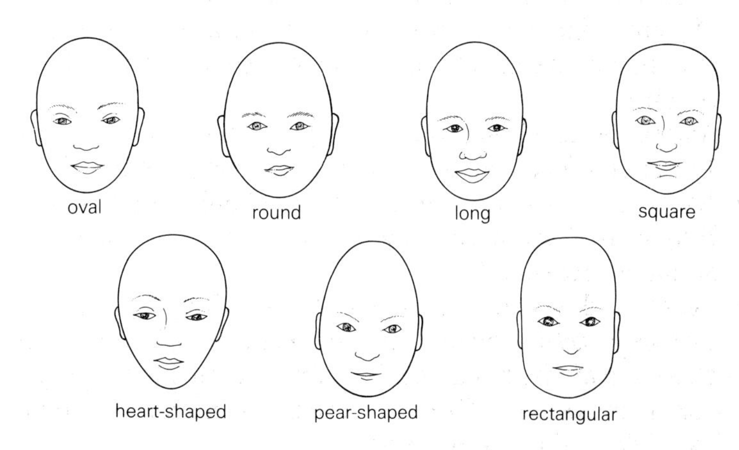

Face and head shapes

Features of the face, head and body

- Note the size, shape and characteristics of your client. The way the head and body are held is important – you can see this best when you first receive the client.
- A prominent or large nose may be 'diminished' by dressing the front hair at an angle, or avoiding a central parting.
- Square jawlines may be softened by fuller side dressings; protruding ears are best covered.
- A double chin is exposed if hair is taken away. A longer, fuller dressing may be helpful.
- Wrinkles round the eyes are made more obvious by straight, hard-line dressings. They may be diminished by softly angling the hair away from the eyes.
- Low, high, wide or narrow foreheads may be disguised by angling the hair and varying fringe positions.

TIP

A common fault when trying to disguise a defect is to make it more obvious by using too much hair to hide it.

- A large, fussy style on a big person can look unsightly. Yet a small, head-hugging style may be completely out of proportion.
- High-dressed styles accentuate height. Flat styles make short people look shorter.
- The shape of facial features – their lines and the shadows they cast – should be used to counterbalance the hair bulk, and enhance or soften overall features.
- Spectacles and hearing aids will influence your choice of style. Keep hair off the face and away from spectacle frames. Bring hair over the ears to disguise hearing aids.

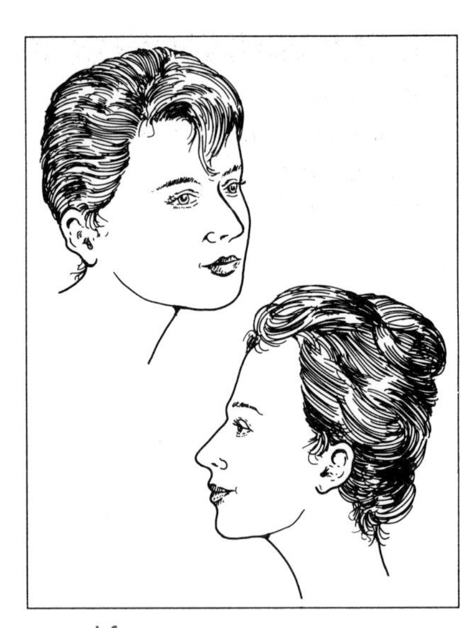

Facial features

TIP

The more the unwanted features are highlighted, the less suitable the style will be. The most suitable style is one that is individually designed.

Dress and occasion

The dress and occasion for which the style is to be worn will help you decide on a suitable hairstyle.

- A style suitable for a special occasion may differ from one worn at work: a beautiful evening gown requires an elegant hairstyle, normal working clothes may require one that is smart and unexaggerated.
- Many clients require styles that are practical and easy to manage. Practicality is less essential for special events, but remember that the hair has to be returned to normal afterwards.
- Particular jobs require particular hairstyles. For example, nurses and canteen workers need to wear their hair off the face and shoulders, and many people wear hats as part of their uniform. Do not choose a hairstyle that makes this difficult.
- Usually, lower necklines require longer hairstyles. Higher necklines allow higher dressings. There are exceptions:

WELLA

TIP

Set a good example yourself by wearing a suitable hairstyle that reflects current fashion.

dancers and ice skaters will not want loose, flowing styles that will impede movement or vision.
- Models require specific and often elaborate hairstyles for demonstrations or photography.

The quality and quantity of hair

- Hair that is in poor condition and poorly textured never looks attractive and will not style well. Shining, healthy hair is essential for good styling.
- Thin, scanty hair is difficult to manage and requires attention. Styles which make it appear thicker and fuller are usually successful.
- Very fine, thin hair is soon affected by damp and loses its shape. Use setting aids, hair thickeners and practical styles.
- Dry, thick hair requires sleek, smooth, styles to contain it. This hair type soon fluffs and loses its shape. A control dressing (a cream, gel or spray) may help.
- Very tight curly hair requires careful and frequent combing. It looks shorter than it really is. As it is combed the true length becomes apparent. With wavy hair, you need to avoid cutting across the wave crests, which could make the hair unmanageable. Try to remove hair below the crests and carefully blend the ends. Straight hair, particularly if it is fine-textured, can be difficult to cut. Cutting marks or lines can easily form if sectioning and cutting angles are not accurate. The sections you take should always be small.

The age of the client

Men and women of different ages may require different styles.

- Children require simple hairstyles that don't require much dressing at home. Shorter styles often suit younger children best.
- Young men and women can wear most styles. Striking, often odd, effects are used by this group. Straight or curled, long or short, hard or soft effects may be used to advantage. A younger client may want a style that is unique and individual, or something 'trendy'. Teenage fashion tends to exclude

styles worn by older men and women. The more extreme glamorous styles are generally requested by young women.

- Young career women and men generally go for fashionable styles which they wear as part of their everyday dress. Such hairstyles need to be practical and easy to manage as well as fashionable.
- Older women require greater consideration for suitable styling. Facial features – lines, wrinkles and double chins – need to be 'styled out' (made less obvious).
- Young businessmen may require the smart, well-shaped, perhaps less extreme styles favoured by teenage boys.
- More mature men usually require flattering or classic, practical shapes, generally less 'fussy' and easier to manage than most women's hairstyles.

L'OREAL

Hair position, proportion and form

- The outline formed by hair in relation to the shape of the face contributes to the overall effect.
- Dressing the hair varies this outline. It is important that you maintain balance between hair and face to achieve a suitable distribution and shape.
- Consider hair growth directions or distributions – strong movements and natural partings, hair streams, hair whorls, cowlicks, widows' peaks, and double crowns. Make allowances for these when cutting and dressing, and particularly when designing the style.
- Hair growth patterns and the way the hair falls or moves is best seen when the hair is wet. Hair styling can disguise the natural position and form of the hair.
- A hairstyle that follows the natural fall and growth is more likely to retain its shape for longer between salon visits.
- Cutting a nape whorl too short produces difficulties – the hair may stick out in all directions.

Styling requirements

You will often come across the terms *suitability, balance* or *imbalance* and *weight distribution, soft and hard effects*, and *originality*. You should understand what these terms mean, so that you can choose different hairstyles with confidence.

Suitability

Suitability refers to the effect of the hair shape on the face, and on the features of the head and body. A hairstyle is usually suitable when it 'looks right'. This is achieved when the moulded hair shape fits the other shapes of the head. A line of the face may be accentuated when the hair lines are continuous with it. It may be softened when they are angled away.

A young, fashionable style dressed on an older woman may be unattractive. This is because the lines of the face, eyes and forehead are accentuated by the harder lines of 'younger' styles.

Most fashion styles are designed for younger women and must be adapted if they are to meet the needs of older women.

Hairstyle with balance

Balance

Balance is the effect produced by the amount, fullness and weight distribution of hair throughout the style. **Imbalance** is lack of proportion. **Symmetrical**, 'even' balance is achieved when the hair is similarly placed on both sides of the head. **Asymmetrical**, 'uneven' balance is achieved by, for example, dressing long hair on one side of the head and countering the weight with one earring on the other. Here the lines and proportions created by the dressing produce the 'balanced look'. A good hairstyle should be balanced from all angles of view.

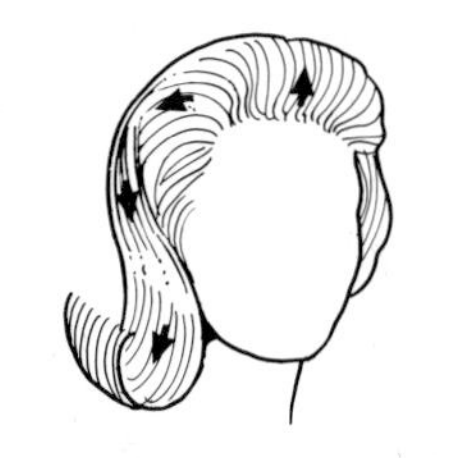

Hair direction and flow

The line of the style

Style **line** is the direction, or directions, in which the hair is positioned. It should 'flow' throughout the shape. If the line suddenly ends, the style becomes unbalanced and the wrong effect is produced.

The line of the style is affected by the way it fits in – or fails to fit in – with the features and contours of the face. It should carry the eye of the viewer along the directions in which the hair is placed. Many style lines produce **illusionary effects** by accentuating or diminishing different facial features.

THE JOHN GILLESPIE SALON FOR L'OREAL

Hairstyle with movement

Partings

Partings have a strong effect. A long, straight, central parting appears to make the nose more prominent. A short, angled parting 'diminishes' a prominent nose. Round, fat faces appear larger with central partings and smaller with side partings.

Movement

Movement is the name given to varying directions of style line. The more varied the line, the more movement there will be. Curly or wavy hair displays movement. Style line should move from one point of the head to another in a fluid fashion reaching to the ends of the hair. Styles with movement are usually complimentary to older women.

hard line (Egyptian)

soft line (classical Greek)

Hard and soft effects

Hard and soft effects

Hard and soft effects depend on balanced lines and movements. Hair dressed without divisions, without sudden line variation and without any abrupt finish to the movement looks natural and soft. Careful colouring enhances soft effects – careless colouring produces hard, unwanted effects. Lack of movement and irregular, unbalanced shapes together produce hardness. Rhythmical movement and balancing are softening.

Originality

Creating completely new style lines requires a great deal of thought and work. You can adapt styles and fashions to create interesting and sometimes original variations. Displays, demonstrations and competitions offer more opportunities for original hair styling. Whatever hairstyle you choose, it should be designed for the individual client.

VIDAL SASSOON

Types of hairstyle

You need to be able to cut and dress hair in a range of styles to meet the requirements of different clients. The following are some in general use:

- **Day styles** should be attractive, uncluttered and easy to manage, without extreme ornamentation, colour or elaboration.
- **Evening styles** are generally more elaborate, not necessarily practical, and suitable for special occasions. They are usually augmented with colour or ornament.

REGIS REGIS REGIS VIDAL SASSOON

Children's hairstyles

TIP

Some basic shapes can be cut into different styles.

- **High fashion (haute coiffure)** refers to the latest style trends. At first they may appear to be extreme; they become more acceptable when better understood. This type of styling requires originality, good techniques and experience.
- **Fashion styling** (usually adapted from high fashion) is favoured by the smart and trendy. There seems to be an endless round or range of fashions stimulated by events, advertising, dress designs and other sources of inspiration.
- **Children's styles** should be natural and suitable, never artificial – in general, the simpler the better.
- **Men's styles** are based on principles similar to those that apply to women. They should be natural, balanced and suited to the client's face and features. (See Chapter 9, 'Barbering').

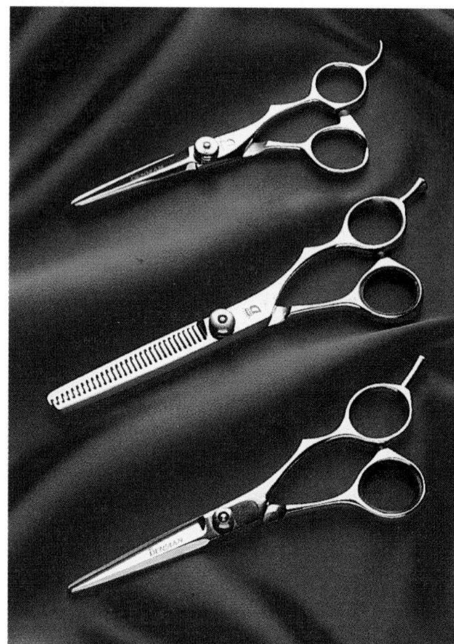
DENMAN

Scissors

EQUIPMENT AND SAFETY

You have considered the 'artistic' part of hairstyling – choosing a style to suit your individual client. Now you need to consider the practical part – the tools used for cutting and how to use them safely, and the terms and techniques used in cutting into style.

Cutting tools

Tools should always be clean, sharp and well balanced. They should fit the hand and feel comfortable in use.

- **Scissors** with straight or curved, and long or short blades may be used. They should never be too heavy, nor too long, to control. Since scissors need regular resharpening, you will need at least two pairs, preferably of the same type. Choose the scissor size that best suits the size of your hand – this will help you to cut neatly, quickly and efficiently.

  The best way to hold a pair of scissors is with the thumb through one handle and the third finger through the other. This ensures ease of use, good control and little effort. It also minimises stress on your hands, arms, back and body.
- **A razor** – the open, 'cut-throat' type – consists of an edged steel blade protected by the handle. A solid or hollow ground blade may be used for cutting hair or shaving. Modern counterparts are called **hair shapers**. The modern razor-like hair shaper has a replaceable blade and a protecting handle. There are other types and shapes.

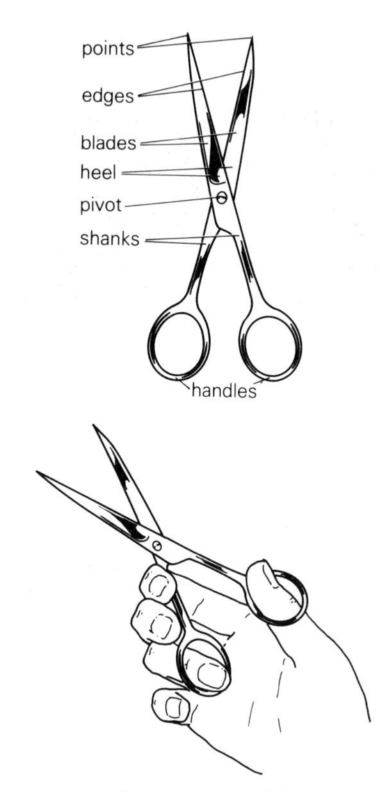

Scissors: their parts and how to hold them

ACTIVITY

Visit a hairdressing wholesaler. Note the different types of cutting tools and their prices. You will see that there is a great variety of scissor lengths and weights. It is important that scissors and other tools are comfortable to use. Ask a senior or your trainer to advise you on the best tools to purchase.

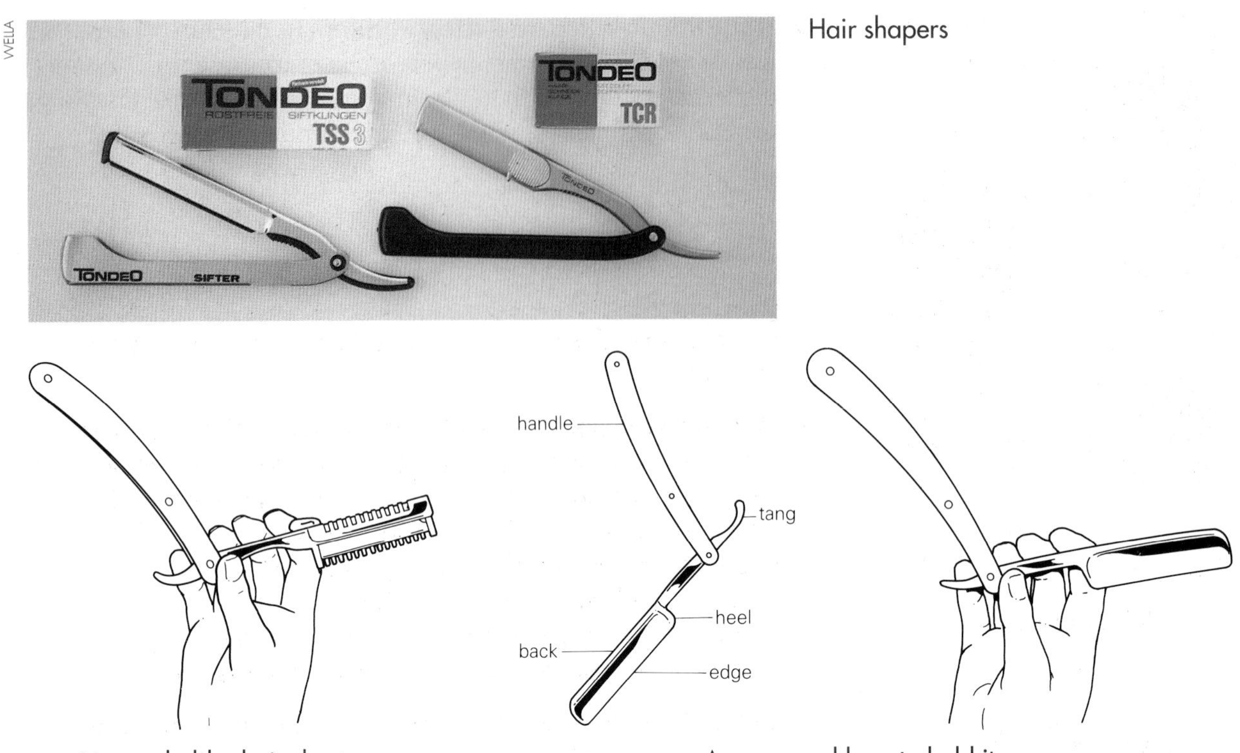

Hair shapers

How to hold a hair shaper

A razor and how to hold it

With the handle open, the thumb and index finger hold the back of the guarded blade, between the pivot and the tang. The two middle fingers rest on the tang, on either side of the handle. The guard restricts some razoring movements; this may be overcome by using shorter strokes.

HEALTH AND SAFETY
The disposable blade or razor is now recommended for general use.

- **Thinning scissors** have one or both blades serrated. The size of the serrations determines the quantity of hair that is removed at each cut: the more often they are closed on the hair section, the more hair is removed. They may be held in the same way as cutting scissors, but are used in an opening and closing fashion. They cannot be used in a slithering action.
- **Clippers** – both hand and electric (the latter are now more popular) – consist of two blades, with sharp-edged teeth. The blades are positioned in such a way that one blade remains static and the other moves across it. Hand clippers are operated by pushing the handles together; electric clippers are operated by a motor. The distance between the blade points and the spacing of the teeth determine how closely the hair can be cut.

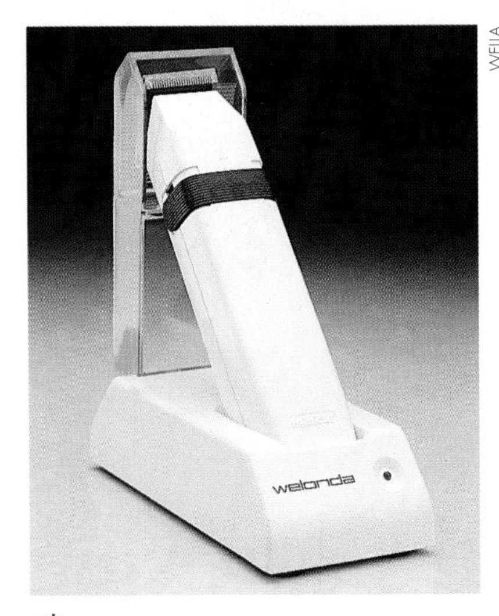

Clippers

HEALTH AND SAFETY
Do not use clippers if the top, movable blade protrudes beyond the bottom, static blade – you might cut or damage the skin.

Mirror reflections

- **Combs** suitable for use while cutting are thin and pliable, with both fine and coarse teeth. Fine teeth allow the hair to be controlled and closely cut. Coarse teeth allow for repeated combing and positioning of the hair. The comb should be comfortable in use and easily positioned.

  Hold the comb so that both ends are supported, to prevent breaking. When cutting over the comb, one end should be held between the index finger and thumb, with the finger on the teeth edge and the thumb on the back of the comb. As the comb is turned, so the finger and thumb grasp the back of the comb.

- **Mirrors** are important while cutting so that the shape can be seen clearly from different angles. The client, too, will want to see the final result: hand mirrors can be used for this. Three different types of hand mirror are available:
  - *plane* mirrors, which give a normal view
  - *concave* mirrors, which magnify
  - *convex* mirrors, which give a smaller, distant image.

  The plane mirrors are commonly used in the salon.

- **Cutting collars** are useful pieces of equipment. They are placed over the shoulders, around the neck, and remain firmly in position. They do away with towels which can constantly slip and disrupt cutting procedures.

A cutting collar

Cleaning cutting tools

- Never use dirty or broken tools. Germs breed in the many corners and may be transferred from one client to another.
- Clean all tools before disinfecting or sterilising. Remove all loose hairs. Use spirit or alcohol to remove any grease.
- Special disinfectant oils may be used to lubricate moving parts.
- Some disinfectants corrode metal and blunt edges. Check the manufacturers' advice before using any disinfectant.
- If corrosion or rusting occurs, light rubbing with emery paper helps to restore the metal surface. Badly marked tools may be corrected by professional servicing.
- Scissors and razors are easier to clean than clippers. Hand clippers can be dismantled. It is not advisable to take electric clippers apart, though some clipper heads are removable for cleaning.
- All repairs should be carried out by the manufacturers, or by qualified electricians.
- All clean and sterile tools should be stored in a dry disinfectant cabinet, or at least covered.

ACTIVITY

In case of accidents at work, or someone being taken ill, it is important to know what to do. With a trained first aider in your salon, you are prepared for any emergency. Think about taking a first aid course yourself.

HEALTH AND SAFETY

Precautions when cutting hair

Examine the hair and scalp thoroughly – signs of disease indicate that you should not proceed with cutting.

Do not place sharp tools in overall pockets – this is unhygienic and dangerous. You might cut your hands, or stab youself when bending.

Make sure that the edges of all sharp tools are covered when they are not in use.

Allowing loose, cut hair to gather on the floor is unsightly, dangerous and unhygienic. It is easy to slip on loose hair.

Take care not to cut yourself when replacing shaper blades or using razors.

Do not use clippers with broken teeth – they can pull, drag or tear the scalp.

Use only tools that are sharp, to prevent splitting or breaking hair.

Beware of clients moving suddenly, particularly children.

Watch out for a sneeze – you might stab your client!

Clean tools after use and store them in a safe place.

First aid

If skin is cut, take the following action:

1. Bathe the area with cool water.
2. If it is a minor cut, apply antiseptic and cover with plaster.
3. If it is severe, apply pressure to stem the blood flow. If bleeding does not stop, seek medical help as soon as possible. If necessary, treat your client for shock.
4. Avoid contact with blood, to prevent cross-infection.
5. Wash and disinfect any bloodstained surfaces.

CUTTING AND STYLING TECHNIQUE

Cutting hair to fit the shape of the head is one of the most important hairdressing processes. It forms the basis of all hair shapes and styles. When a client washes her own hair, the cut shape is what remains. The cut affects the way that the hair lies on the head and influences all other hairdressing processes. A well-shaped head of hair should be pleasing to look at and easy to manage.

THE HAIR SHOP FOR L'OREAL

Terms and techniques

When different people use particular terms they don't always mean the same thing. Below is a list of useful terms, with explanations of what they mean in this book.

Cutting: scissor tapering (always on dry hair)

Cutting: razor tapering (always on wet hair)

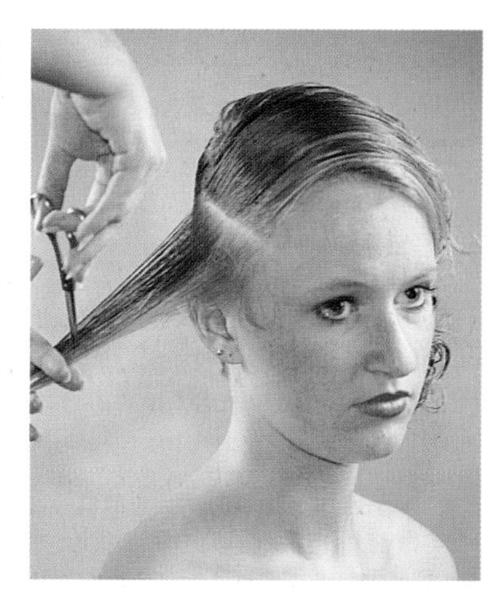

Cutting: point tapering

VIDAL SASSOON

VIDAL SASSOON

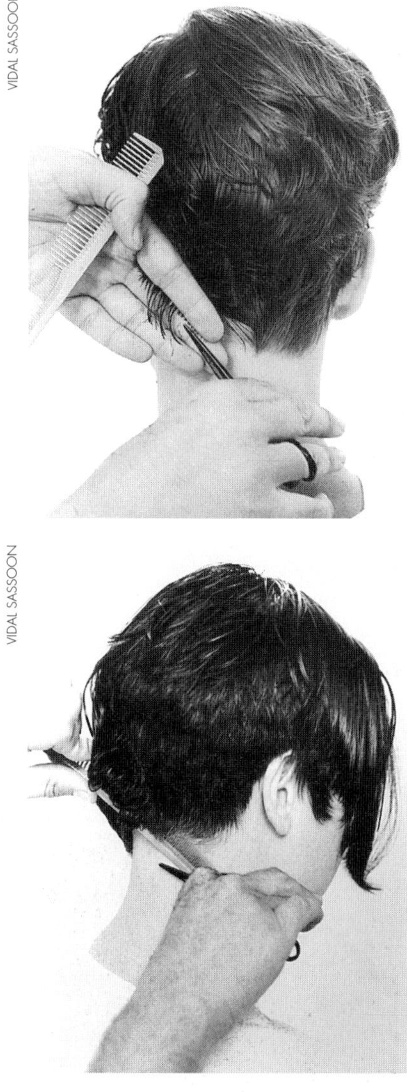

Cutting: clubbing
over finger (*above*)
over comb (*below*)

Tapering

Tapering or **taper cutting** means reducing hair so that it tapers easily to a point and unwanted weight is removed. It may at the same time be used to shorten the hair.

- **Scissor tapering** – used on dry hair – is done with a slithering, backwards-and-forwards movement along the hair section. The hair is cut in the heel of the blades from the third of the section that includes the points.
- **Razor tapering** – used on wet hair – achieves a taper effect. The razor is placed, at a slight angle, on or under the hair section. The hair is cut in a series of slicing actions. The length may be reduced at the same time. Cutting should be restricted to the third of the section that includes the points.
- **Point tapering** achieves a taper effect by using the scissors points to remove hair from the point ends of the hair section.
- **Feathering** is another name given to tapering. It also describes the overall effect of dressed, tapered hair.
- **Backcombing taper** achieves its effect by first backcombing a section of hair. The points ends remaining in the hand are then tapered with a sliding, slithering action of the scissors or razor. The amount of backcombing determines the degree of taper.

Clubbing

Club-cutting or **clubbing** is a method of cutting hair sections bluntly, straight across. It reduces all the cut hairs to the same length. It may be used on wet or dry hair. If too large a section is clubbed the resulting line of the hair ends will be irregular. You need to cut small sections of hair at a time.

- **Scissor clubbing** – of wet or dry hair – is the most common. Small slicing actions ensure a clean cut.

ACTIVITY
Taper one hair sample and club cut another. Then curl them both, and dry them. Note the difference in the amount of curl shape achieved.

Thinning

Thinning reduces the length of some of the hairs in a section without shortening the hair overall. The hair's bulk is reduced. Hair is cut at the middle third of the section – if cuts are made too close to the scalp, thinning will cause short stubble to stick out.

- **Scissor thinning** is achieved with scissors used in a long tapering action. It can also be achieved by deep backcombing and tapering, or by point cutting at the middle third of the section.
- **Thinning scissors** have serrated blades. When closed on to a section they thin it automatically. Cuts should be made at the middle third of the section and towards the points.
- **Razor thinning** reduces thick bulky hair. Make long slicing cuts from mid-lengths to the hair points. Use little pressure or you will cut through the section.
- **Modern hair shapers** with removable blades are used in short, sharp movements to thin hair. The blade is angled slightly and cut from mid-section to points.
- **Root thinning**, with scissors or a razor, is achieved by cutting small hair sections level with the scalp. It is a drastic method, rarely used on the average head: it is used in some fashion and competition styles.

Cutting: thinning

ACTIVITY
Using hair samples that are naturally curly, note the effects of clubbing, tapering and thinning on the curl strength.

Producing varied lengths

Texturising, **castle serrations**, **slicing**, **chipping** and **chopping** are terms used to describe methods of varying lengths of hair within a section. They also describe the look of the cut hair, which gives the effect of some hairs being lifted and supported by others.

- **Castle serrations** are produced with special serrated scissors which drastically reduce parts of the hair section. The amount of hair to be removed is determined by the style effects required.

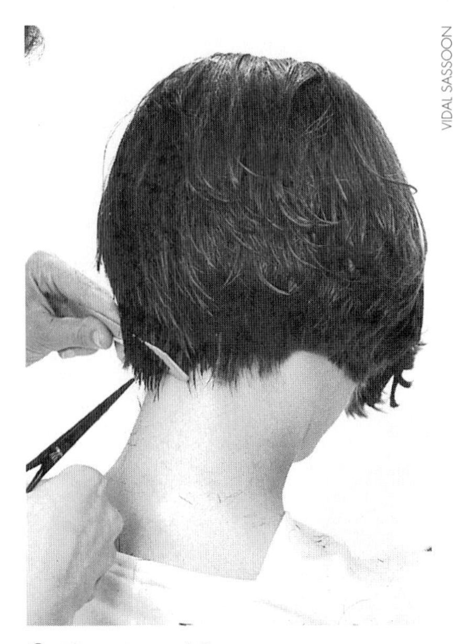

VIDAL SASSOON

Cutting: texturising

Wet and dry cutting

Wet and dry cutting refers to methods of scissor or razor cutting. *Scissors* may be used on wet or dry hair. Scissor tapering

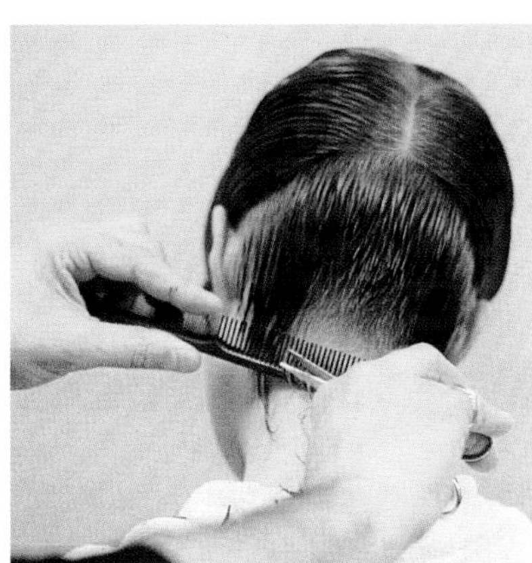
Cutting: graduation

Cutting: reverse graduation

should not be used on wet hair as the action of the blades is restricted. *Razors* and *modern shapers* are commonly used to taper or thin wet hair; they are never used on dry hair as they drag and tear it, cause the client pain, and blunt the cutting edges. *Clippers* and *thinning scissors* are best used on dry hair.

Graduation

Graduation is process of creating a difference in length between the upper and lower layers of a section of hair. It refers to the slope produced, from longer to shorter hair, by the ends of the hair.

If a section of hair is held out at right angles to the head, and cut at right angles to the section, the hair will lie evenly on the head. The angle of the cut and the contours of the head together make the ends lie neatly over each other, producing a graduated curve (**uniform layering**). This may best be achieved by clubbing.

- A **graduated cut** can be produced by clubbing the hair, to make it short in the neck graduating to long at the crown, or longer at the nape and shorter at the crown.
- **Reverse graduation** refers to a graduated line being shortest at the lowest layers and longest at the higher layers. This is used where the hair is required to 'turn under', as in some long or short 'bob' styles.

Layering

Layering is the term given to the process of cutting sections of hair to similar lengths. It produces a uniform, unbroken shape. A uniform layer can be produced by holding hair sections out at right angles to the head and cutting across them at right angles.

'Layering' is also used to describe thicker and more distinct layers, cut directly into the hair shape. These layers are *not* uniform: there is a sharp difference in section length.

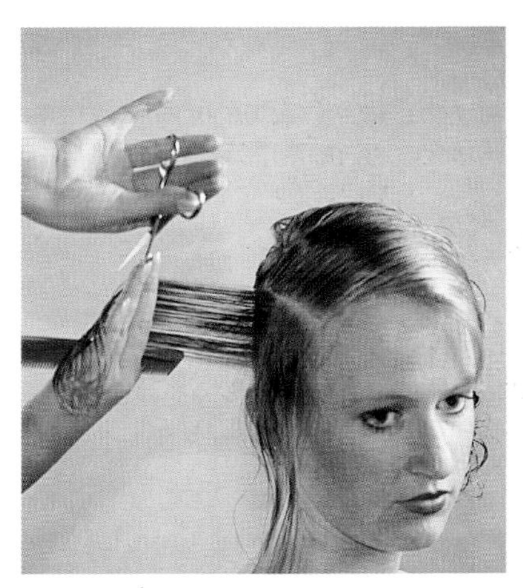
Cutting: layering

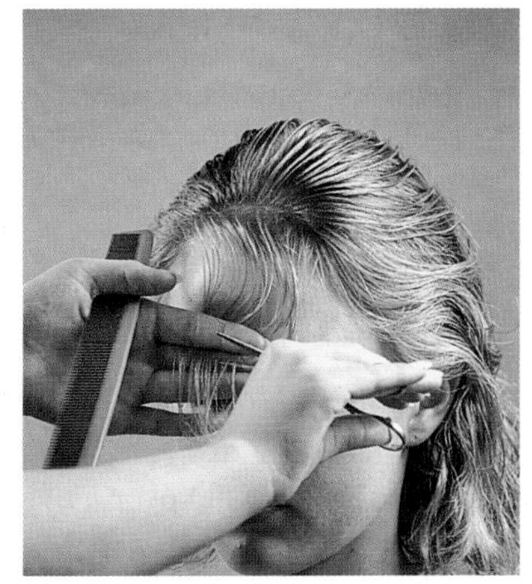
Freehand cutting

Freehand cutting

This is the process of taking small sections of hair, gently pushing them and allowing the natural movement to take the hair section, and then cutting the section without stretching the hair out of its natural line. The hair must be free from any forced directional pull. Pushing (or lifting) the weight of the lengths of hair allows them to move in their own natural manner.

This is a useful technique for dealing with hair growth patterns, such as 'calf lick'.

> **TIP**
> Always use part of the previously cut hair as a guide to cutting and shaping the next part.

Controlling the shape

- **Angles** must be considered when you are applying any method of cutting. Two in particular are important:
  - the angle at which the hair section is held out from the head
  - the angle at which the cut is made across the hair section.

  By varying these two angles you can produce a wide variety of effects.
- **Cutting lines** or **perimeter lines** are the lines described by the hair-ends when they are held directly out from the head or combed flat to the scalp. They encircle the contours of the head and must be followed carefully throughout any cutting procedure. The curves of these lines determine the shape of the cut style. The main ones to consider are:
  - the head contours from top to bottom
  - the head contours from side to side across the back
  - the outer circumference of the hair lines (nape, sides and front, for example), which also act as cutting guides.
- **Guides** for cutting are specially prepared sections of hair. Each is cut so that both the length and the cutting line are visible. The guide can be followed throughout the cutting process to produce even and precise results. Cutting haphazardly, without guides, produces peculiar and usually unwanted effects.

  To prepare guide sections you should carefully note the features of the head – the position of the eyes, ears, nose, hairline points and so on. Further guides may be prepared in the neck, at the sides and at the front, to be followed throughout the cutting process.

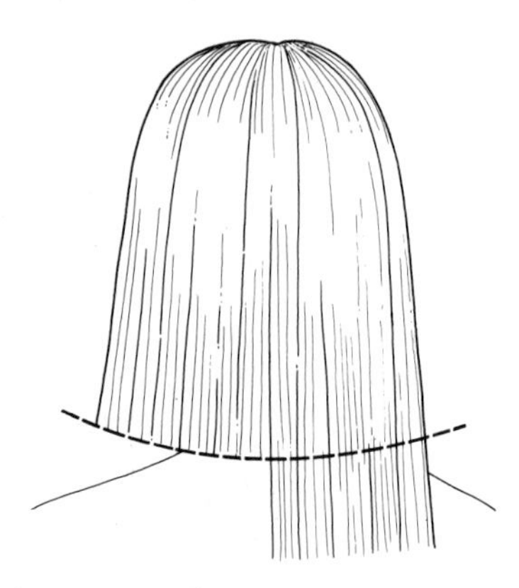

Cutting: guides

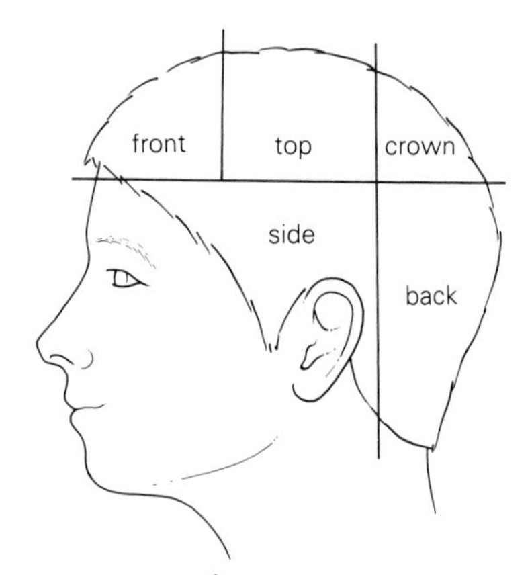

Cutting: guide sections

Cutting practice

To a certain extent, you can learn and practise tool movements and positions, combing hair at different angles, control of hands, hair and so on before you start cutting. Use practice hairpieces (**slip-ons**) which slip over a block. These allow your first cutting attempts to be monitored by your supervisor. You will soon be able to practise on live heads.

Cutting for the first time can be successful if you use a simple pattern and take a slow, methodical approach. You will only

> **TIP**
> It is important to consider the amount of hair that will be left on the head after cutting. The closer the cut is made to the head, the more hair is removed.

JOHN CARNE

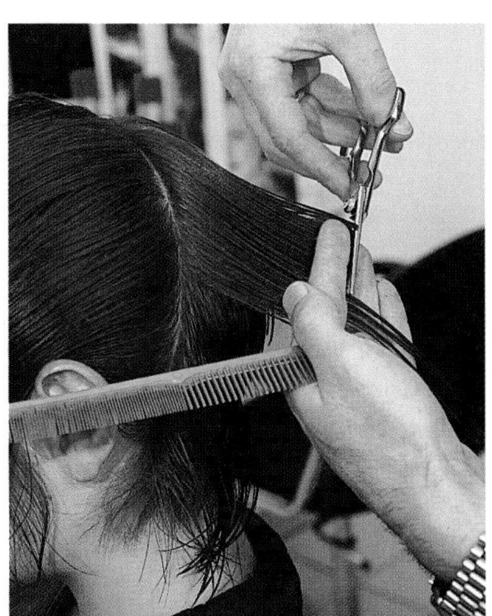

Cutting: angles

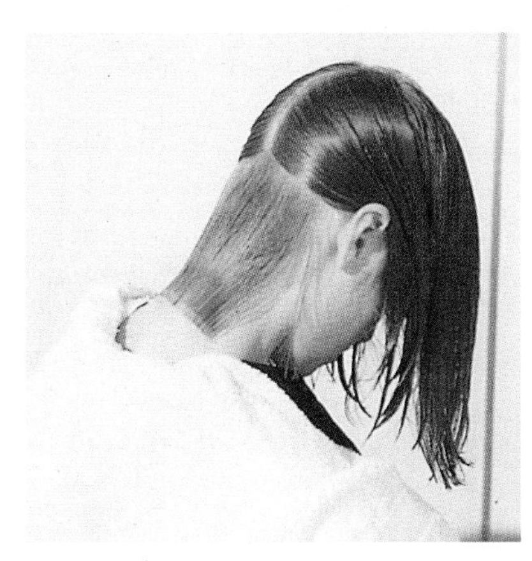

Cutting: lines

achieve speed in cutting after lots of practice. Never cut fast at the expense of a good hairstyle.

Cutting the lines and angles

Comb the hair and hold neat sections of it away from the head. The position in which you hold and cut the hair determines the positions the cut sections take when combed back on to the head.

The angles and lines of cutting depend on the different lengths required by the style. The first cutting line – the outer perimeter line – may be determined in the nape, as well as determining length. The second cutting line – the inner perimeter line – depends on the different lengths required throughout the style.

General style cutting

Although the methods of cutting you use may vary, the end results should not. Whether cutting horizontally, vertically or diagonally, or any combination of these, the hair should fit the head. There should be no visible steps, broken curves or lines, unless these effects are actually required. The finished cut should

TIP

A section of hair held out at right angles (90°) to the back of the head and cut at right angles (90°) to the section, produces a 45° **angle of graduation** – that is, the gradient between the top and bottom of the hair section when positioned back on the head.

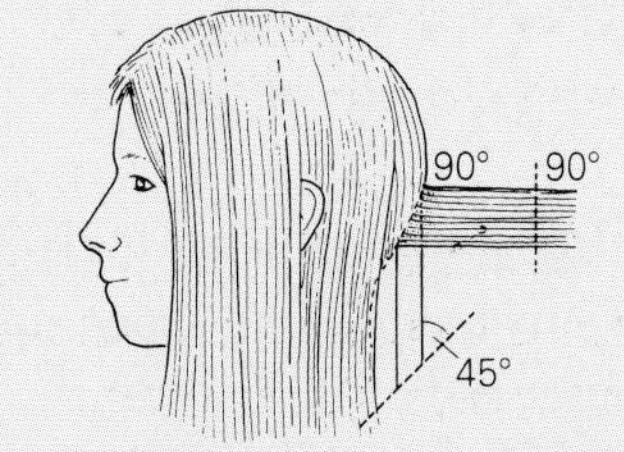

hair held at a 90° angle,
cut at a 90° angle,
gives a 45° angle of graduation

A section of hair held at 90° and cut at a 45° angle produces a steeper graduation.

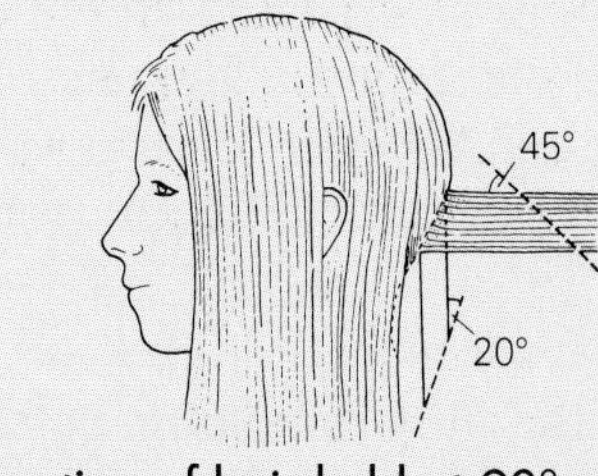

hair held at a 90° angle,
cut at a 45° angle,
gives a 20° angle of graduation

A section of hair held at 90° and cut at a 145° angle produces a 'level length', in which all the ends of the hair fall level, without graduation.

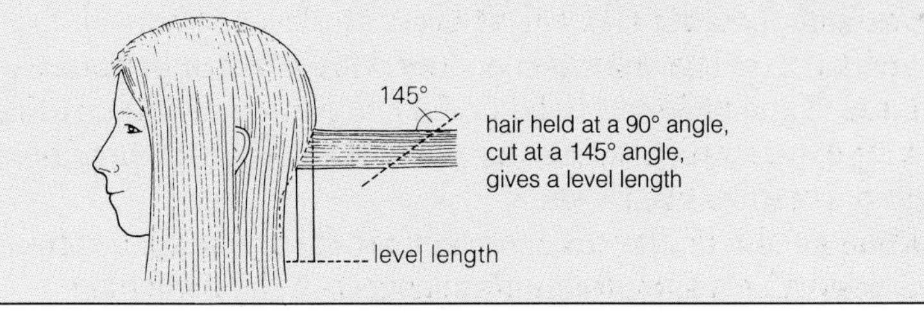

ACTIVITY

Using hair samples, practise the various haircutting techniques. Sketch the effects or shapes produced with each of the hair samples. Note the effect on the samples when trying to curl or wind them.

not need to rely on blow-drying, setting or dressing for its shape – you should use these techniques only to enhance and position the cut hair.

- A good approach to cutting is to choose a suitable starting point, providing yourself with a clear, visible guide for continuous cutting lines. This will help you to cut the hair easily. Be sure that all guide sections – particularly the first – are accurate so that following sections fit correctly. Consider carefully which techniques to use – tapering, clubbing, cutting the hair wet or dry, using scissors or a razor, and so forth.
- Make sure throughout that you hold the client's head in suitable positions, so that you achieve the required shape.
- When sectioning hair, take sections that are small enough to hold comfortably. If the sections are too big, you will not be able to control your cutting and the result will be inaccurate.
- At the end, show the hairstyle to your client. Hold the hand mirror behind her at an angle, so that she can see the back and sides of her head reflected in the large mirror in front of her.

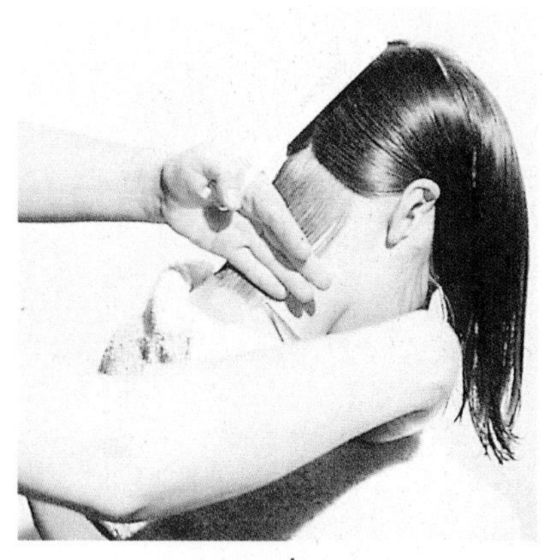

Cutting: perimeter lines

TIP

It is important to follow the contours of the head, and the cutting lines must match the outline, the shape and the lengths required.

One-length shapes

In a one-length shape, or **bob cut**, the top layers of the hair fall into a line level with the underlying layers. With the weight of the hair on the outside, the ends can be made to turn under. The term **level length** is commonly used.

A bob can be produced as follows.

UNERMANS FOR L'OREAL

Bob cut

The nape

1. Section the hair and make sure that the lengths and weight are clipped away from the nape. Sub-section into a position in which the hair can be seen and cut easily.
2. The first cut determines both the outer perimeter line and the length. First comb and hold the centre nape hair, then cut it.
3. Remember that successive cuts should follow a line passing from one side of the nape to the other. (Use the ears as a guide – 12 mm below each ear may be suitable for shorter lengths.)
4. Take a section (12–18 mm) of the nape hair. Hold this horizontally between two fingers, the fingers resting on the neck. Using scissors, club this section in a smooth, slicing action, making several cuts.
5. Working on either side of this first cut, make a series of further cuts. The cutting line should follow an unbroken curve from ear to ear. Each new section taken along this line should overlap a previous one, so that a part of the previously cut hair can be clearly seen.
6. When complete, the cut nape hair serves as a guide to the cutting of the other sections and layers of the back hair.

Bob cut step-by-step
(a) Before

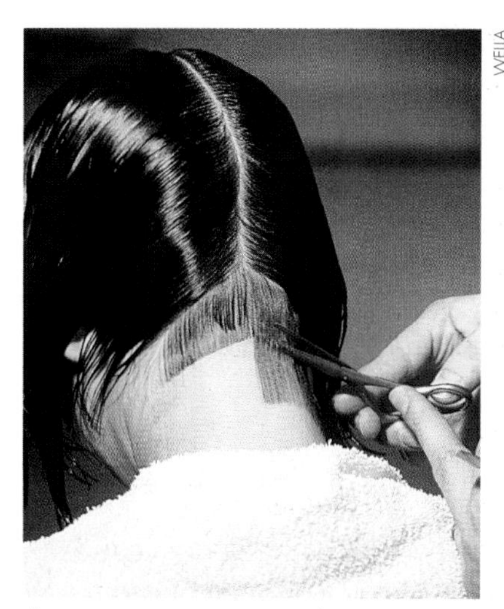

(b) Preparing nape and guide lines

(c) Following sections, cut to guide lines

(d) Side cut in line with nape

The back

7 The next section, above the nape, should be about 12 mm deep, depending on the thickness of the hair. Comb it down, sub-divide it, and then cut it as you did the underlying nape hair. Remember not to stretch the hair or pull it too tightly; if you do, the hair will retract above the nape line and will be uneven. It is better to cut the second section of hair slightly below the first cut nape sections.

8 Allow the cut hair to remain in its natural position so that following sections can be cut in line with it. If you cut the hair out of its natural fall or position, the shape may be distorted when the hair has dried.

The sides

9 Comb the first section at the base of the side, and hold it horizontally between your fingers. Line it up with the cut nape hair, then cut it to continue the curve round to the side. Do not hold the hair too far away from the head or you will produce graduation. Do not pull the hair tight, either, or make it flatten the ear. Make allowance for the hair to lie over the ears without 'shrinking' when dry.

10 Now you can section and cut the higher layers of the sides, using the previously cut hair as a guide.

(e) Completed bob cut

The fringe

11 The process of cutting the fringe depends on the type and shape required. The fringe area covers the top front of the head.

12 Section and comb the hair forward on to the forehead. The perimeter line can be cut to a variety of shapes. Then cut the upper sections, placing them on to the lower, previously cut, sections. It is important to determine the type and texture of

shape so that the correct techniques – such as feathering, chipping or clubbing, see page 95 – can be used.

In a successful bob cut the ends of the hair fall evenly. The client's position throughout the cut must be maintained to avoid distorting the level and shape.

Reverse graduation (see page 97), in which the top layers are longer than the underlying ones, is often used to encourage the hair to turn under. It produces full, swinging hair, which should return naturally to its position.

MICHAEL LAWLESS FOR JOHN CARNE

Hairstyle with a fringe

Layering the hair

Most cutting techniques, except for those aimed at a one-length look, produce a layered effect to some degree. You can produce different layered looks by cutting the hair to different lengths – below or above shoulder length – or with or without partings or fringes.

Layered looks: inner lengths same as outer lengths

This cut ensures that all sections of hair are cut to the same length throughout. It is known as a **short layered cut**. It can be long or short, but is more commonly used for short styles. If you use this cut on longer hair, the top layers will fall over the lower ones, producing a degree of graduation.

TIP

Different layering techniques can produce quite different effects.

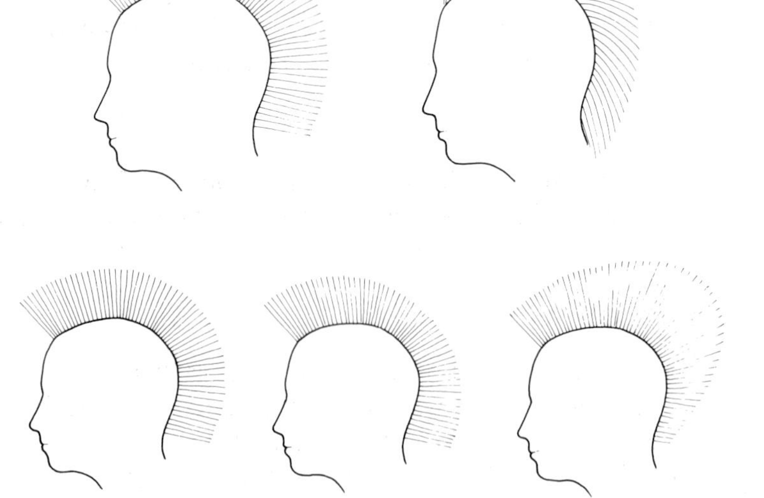

Cutting: same lengths

Cutting: inner line

The nape

1. Section the nape hair and cut the length, and the first part of the perimeter line, horizontally.
2. Cut the inner line by sub-dividing the nape hair and taking the sections vertically.

Cutting:
The back (*top left*)
The sides (*top right*)
The fringe (*below left*)
The nape (*below right*)

3 Hold the hair directly out from the head at 90°, and cut it at 90° to the section. This gives uniform lengths.

The back

4 Each of the higher sections is then sub-divided and cut vertically only. The lower, previously cut sections are used as a guide.

The sides

5 Treat the sides similarly. Cut the perimeter section horizontally and then vertically – this ensures that both the outer and the inner perimeters are shaped.
6 Are the sides to be dressed back or forwards? Angle and cut them accordingly.

The fringe

7 Fringes may be cut by combing the hair forward. Determine the length and shape by reference to the nose, eyes, eyebrows and other features of the face.

MICHAEL LAWLESS FOR JOHN CARNE

Hairstyle with a fringe

Layered looks: inner lengths longer than outer lengths

This cut can be used to produce a shorter shape in the nape sections and longer layers at the crown. The nape can be cut very short, the length graduating to the longer lengths of the upper layers. The terms **shingling**, **semi-shingling** and **Eton crop** have been used for this style of cut; now it is known as a **graduated-wedge cut**. The cut can be varied, depending on the hair lengths required in the nape and crown.

ACTIVITY

Using sketches, try to outline a cut style so that it can be easily followed by another 'junior'.

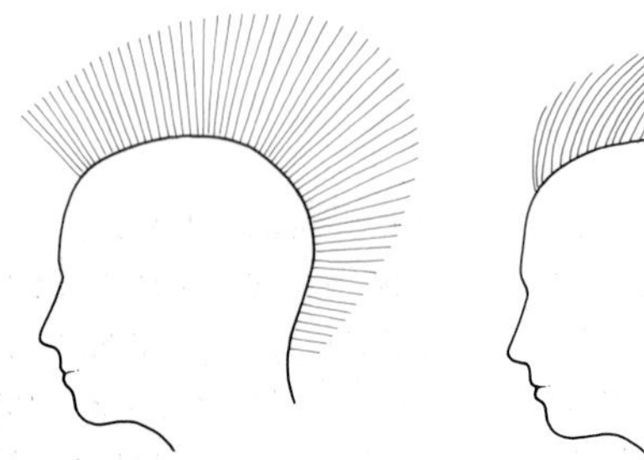

Cutting: inner layers longer

The cutting method

1. The method follows that for the short, layered cut, except that as the sections are sub-divided and cut vertically the angle of cut is changed. Hold the hair section out at 90°, and cut the hair across at 145° to the section. This gives longer lengths in the layers.
2. Use the same angle of cut throughout, so that as the layers are allowed to fall back on to the curve of the head a soft, unbroken line of graduation is achieved. Harsh lines and divisions may be produced if this is not carried out correctly.

Layered looks: inner lengths shorter than outer lengths

This cut, the **long layered cut**, may be used to produce shapes with longer nape hair (a longer outer perimeter) and shorter layers on the higher and inner perimeter. You can use this cut to produce a variety of shapes, depending on the lengths of the hair. Softness may be suggested by the longer lower lengths and by the fullness around the lower ears and jawlines.

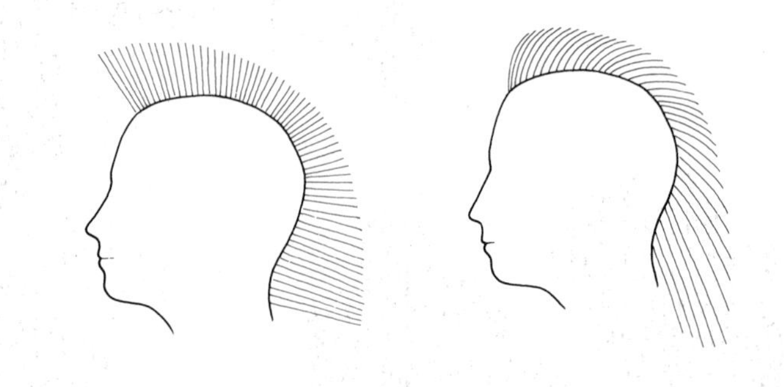

Cutting: inner layers shorter

TIP

A combination of techniques can achieve good results. Practice is essential.

The cutting method

1 Section and sub-section the lower nape hair. Taking a small section, usually mid-nape, cut the first part of the outer perimeter line horizontally.
2 Re-comb the section and hold it out from the head at 90°. Cut the hair at 45° to the section. Then use this as a guide while cutting the hair above.
3 Take down this upper hair in approximately 12 mm sections. Carefully cut it on the previously cut sections of hair, leaving longer nape hair with the upper hair getting gradually shorter.

Fashion looks

High-fashion styles represent the very latest trends in hair styling. These styles are intended to be worn by the model only, or at most a few others. Without adaptation, they are generally unsuitable for most women. At first sight they may appear to be extreme, and are often disliked, but they become more readily accepted as the fashion becomes understood, worn and seen. You need originality, good technique and experience to carry them out well.

Fashion styles are adapted high-fashion lines. They are created to suit different types of head or hair, or for different clients. These are favoured by the smart, well-dressed client and by people who like to look trendy. The new, different fashion styles and shapes – sometimes a return to older ideas – reflect the constant demand for novelty, ideas stimulated by an endless variety of events, moods and habits, and above all the wish to be different. As fashion styles become current and familiar, new ones appear to replace them.

Before starting to cut a client's hair to achieve a particular

TIP

People don't always mean the same thing by 'an inch' (2.5 cm). Make sure that client and stylist agree about what they mean.

VIDAL SASSOON

Fashion looks

fashion look, you must closely examine and analyse her head and hair. Carefully assess the techniques you could use to produce the effects she wants. Various questions need answering before you begin; these might include the following:

- How long is the client's hair now?
- Is the hair long enough for the required shape?
- How short will the hair be after cutting?
- Does the client agree to this?
- Has the hair texture sufficient body for lifted, full or sweeping movements?
- What does the client mean by phrases like 'cut it long', 'a full forward fringe', 'short at the side' or 'make it thicker'?
- What effects are realistically achievable? Are they practical? Will they last?
- Will the effects requested be suitable? Can simple sketches help? When should you, as stylist, take the initiative?

MAHOGANY

ERROL DOUGLAS AT NEVILLE DANIEL

Fashion style cutting

This involves cutting hair to a particular shape. It requires a blending of effects, methods and techniques. For you to achieve unique creations you should prepare your patterns of work, and carefully follow them exactly. Base them on the elements of styling as well as cutting.

Different parts of the head require different effects and techniques. The fringe hair may be 'skinny' and little reduction of length and body needed. The back hair may be thick and bushy and may well need to be 'tamed' or shaped. You can only feel confident with a technique when you have practised it thoroughly. Then you can go on to attempt and perfect others: advanced fashion styles are rarely based on a single technique. Fashion styling is attained by progressing from the basic principles to more intricate aspects. Once you have grasped the essentials of cutting – cutting guide lines, understanding angles, holding sections – and can work accurately, then you can progress to the combination of techniques and effects that fashion requires.

Necklines

These may be shaped in various ways. They may be cut curved, straight or pointed, or graduated high or low. Low graduation produces soft effects. When cutting above the natural hairline, be careful to avoid harsh effects. Where hair is cut shortest, particularly at the nape, make sure that hair growth patterns do not distort the effects required.

Trimming

This is a term used for the removal of small amounts of hair. It is usually done to retain the original cut style. To reproduce the original shape, use techniques, cutting lines and angles similar to those used for the original cut.

REPRODUCED COURTESY *HAIRDRESSERS JOURNAL*
HAIR BY TERENCE RENATI

Step-by-step: (a) Before

(b) Diagonal section is taken to retain weight/length

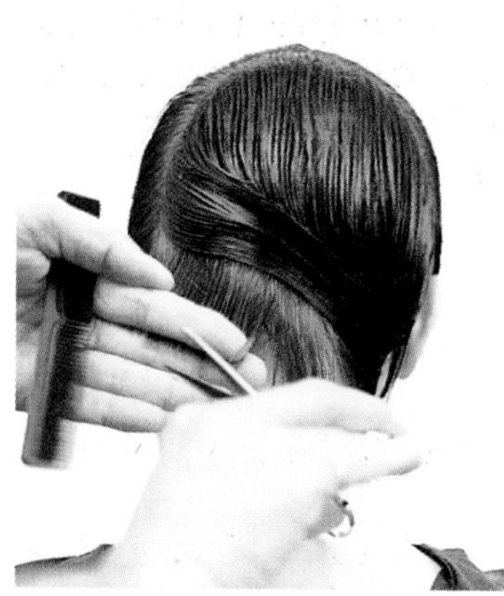

(c) Line followed through, with hair held at 45° angle

(d) Side hair held at 90° angle slightly forward to blend in back and sides

(e) Sections over ear snipped into, scissor over comb, to soften line

(f) Sides cut with hair flat on skin for a squared effect

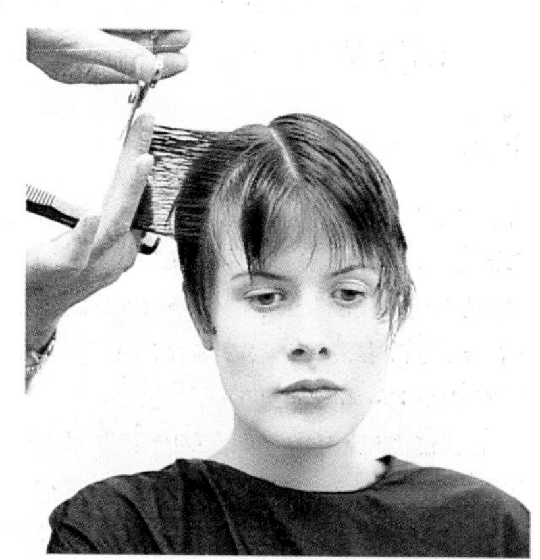

(g) Sections at crown blended into sides; hair slightly forward to retain length

(h) Fringe baseline cut to required length

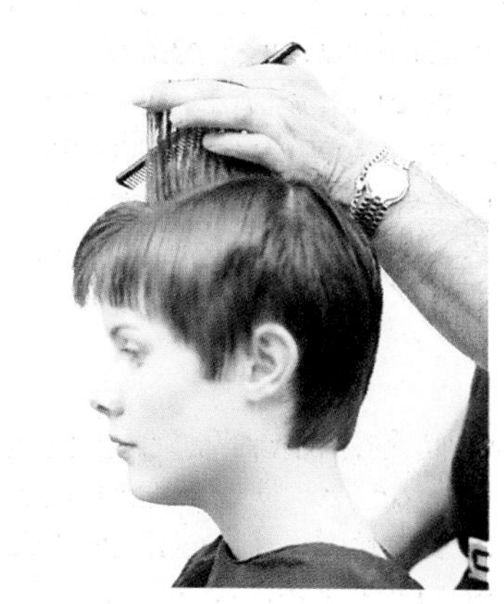

(i) Top fringe shaped; sections lifted to graduate lengths

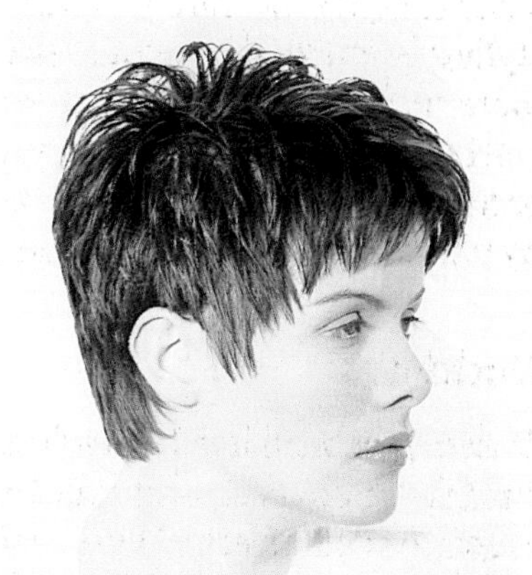

(j) Hair sprayed with spritz and styling spray, then finger blow-dried for finished effect

TIP

Cutting techniques should be adapted and combined as required.

Re-styling

To **re-style** is to design a completely new hair shape. You need to check that the hair is long enough for the style requested. Some styles require certain lengths, and it may take time for the hair to grow before these can be achieved. If your client is particularly keen to have a certain style, you may need to work on it gradually over several months – for instance, to allow earlier layering to grow out.

TIPS

Increase volume by texturising.

Increase body or weight by club cutting.

Decrease volume by thinning.

Increase curl tendency by tapering.

Increase texture by razoring or pointing.

Step-by-step: (a) Before

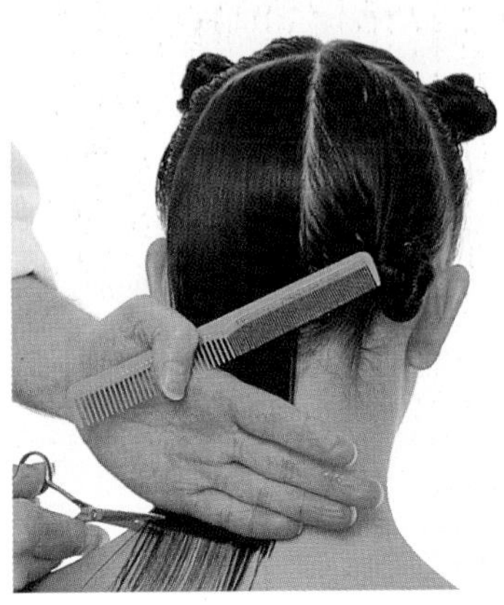

(b) First section taken parallel to hairline; hair cut flat on skin

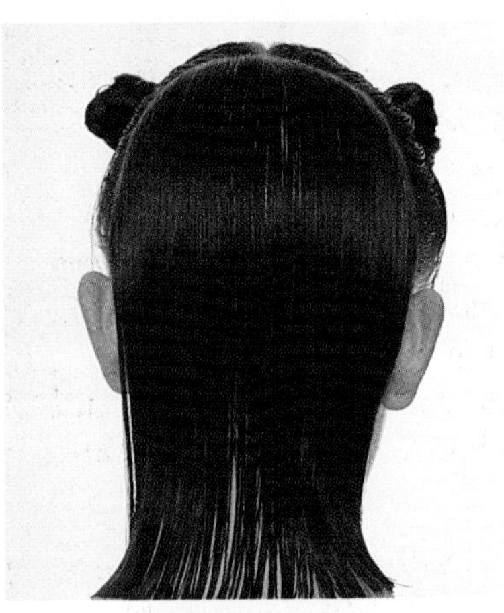

(c) Both sides of parting cut the same way

(d) Side: parting taken temple to nape, and another across crown; line followed through

(e) Line continued to centre parting in parallel sections

(f) Fringe: V-shaped sections cut into hair

(g) Irregular effect achieved

(h) Texturised by skidding scissors over top sections

(i) Cut complete

(j) Styled with mousse worked through lengths before blow-drying; finished lengths smoothed with silicone shine for gloss effect

ASSIGNMENTS: CUTTING AND STYLING HAIR

A practical activity

Closely watching your senior colleagues and tutors working is an invaluable means of learning. At first, cutting hair can be slow and difficult. With practice this soon changes.

To gather together information on cutting and styling you will need to visit hairdressing demonstrations, exhibitions and competitions. Using photography and video recording is ideal. Practising first cuts, or experimenting with the various techniques, can be carried out on practice blocks, slip-ons and models. You need to record as much as you can. Include the following:

1. Carefully list the movements and techniques that you see and outlining the effects produced. Try to capture the section positions taken, angles of cut, direction of cutting lines and so forth.
2. Practise cutting as soon as possible after seeing or recording a movement. Remember that your cutting actions will be slow to start with and that will affect your results.
3. Outline the plan of the cut and list the important factors to consider.
4. How do the different growth patterns affect your cutting? Describe these and try to illustrate them.
5. Try to describe the different cutting procedures and refer particularly to the different parts of the head – the fringe, sides, nape, top and back. Say how these parts are blended together.

For you to find out

Investigate the sources of haircutting information. In addition to demonstrations, competitions and seminars, wholesalers and manufacturers of cutting tools are extremely helpful. Video tapes of a wide range of methods and techniques are available. The information you collect should include these items:

- how to choose suitable cutting tools
- the effects produced by the different tools
- how metal cutting tools are maintained and cleaned
- how to select the right tool for the effect required
- the difference between wet and dry cutting, and the tools used for each
- how tools should be used safely
- which razors are considered to be most hygienic.

A case study

A new client has come to you for cutting and restyling. The hair is fine, shoulder-length, and in poor condition. Outline how you would deal with this client. Work through the following sequence:

1. List the questions and points you wish to make.
2. What styles may be suitable for your client, and why?
3. Discuss face shapes, hair growth patterns, and other important factors.
4. Is a fringe to be cut? Should the hair at the sides sweep back or forward? What type of neckline is required?
5. Which cutting technique or combination of techniques should be applied?
6. Should partings be used?
7. List the problems that you might meet. How could you overcome them?
8. Do you need to demonstrate how to maintain the new style?
9. What action would you take if the client did not like the new style?
10. What after-care advice do you need to give your client?

PREPARING FOR ASSESSMENT

In preparing for assessment on cutting and styling hair the following checklist may be helpful. Check that you have covered and now fully understand these items:

- determining the client's needs
- advising on style suitability, practicability and so on
- agreeing with the client the final cut, shape and style
- selection of tools
- choice and application of techniques
- need to maintain the client's confidence throughout cutting
- explanation to client of methods and procedures taken
- completion of styles such as one-length bobs, layering and graduation
- achieving client satisfaction.

When you feel that you are ready, talk to your trainer and arrange a suitable time for your assessment.

CHAPTER 6

Setting and dressing hair

STEPHEN REAY FOR TRESemmé

INTRODUCTION

Setting and dressing hair are important hairdressing techniques. they have alternated in popularity over the years.

Setting is the process of placing tension on the hair (stretching it) at various points along its length. Setting hair, wet or dry, involves curling, rollering, waving, twisting, pinning, clipping, positioning, placing and fixing it. This gives hair spring, body, volume and direction, achieved by the structural changes brought about by the altered tension.

Dressing blends the set movements and the directions of the hair, and finalises the style.

The following are some of the topics covered in this chapter:

- setting
  - what it is and what it does
  - techniques and methods
- dressing
  - what it does
  - shapes and styles.

Read too about **heat moulding techniques**, which are dry forms of temporarily shaping or setting dry hair (see page 72).

SEAN HANNA FOR L'OREAL

SETTING – WHAT IT IS

Like blow-styling, setting is a method of forming wet hair into shape. Hair can also be moulded dry. Setting is used to produce a variety of looks. You can make hair straighter, curlier, fuller, flatter or more wavy.

Setting involves placing wet hair in chosen positions, and holding it there while it dries into shape. You may roll the hair round curlers, secure it with clips or pins, or simply use your fingers. Once dry, you complete the process by dressing the hair with brushes and combs. Hair that has been set is called a **pli**. This term comes from the French *mis-en-pli*, meaning 'put into set'.

Hair must be controlled effectively, using initiative and a creative interpretation of the client's wishes, taking into account the same factors you consider when you are cutting or styling (see Chapter 5).

Dexterity – skilled, competent hand and finger movements,

> **TIP**
> Hair positioned and secured when wet will retain its shape when dry. In the end, you will get the shapes that you form.

> **TIP**
> Root direction determines hair flow.

ACTIVITY
Using sketches or photographs, compile a style book. Collect those styles that appear to you to be suitable and complimentary to the wearer. Also collect hairstyles that are totally *unsuitable*, and note why you think this is. Discuss these styles with your colleagues and tutors.

achieved after much practice – enables you to attain both effective control and shape variety.

As with other techniques, setting produces only a temporary change in hair structure. The pli will be lost as moisture is absorbed by the hair. Various setting aids are available which slow down this process, holding the shape longer (see page 114).

Different effects can be produced by different techniques:

- increasing volume – adding height, width and fullness, by lifting bases when rollering or curling
- decreasing volume – producing a close, smooth, contained or flat style by pincurl stem direction, or by dragged or angled rollering.
- movement – variation of line, waves and curls, produced by using differently sized rollers, pincurls or finger waving.

Straight hair effects can be produced by wrapping hair or by using large rollers (see page 163).

Different techniques are used for hair of different lengths:

- Longer hair (below shoulders) requires large rollers, or alternating large and small rollers, depending on the amount of movement required.
- Shorter hair (above shoulder) requires smaller rollers to achieve movement for full or sleek effects.
- Hair of one length is ideal for smooth, bob effects.
- Hair of layered lengths is ideal for full, bouncy, curly effects achieved by, say, barrel or clockspring curls (see page 117).

Different techniques can also be used to improve the appearance of hair of different textures:

- fine, lifeless hair can be given increased body and movement
- lank hair can be given increased volume and movement

Setting hair: different hair lengths

DANIEL GALVIN FOR L'OREAL

ANDREW COLLINGE (PHOTO: JOHN SWANNELL)

DANIEL GALVIN FOR L'OREAL

- coarse, thick hair requires firm control
- very curly hair can be contained and made smoother, and its direction varied
- the volume of unruly hair can be decreased.

SETTING – WHAT IT DOES

Hair is both flexible and elastic. As hair is curled or waved, it is bent under tension into curved shapes. The hair is stretched on the outer side of the curve and compressed on the inner side. If it is dried in this new position, the curl will be retained. This happens because when hair is set the hydrogen bonds and salt bonds between the keratin chains of the hair (see pages 28–9) are broken. The linking system is moved into a new temporary position. (The stronger disulphide links remain unbroken.)

Hair, however, is **hygroscopic** – it is able to absorb and retain moisture. It does so by capillary action: water spreads through minute spaces in the hair structure, like ink spreading in blotting paper. Wet hair expands and contracts more than dry hair does, because water acts as a lubricant and allows the link structure to be repositioned more easily. So the amount of moisture in hair affects the curl's durability. As the hair picks up moisture the rearranged keratin chains loosen or relax into their previous shape and position. This is why the **humidity** – the moisture content of air – determines how long the curled shape is retained.

The condition and the porosity of hair affect its elasticity. If the cuticle is damaged, or open, the hair will retain little moisture, because of normal evaporation. The hair will therefore have poor elasticity. If too much tension is applied when curling hair of this type it may become limp, overstretched and lacking in spring. Very dry hair is likely to break.

The client

- Prepare your client by carefully gowning her and making sure she is comfortable. Remove damp towels and any loose cut hair before setting commences.
- Communicate with the client about what you are going to do next. Discuss the final effect you are aiming for. Pictures of styles in magazines and style manuals may be useful.
- Examine the hair again – check the natural direction and movement, the effects of previous perming, and the condition of the hair. Whether a given style is suitable will depend on its texture and condition.
- Agree with your client what you will do. Estimate how long it will take and tell her if there will be any additional costs.
- Analyse the techniques you will need.
- Discuss any setting aids you plan to use (see page 114) – your client may have personal preferences.
- Assemble the tools you will need, so that they are to hand as you carry out any rolling or pinning.
- Advise your client on how to manage the style at home.

SETTING AIDS

When you have towel-dried and combed your client's hair, and before you start work on the pli, you may decide to apply one of a range of **setting aids**. These products help to hold hair in shape, maintain the curls and waves, and thus make the set last longer. They include lotions, sculpting creams, mousses, gels, glitz, waxes, sprays, moisturisers and hair thickeners. Some setting aids also add glaze, glitter, shine or colour to the hair. They contain **resins** or **plastics** (polymers such as **PVP** and **PVA**). These soften the hair, allow shapes to be formed, prevent flyaway effects and coat the hair with a fine plastic film which slows down the absorption of moisture.

When applying setting aids, remember the following:

- If the hair is too wet, the setting aid will become diluted and will be less effective.
- If the hair is to dry, it will become sticky and difficult to manage.
- Don't apply too much. Apart from being wasteful, it will make the hair sticky.
- Apply setting aids evenly. Massage or comb them through the hair to make sure each hair is completely covered.
- Protect your client's face – chemicals can be irritating to the skin and harmful to the eyes.
- Always follow manufacturers' instructions

TIP

Each technique creates its own effects. Learn these, to make yourself adaptable.

WELLA

Setting aids

CURLING TECHNIQUE

Curls are series of shapes or movements in the hair. They may occur naturally, or be put there by hairdressing – chemically by perming, or physically by setting. Curls add 'bounce' or lift to the hair, and determine the direction in which the hair lies.

Each curl has a **root**, a **stem**, a **body** and a **point**. The **curl base** – the foundation shape produced between parted sections of hair – may be oblong, square, triangular and so on. The shape depends on the size of the curl, the stem direction and the curl type. Different curl types produce different movements.

You can choose the shape, size and direction of the individual curls: your choice will affect how satisfying is the finished effect, and how long it lasts. The type of curl you choose depends on the style you're aiming for – a high, lifted movement needs a raised curl stem; a low, smooth shape needs a flat curl. You may need to use a combination of curl types and curling methods to achieve the desired style – for example, you might lift the hair on top of the head using large rollers, but keep the sides flatter using pincurls. Think about this when designing the pli.

STEPHEN REAY FOR TRESemmé

A curled dressing

Rollering

There are various sizes and shapes of **roller**. In using rollers you need to decide on the size and shape, how you will curl the hair on to them, and the position in which you will attach them to the base.

TIP

Evenly tensioned curls produce even movements. Twisted ones produce difficulties.

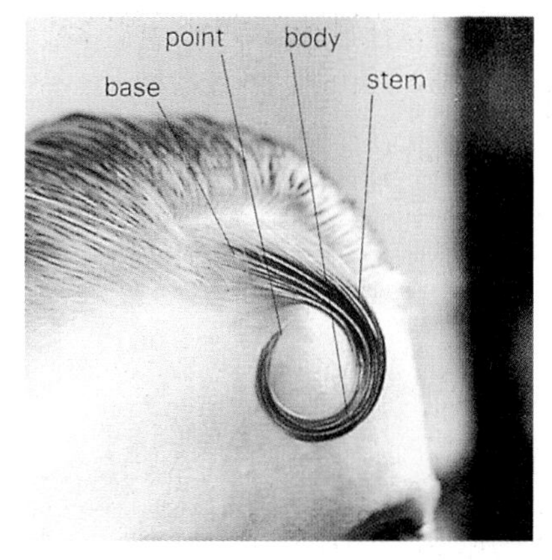

Curl parts

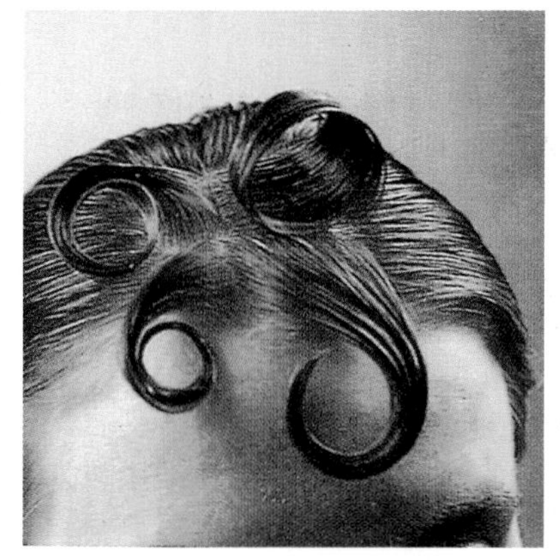

Curl types

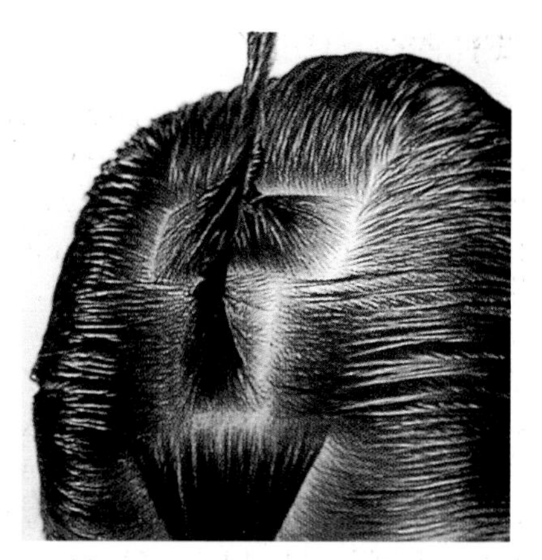

Curl bases

Roller setting:
Wound rollers (*left*)
Completed effect (*right*)

TIP

If you're not sure which size of roller is best, use smaller ones – if necessary you can brush out too tightly curled hair later. Loosely curled hair will drop more easily, so you may not achieve the style you were aiming for.

- Small rollers produce tight curls, giving hair more movement. Large rollers produce loose curls, making hair wavy rather than curly.
- Rollers pinned on or above their bases, so that the roots are upright, produce more volume than rollers placed below their bases.
- The direction of the hair wound round the rollers will affect the final style – do you want the hair to flick upwards or turn under?

Hair rollers/wavers

HEALTH AND SAFETY
Don't position metal clips or pins on the scalp itself. They will get hot when you dry the hair, and may burn the skin.

Never allow a pin to pierce the skin. Watch what you are doing!

Method

1. Begin at the point from which the curled hair is to flow, at a place that is comfortable for the client and convenient to work from.
2. Section the hair to avoid unwanted divisions after setting and drying. Use a tailcomb with which you can divide and control the hair easily.
3. As you work, make sure that any fine, wispy hair is included on the roller. Don't overstretch the hair – this could make the hair break or become limp.
4. If you are using pins to secure the rollers, make sure you don't pierce the client's scalp, or disturb hair that has already been wound.
5. Cleanly comb a section of hair – no longer or wider than the roller size being used – straight out from the head.
6. Place the hair points centrally on to the roller. Use both hands to retain the hair section angle and keep the hair points in position.
7. As you turn the roller, 'lock' the hair points against the body of the roller. Then wind down the hair and roller evenly. Don't move the hair from side to side when winding: if you do, the hair will slip out.
8. Place the wound roller centrally on to the sectioned base to achieve the full height effect. Secure the wound roller by pinning through it to prevent unwinding.

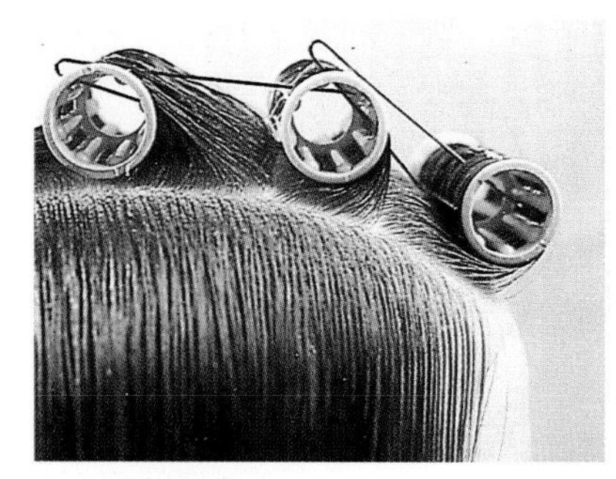

Securing rollers

Pinning rollers

TIP
More tension is required when rollering coarser hair. Chemically treated hair, and very fine hair, require little tension.

TIP
Curled or rollered hair will kick out if kinked.

Common faults

- If you don't secure the wound roller carefully on its base you may get a dragged or flat effect, without the volume you had intended.
- If the hair sections are too big or too small, you will find it difficult to blend the curls when dressing.

ACTIVITY
Practise setting a circle of curls. This will help you to achieve control of stem directions.

ACTIVITY
Practise setting one row of curls with stems to the left, the next with stems to the right, and the third with stems to the left. Dry in position, then brush the hair and blend the curls. You should have achieved a wave shape.

- Don't allow roller pins to scratch the skin. It is better to pass them through another roller.
- Longer hair requires a large roller, unless very tight effects are required. Large rollers in short hair make control difficult and the effects produced are weak.
- Dragging hair from either side of the roller produces divisions which will not dress out easily.
- If you bend back the hair points you may cause 'fish-hooks'.
- Twisting hair as you roll it will distort the movement of the hairstyle.
- Working untidily can lead to sloppy rollering, which in turn causes dressing problems and distorts the movement directions of the final style.

Pincurling

Pincurling is the technique of winding hair into a series of curls which are pinned in place while drying. The two most common types of curl produced in this way are the barrelspring and the clockspring.

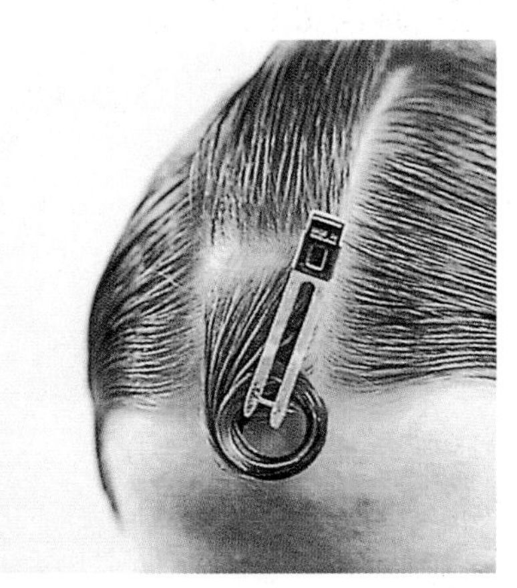

Barrelspring curl

- The **barrelspring curl** has an open centre and produces a soft effect. When formed, each loop is the same size as the previous one. It produces an even wave shape and may be used for **reverse curling**, which forms waves in modern hairstyles. In this, one row of pincurls lies in one direction, the next in the opposite direction. When dry and dressed, this produces a wave shape.
- The **clockspring curl** has a closed centre and produces a tight, springy effect. When formed each loop is slightly smaller than the previous one. It produces an uneven wave shape throughout its length. It can be suitable for hair that is difficult to hold in place, but is not often used nowadays.

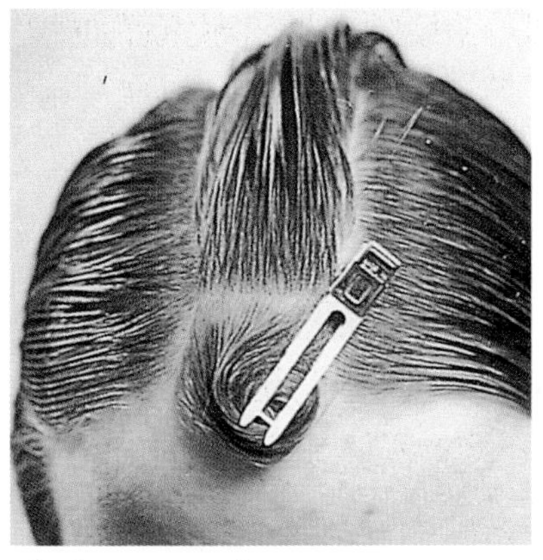

Clockspring curl

Method

The following method of curling can be used for curls that are tight or loose, big or small, and for even and uneven shapes.

1. Neatly section the hair and comb cleanly through it. (The section size is determined by the effect required.)
2. Hold the hair in the direction in which it is to lie after drying and dressing.

ACTIVITY

Set the hair of your practice block in rollers. As you place the rollers, ensure that you form a brick-like pattern with no partings. Set another block, placing one roller level with the next where possible. When dry, brush out both blocks and note the difference between them. The second block will have harsh divisions or partings which are difficult to dress out.

3 Hold the hair, at mid-length, in one hand, using the thumb and forefinger, with the thumb uppermost. Using the thumb and finger on the other hand, with the thumb underneath, hold the hair a little way down from the hair points.
4 Turn the second hand to form the first curl loop. The hand should turn almost completely round at the wrist.
5 On completion of the first loop, transfer the hair to the finger and thumb of the other hand.
6 Form a series of loops until the curl base is reached. The last loop is formed by turning the curl body into the curl base. The rounded curl body should snugly fit into the curl base.
7 Secure the curl without disturbing its position on its base. Use clips or pins.

This curling method can be used to produce either barrelspring or clockspring curls. The curl loops may be formed either larger or smaller, as required. It can be used whether you are right- or left-handed.

Stand-up pin curls

Common faults

- Tangled hair is difficult to control. Comb the hair well before your start.
- If the base size is too large, curling will be difficult, particularly if the hair is short.
- If you hold the curl stem in one direction but place it in another, the curl will lift.
- If you don't turn your hand sufficiently you will find it difficult to form loops.

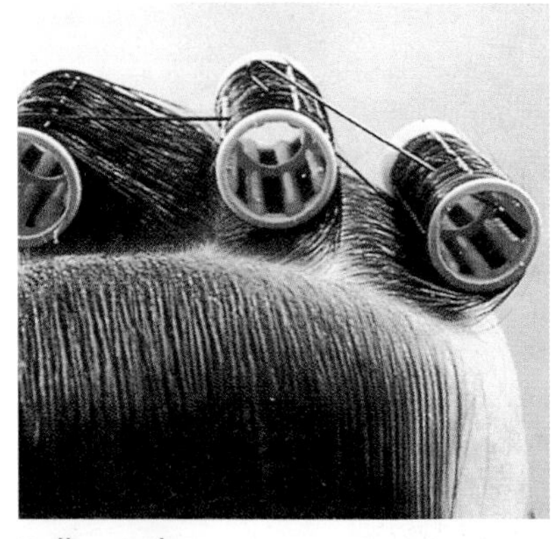
Roller curls

Curl variations

Roller, stand-up and barrel pincurls are similarly formed. Each has its stem directed up from the head, which produces height and fulness.

- The **stand-up pincurl** is formed on an oblong base – longer than it is wide – and has an open centre and a lifted base. These curls produce high, soft, casual, loose shapes. Their main advantage is individual direction and shape.
- **Roller curls** are similar to stand-up curls but do not have the individual shape and movement produced by separate curls. The main difference between these curls is the tension used, and their size.
- The **barrel pincurl** is formed on a smaller base than that used for rollering. Variation in stem direction produces interesting shapes. The curl is formed from its points, or held in the centre and the points placed on to the base. A clip retains the lifted base and curl position. Barrel pincurls are normally wider than stand-up pincurls, and narrower than roller curls.

Barrel pincurl

ACTIVITY
Try securing some pincurls with hairpins, some with setting clips, and some with hairgrips. When dry, dress each of them and note the differences produced.

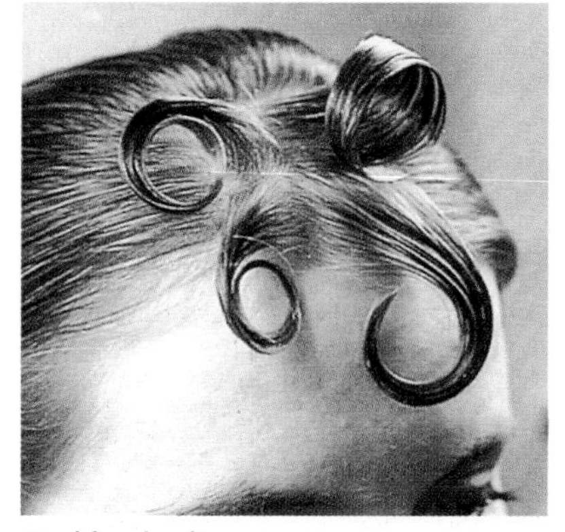
Curl body directions

Curl body directions

A flat curl may turn either clockwise or counter-clockwise. The body of a clockwise curl moves to the right, like the hands of a clock. The counter-clockwise curl moves in the opposite direction. Roller and stand-up pincurls are formed with their stems directed up from the head.

Make sure that you place the hair carefully to get the curls going in the right direction for the style you have chosen.

Reverse curls

Using alternate rows of clockwise and counter-clockwise barrelspring curls, you can create a wave shape. Double rows of reverse curls – two rows clockwise, then two rows counter clockwise – produce larger waves. Wave size is determined by the hair length and the curl size, and by the use of single or double rows.

HEALTH AND SAFETY
Never place clips or pins in your mouth – this is unhygienic and dangerous.

Never place tailcombs in your pocket – they may pierce the body when you bend over.

Never work on a wet, slippery floor.

Always use clean, sterile tools, towels and equipment, to avoid cross-infection.

ACTIVITY
List the movements and directions produced by the different types of curl.

ACTIVITY
Using three separate blocks, form, dry and dress three different curl types. Look carefully at the different effects and consider how you might use each kind of curl in your designs for setting.

Drying a pli

The pli is usually dried using a hood dryer, carefully lowered to cover the set head of hair.

1. Make sure the client is comfortable.
2. Set the dryer to a temperature that suits the client. Most dryers have thermostatic controls, but it is a good idea to check with the client from time to time. Fine hair should be dried at lower temperatures.

3. Drying will take about 20–30 minutes. The time will depend on the thickness of the hair: the thicker the hair, the longer the drying time. The dryer may have an automatic timer which reminds you when the time is up.
4. Allow the hair to cool fully before removing pins, clips and so on. If you unwind the hair while it is still warm and soft the shape will soon drop.

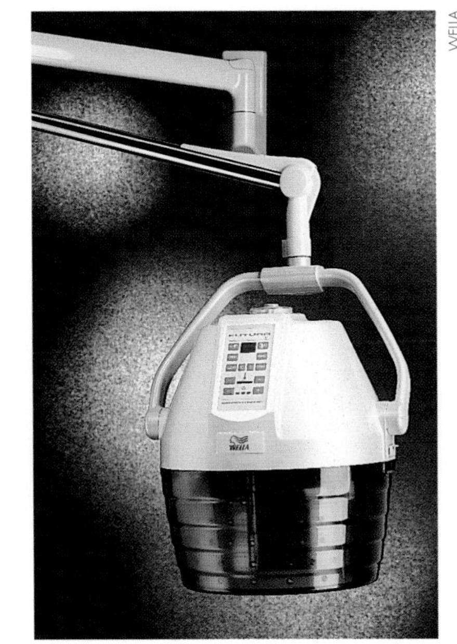

WELLA

A hood dryer

Steam setting

The **steam set** relies on the setting of clean, dry hair, with moisture supplied by a steamer.

1. Wash and dry the hair.
2. Place the dry hair into the pli.
3. Steam the hair for three minutes.
4. Place the hair under a dryer for 5–10 minutes, depending on the length of the hair.
5. Allow the hair to cool, then dress it.

This type of set produces a quick shape; the hair is shiny and easy to dress. It takes about half an hour for long hair.

Successful curling

L'OREAL

Learning to curl, like other practical techniques, requires patience and practice. You need to experiment, preferably on practice blocks. Try combing, sectioning, sub-dividing smaller hair sections, handling different hair textures, and practising the sequence of movements required to form the curl.

When you are fairly competent, transfer your skills to 'live' models. In a way, this is like starting again. Dealing with the model, and coping with different hair textures, hair lengths and style requirements, creates further opportunities for you to explore techniques of curling.

Reasons for poor results

ERROL DOUGLAS AT NEVILLE DANIEL

- Wet hair stretches more than dry hair. If the hair is too dry the curl spring will be reduced.
- Hot hair is soft. If you start to dress it before it has cooled, spring and shape will be lost.
- To form a movement you need to make several similar curls. If you use too few the shape becomes skimped.
- If the hair is not free of grease and other materials before setting, the shape will be loose and lank.
- If you don't dry the hair sufficiently after setting, the shape soon falls.
- The larger the curl, the looser the effects. Large rollers placed in short hair produce straight effects.
- Frizzy ends may be produced by fish-hooking or overstretching.
- Stem direction determines hair movement. If the directions are varied by too much dressing, control becomes difficult.

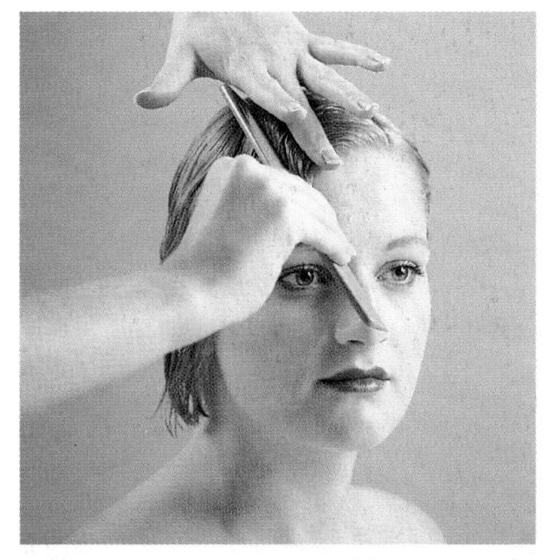

Finger waving: first crest

Finger waving: second crest

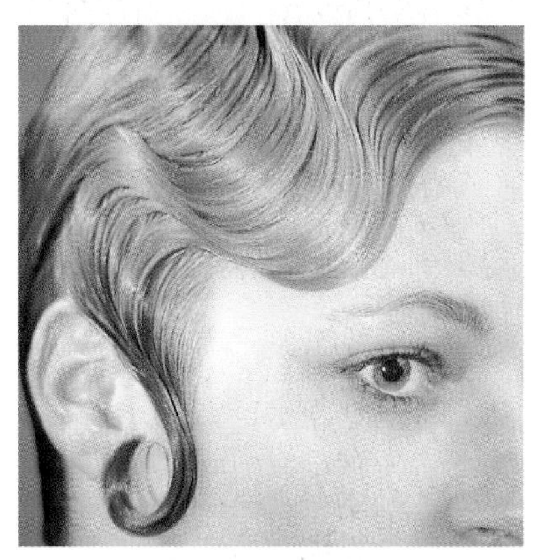

Finger waving: third crest

Finger waving

Finger waving is a technique of moulding wet hair into 'S' shaped movements using the hands, the fingers and a comb. It is sometimes called **water waving** or **water setting**, as the result resembles waves in the sea. In **horizontal waving** the waves go from side to side; in **vertical waving** they go up and down.

The technique was most popular before rollers were widely available. You can see the effect in the flat, waved hair of early movie stars. Nowadays hairstyles are generally fuller, but finger waves may be used within the overall style – for example, at the lower part of the back of the head, or at the sides. They usually look better if they are at an angle. As with all styling, the use of these movements depends on the individual client's features and head shape.

Forming the wave

1. Use one finger of one hand to control the hair and to determine the position of the wave. Comb the hair into the first part of the crest, and continue along the head.
2. Place the second finger immediately below the crest formed, and comb the hair in the opposite direction.
3. Form the second crest similarly, to complete the final wave shape.

The elbow and arm should be held above the hand when it is placed on the head. Only the index finger should touch the head. This gives the required control and pressure. A comb with both widely and closely spaced teeth is the most suitable.

Points to remember

- Finger waving is most successful on medium or fine hair that is about 10 cm long. Coarse or lank hair can be difficult.
- Setting lotion, gel, mousse or emulsion will be needed to hold the waves.
- Keep your foream level with or slightly higher than the wrist, to control the hair and your hand during waving.
- Hold the comb upright and don't use too much pressure when combing, to avoid tearing the scalp.
- Keep the waves the same size and depth. About 3 cm (the tips of two fingers) between crests is usually best.
- For vertical waving, use strips about 5 cm wide.
- For short hair, make shallow rather than deep waves.
- Pinching or forcing the crests will distort the waves. Correct control and angling will produce the best waves.
- Positioning is important. Comb the hair to make it lie evenly, and return it to this position after each wave movement is complete.
- Keep the hair wet (but not dripping) during waving. If you find that it is drying out, dampen it while you work and apply more setting lotion if necessary.

- Dry the completed shape under a hood dryer, if possible. This helps to prevent the movements from being disturbed.

Finger waving: whole head

Waving all of the hair

1. Begin the waving about 75 mm from the front hairline, at the parting. The parting should ideally be placed midway above the eyebrow. Start with the larger side of the hair.
2. Place the finger at right angles to the parting, with the crest curved round to the front.
3. If there is to be no parting, begin at the hairline on one side.

SCHWARZKOPF

Dressing the waves

The waved head of hair is not usually brushed. It should be disturbed as little as possible.

1. Place the coarse end of the comb between the two lowest crests and comb through to the ends. Support and hold the crests and hair above the combing, to prevent dragging. A slight pushing and moulding action with the hand produces full, soft wave shapes.
2. Repeat this, starting between the next higher crests.
3. Complete the dressing with the fine end of the comb.

WELLA

Completed dressings

ACTIVITY

On a practice block set the section with the rollers so that it is over-directed. On another block set the top section with rollers on their bases. On a third block set the rollers below sections. Dry and dress all three. Note the shape and the hair direction produced in each.

ACTIVITY

Finger wave different parts of a block or head, and dry the hair in position. Assess the wave shape formed: better waves remain in one position, poor ones drop.

DRESSING TECHNIQUE

After all the planning and preparation, dressing is the process of adding the finishing touches to well-conditioned, cut and set hair. Setting gives movement to hair in the form of curls or waves. **Dressing** blends and binds these movements into an overall flowing shape, the style you set out to achieve. It produces an overall form that flows, lightening the head and face and removing dull, flat or odd shapes. The completed shape is called a **dressing**, **coiffure** or **hair-do**. It is this that the client takes away from the salon – ideally, a correct and satisfying interpretation of what was required.

Dressing uses brushing and combing techniques, and dressing aids such as hairspray to keep the hair in place. If you have

DENMAN

Brushes for dressing hair

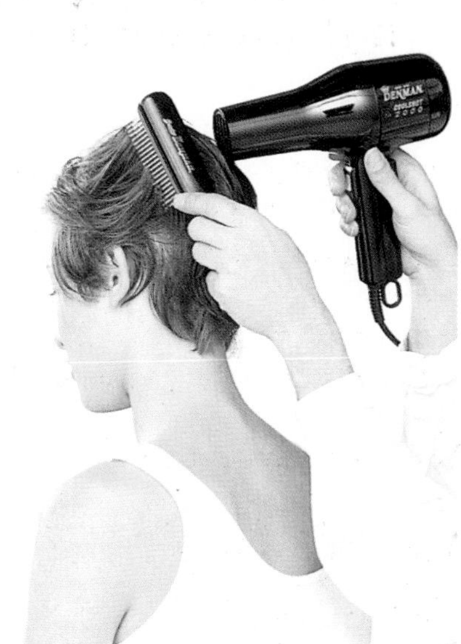
RICHARD THOMPSON, MAHOGANY

Dressing with a brush

planned the pli carefully and set the hair accordingly, only a minimum of dressing will be needed.

Brushing

Brushing blends the waves or curls, removes the partings left at the curl bases during rollering, and gets rid of any stiffness caused by setting aids.

1. One way of achieving the finished dressing is with a brush and your hand. The thicker the hair, the stiffer the brush bristles need to be. Choose a brush that will flow through the hair comfortably.
2. Apply the brush to the hair ends. Use firm but gentle strokes.
3. Work up the head, starting from the back of the neck.
4. Brush through the waves or curls you have set, gradually moulding the hair into shape.
5. As you brush, pat the hair with your hand to guide the hair into shape. Remember, though, that overdressing and overhandling can ruin the set.

The technique of **double brushing** uses two brushes, applied one after the other in a rolling action. You may prefer to use a brush and comb.

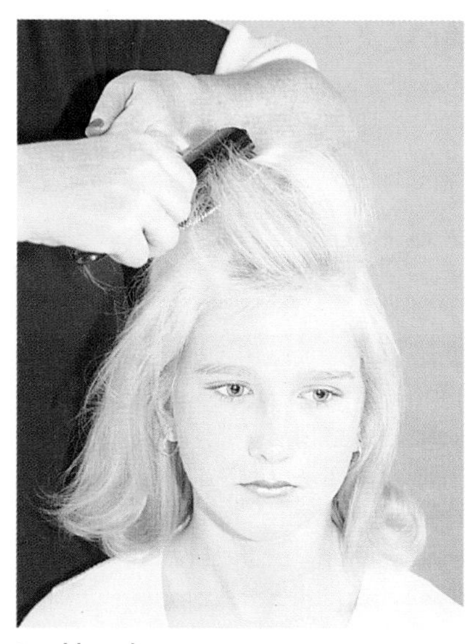

Backbrushing

Backbrushing

Backbrushing is a technique used to give more height and volume to hair. By brushing backwards from the points to the roots, you roughen the cuticle of the hair. Hairs will now tangle slightly and bind together to hold a fuller shape. The amount of hair backbrushed determines the fullness of the finished style.

Tapered hair is well suited to backbrushing: the short hairs in the sections backbrushed add bulk easily. Clubbed hair, on the other hand, does not respond to backbrushing as it is all of one length. Tapered hair, with shorter lengths distributed throughout, is more easily pushed back by brushing. Most textures of hair can be backbrushed; because it adds bulk, the technique is especially useful with fine hair.

Method

1. Hold a section of hair out from the head. For maximum lift, hold the section straight out from the head and apply the backbrushing close to the roots.
2. Place the brush on top of the section. With a slight turning action of the brush, slide some of the hairs back towards the scalp. If you brush too strongly you will pull the entire section from your hand. After each stroke, replace the section on the head, in the direction you want it to lie.
3. Check the surface of the section. In the final style the underlying tangling should not be visible.
4. You may need to backbrush only a small amount of hair – it depends how much volume you want to add.
5. Offer your client guidance about how to achieve the same effect at home, and about how to remove backdressing without tearing or breaking the hair.

Backcombing

The technique of **backcombing** is similar to that of backbrushing. Here a comb rather than a brush is used to turn shorter hairs in a section, giving support and volume to dressed hair. The backdressing is applied deeper in the hair, right down at the roots, so this technique can add more volume than can backbrushing.

Method

1. Hold a section of hair out from the head. Use different angles with different sections.
2. Place the fine end of the dressing comb underneath the section, near the roots. Don't push it too far in. Gently turn it, and push it back towards the head.
3. Repeat this movement of the comb along the length of the section, moving away from the roots and towards the points.
4. Push the backcombed section out of your way, and comb another section. Continue until you have achieved the desired height or fullness.
5. Finish the dressing by positioning the hair with your fingers. Smooth the hair with the wide end of the comb.

ACTIVITY

Practise differing amounts of backdressing. Notice how backcombing produces firmer and higher effects than backbrushing.

Backcombing

TIP

Backcombing is applied to the *underside* of a hair section. Don't let the comb penetrate too deeply (towards the surface of the section), or the final dressing will drag the backcombing out and lose the effect.

Teasing

After brushing the hair and backdressing it if necessary, you may need to place small areas of hair individually. This is called **teasing**.

It is important at this stage not to disturb the rest of the dressing. Use your fingertips and a pin, the end of a tailcomb, or a wide-toothed Afro comb to lift the hair carefully into position, to finish the balance, or to cover an exposed area.

> **TIP**
> Angle your hands so that the palms don't touch the head, and don't pat the hair too much – you could easily undo the effect of the earlier dressing.

Simple dressing

Hair does not always need backdressing. If the hair has been suitably cut and blow-styled it may already have sufficient shape and bulk. After setting, tonging or hot brushing, for example, this kind of dressing may be quite adequate:

1. Brush the hair firmly, starting at the nape. Gradually work up the head until you reach the front.
2. As you brush, move freely – first *against* the direction of the set, then in the intended direction.
3. Having blended the set in this way, distribute the hair using a comb or brush. Follow the movements of the hair. Lightly stroke the hair with your hand as you position it. Gently push the hair from the head to achieve any extra height.

Overdressing

One of the commonest faults in dressing is **overdressing** – doing too much. You need to plan the whole dressing from the outset, and watch what you are doing so that you recognise when you have done enough. Don't fiddle with the hair: look for the overall shape, balance and movements.

Mirrors

As you work, keep looking in the mirror to check what you are doing. If you spend too long concentrating on one area you will lose track of the overall shape. Step back from time to time and

Mirror reflection

ACTIVITY

Practise the following:

□ combing hair stems in different directions
□ placing stems in different directions
□ rolling your wrist as you curl the hair
□ using your fingertips to hold the hair and the curls.

look at the shapes and movements you are producing. This will save time-wasting alterations later.

At the end, hold a hand mirror at an angle so that your client can see the finished effect from behind and from the side.

Long hair dressings

Long hair needs particular consideration, but is not difficult to manage. If it is in good condition and has been well cut it will hang naturally. Flowing styles can be finished with a hand dryer and a brush.

Because long hair is heavy, it is important to centralise the weight. This will help it to stay in place. You can secure it in position using pins, grips, rubber bands, combs or ribbons.

When the bulk of the hair is in place, you may dress lengths by plaiting (see page 129). If you do use plaits, angle them carefully so that you keep the weight well distributed. Take care not to disturb the *base* of the secured hair – you need this to remain firm.

Long hair can be dressed **symmetrically**, with matching hair arrangements on either side, or **asymmetrically**, with unmatched but balanced arrangements.

The following are popular long hair dressings:

STEPHEN REAY FOR TRESemmé

Long hair dressed symmetrically

Long hair dressed asymmetrically

HEALTH AND SAFETY

Whatever you use to secure the hair, make sure it doesn't damage the hair or scalp.

- a pleat, French roll or vertical roll
- a horizontal roll
- plaiting.

Pleating

TIP

Before securing long hair, give it a slight twist. This will help to keep it in place.

A **pleat**, or **French roll**, is a vertical fold of hair, commonly worn on the back of the head. It is most suitable for long hair, but can be achieved even with shorter lengths. The pleat is one way of dressing long hair to make it appear to be shorter.

A pleat or vertical roll

The steps for attaining a successful pleat are as follows:

1. Brush and smooth the hair into the position required, either to the left or to the right.
2. Secure the crown hair out of the way, if necessary. Otherwise, include it in the pleat. The side hair can be included, or it can be dressed separately.
3. Keep the head upright so that the pleat does not loosen. Backdress the hair to give added fullness.

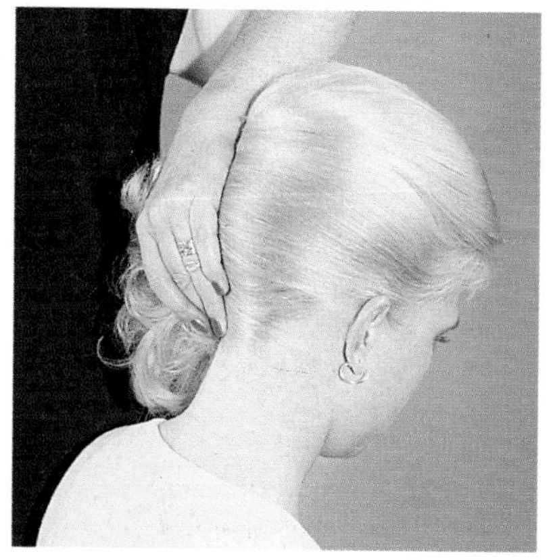

Pleat/vertical roll:
(a) Smoothing hair into position

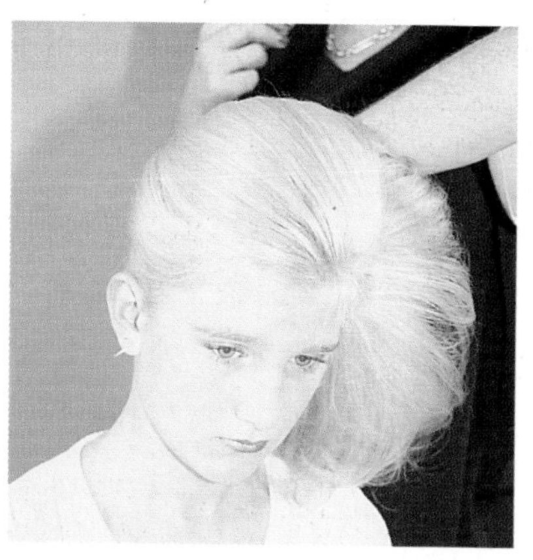

(b) Backdressing

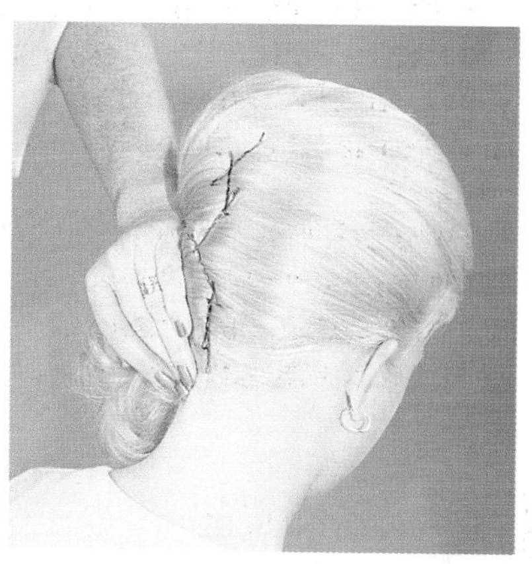

(c) Securing with grips

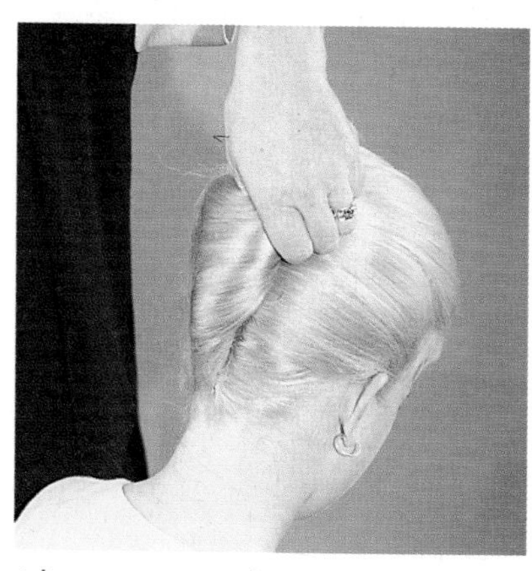

(d) Positioning pleat

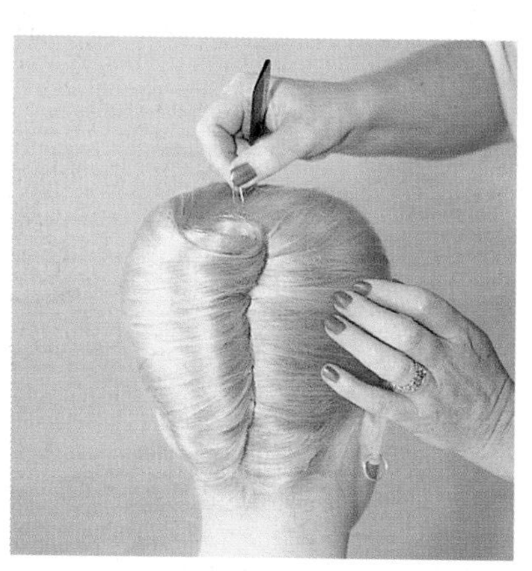

(e) Pinning folded hair

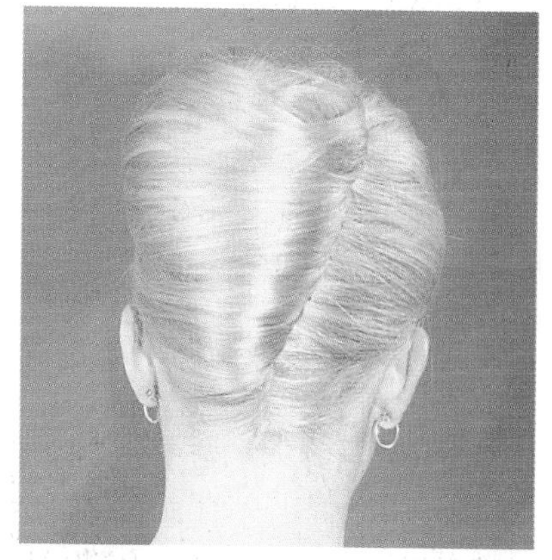

(f) The completed roll

4 Place one hand on to the sweeping hair, at the angle you require the pleat to lie. Secure the hair firmly in position with grips, making sure that you overlap them.
5 Now grasp the hair and tidy it, but without loosening the gripped base. Turn it up and round to cover the grips.
6 You can now slowly slide your hand towards the crown and pin the folded hair into position.
7 With the pleat secured firmly in place, dress the top front or crown hair into place, depending on the look you require. No pins or grips should be visible in the finished dressing.

TIP

During consultation with the client you may find it helpful to manipulate the hair at a styling unit. By moving and changing the hair into different positions, you and your client will be able to see what possible final shapes look like. When styling longer hair, this will save valuable dressing-out time while achieving the agreed final appearance.

The horizontal roll

The steps for attaining a successful **horizontal roll** are as follows:

1 Take the hair into your hands and carefully position the hair bulk where required.
2 Sweep the hair in the direction it is to lie. Securely fix the base using overlapping grips or pins.
3 Fold the hair, in the opposite direction to that of the base. Hide any fixing pins or grips by pushing them in or teasing hair over them.

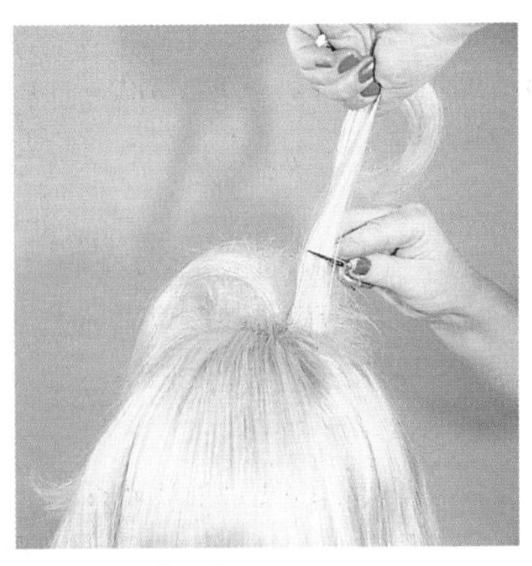

Horizontal roll:
(a) Positioning hair

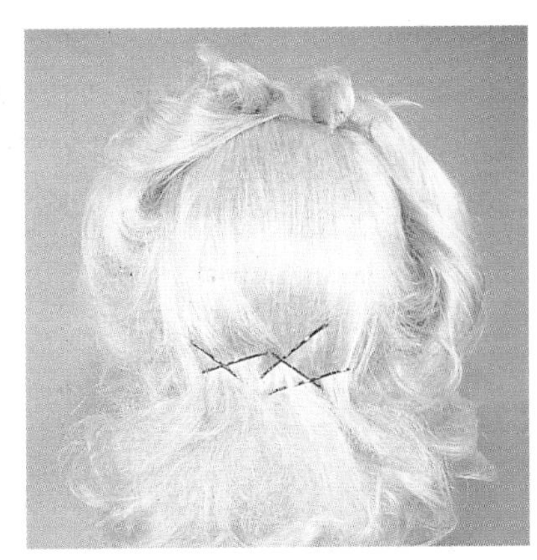

(b) Securing hair

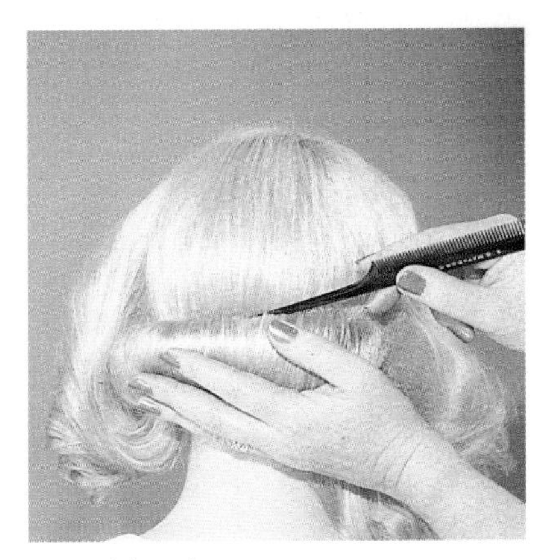

(c) Folding hair

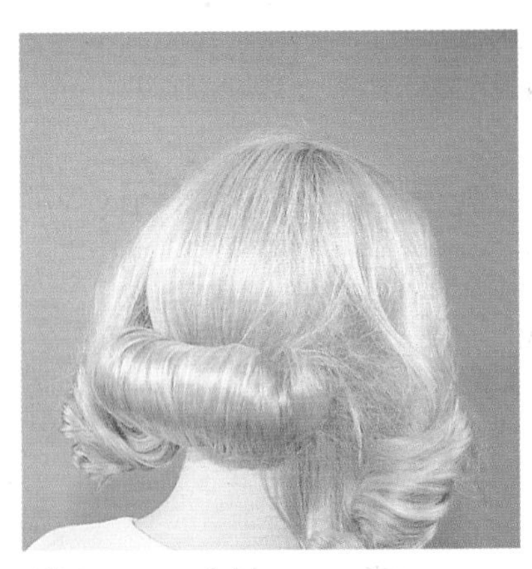

(d) Securing fold

(e) Positioning sides

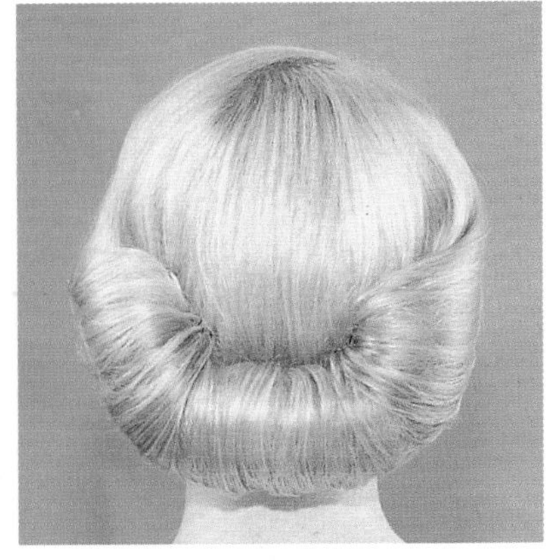

(f) The completed roll

4 Secure the fold in position. (A base of cottonwool, or net-covered pads of various shapes, may be used to lift and round out the roll: this must be placed on the base before the roll is secured.)
5 For greater variety, smaller sections should be taken: a series of rolls can be placed artistically to achieve a pleasing effect.
6 The side hair may be unswept into small or large rolls, covered partially by the top of crown hair. The lower back should be positioned first, and the side and top hair built upon it.
7 The hair may be interlaced to give added support to the dressing. In this process, a strip of hair is taken from one side and crossed and interlocked with another strip taken from the opposite side.

Plaiting

Woven hair, on a block

Plaiting, or **braiding**, is achieved by intertwining sections of hair. It can be an attractive way of dressing long hair. A variety of sizes and shapes is possible. The three-stem plait is the one most commonly used, but others may be used. Plaited or unplaited hair offers a wide range of dressings. Basket-weave shapes have become popular recently. You can interlace coloured materials, if you wish.

- **Cornrowing** Continuous plaits running along the scalp, also called **scalp plaits** or **ethnic plaits**.
- **Dreadlocks** Long thin plaits.
- **Hair extensions** Synthetic hair plaited and added to the natural hair lengths, by heating, to imitate dreadlocks.
- **Hair threading** The process of wrapping plaited, or unplaited, hair with coloured threads.
- **Hair twists** Oiled or gelled hair twisted together to form tufts.
- **Hair wrapping** Coloured ribbon wrapping the hair, or plaiting with ribbons.
- **Hair weaving** The interlacing of strands of hair, over and under one another, to produce a variety of basketweave effects.

There is an almost infinite range of plaiting, braiding, twisting and weaving effects, as you can see among the ethnic groups of the world, particularly those of Africa. Many dressings of international origin are being used in British and European fashions.

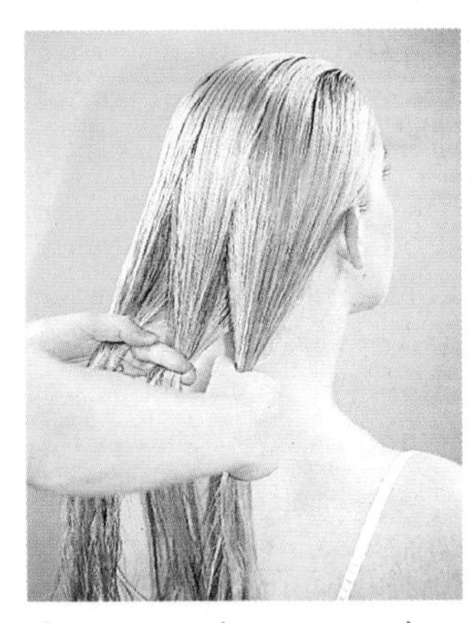

Three-stem plait: (a) Dividing hair into three sections

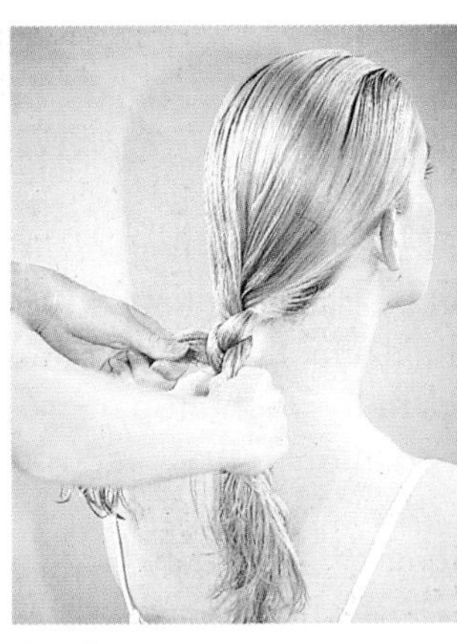

(b) Placing outer sections over centre alternately

(c) Continuing to intertwine the sections

(d) The completed plait

HEALTH AND SAFETY
Avoid pulling the stems too tightly, particularly at the hairlines. Repeated plaiting, and leaving hair in plaits for long periods, can cause traction baldness and hair breakage.

Three-stem plaits

1 Divide the hair to be plaited into three equal sections. Hold the hair above the hands, using your fingers to separate the sections.
2 Starting from either left or right, place the outside section over the centre one. Repeat this from the other side. (Alternatively, place the outside stems *under*, rather than *over*, the central one – keep to the same method throughout, however.)
3 Continue intertwining the outside sections of hair over (or under) the centre ones until you reach the ends.
4 Secure the ends with ribbon, thread or a bow.

Head-hugging patterns

1 Comb the front and top hair together at the crown. Divide it into three equal stems.
2 Starting from the left or right, cross an outside stem over the centre stem. Repeat this action, crossing the opposite stem over the centre stem.
3 With the little finger, take in a further section of hair, about half the thickness of the initial stems. Add it to an outside stem.

Head-hugging plait:
(a) Sectioning the hair

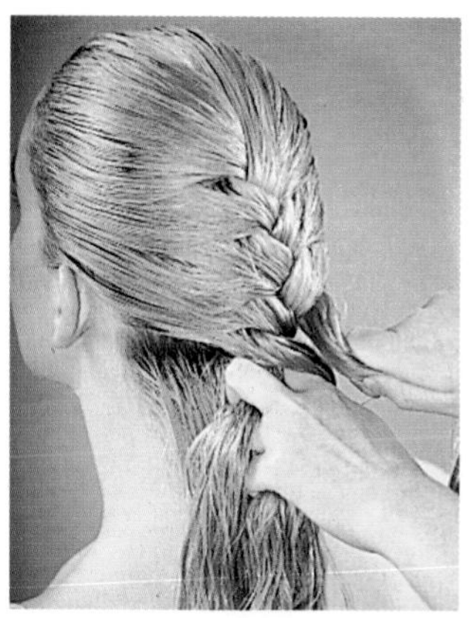

(b) Plaiting the sections in with the main stem

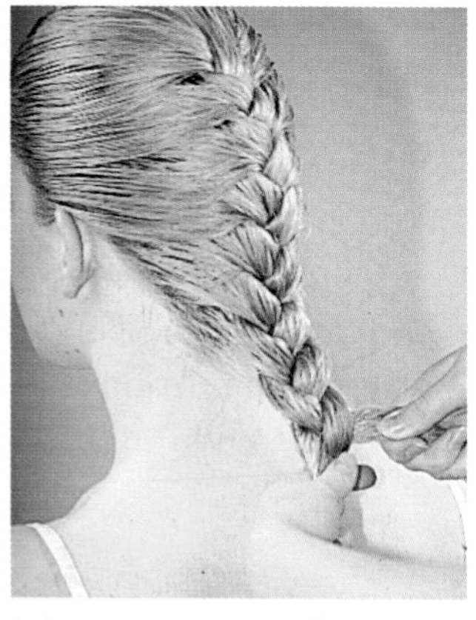

(c) Continuing to plait

(d) The completed plait

4 Cross this thickened stem over the centre one. Repeat this, too, from the other outside stem.
5 Continue in this way, adding hair to each of the outside stems before crossing them over the centre stem.
6 When there is no more hair to be added, continue to plait to the hair ends. Secure the plaits.

Four-stem plaits

1 Divide the hair to be plaited into four equal stems.
2 Begin to plait by crossing the left-hand of the two centre stems *over* the other centre stem.
3 Now cross the outside right stem *over* the next stem.
4 Then cross the outside left stem *under* the next one.
5 Repeat each of these stages until you reach the hair ends.

Four-stem plait

Six-stem plaits

1 Divide the hair into six equal stems. Form these into two groups of three stems.
2 Pass the outside right stem over the next two stems.
3 From the left, pass the outside stem *under* two stems, and *over* one.
4 Repeat this until you reach the hair ends.

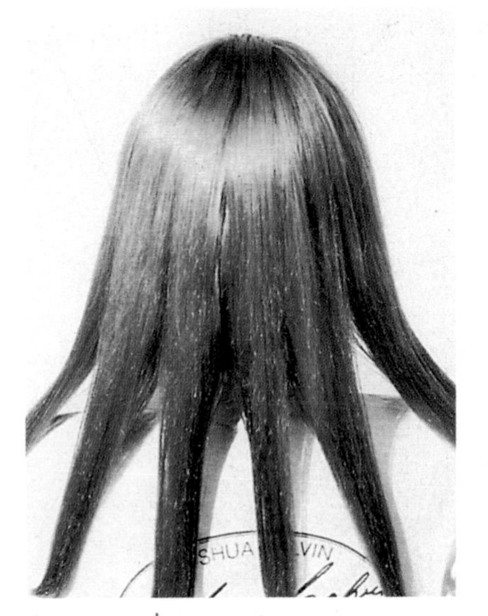

Six-stem plait: starting

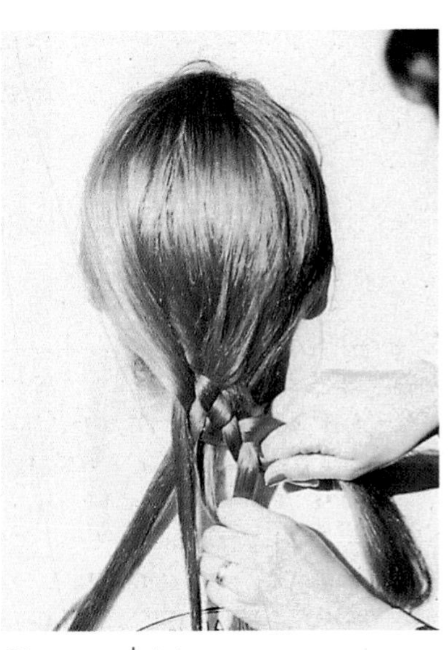

Six-stem plait in progress

The more stems you plait, the more help you will need in handling them. A large variety of multi-stem plaits may be formed: try them out! The hair must, of course, be long enough to plait. Control is easier if you oil, or dampen, the hair. Some tension is required, but it should be evenly distributed throughout the plait length.

ANDREW COLLINGE FOR TRESemmé

Hair ornamentation

Ornamentation

Ornaments can be used to enhance and complete hair dressings. Combs, ribbons, jewels, grips and slides can all be used, as can flowers, feathers, glitterdust, coloured sprays, beads and sequins.

Added hairpieces – also known as **postiche** – can be an attractive means of ornamentation. Apart from covering injuries or scars, bald patches and other defects, they can be decorative and interesting. The means of securing hairpieces vary: most are attached by combs, grips or pins. For a complete change of dressing, styled **wigs** can be used. To see the range of postiche available, refer to wigmaking textbooks or manufacturers' brochures.

ERROL DOUGLAS FOR NEVILLE DANIEL

Dressing and finishing aids

Added colour is a most popular means of augmenting shape and line throughout a dressing. You may like to refer to Chapter 8 ('Colouring hair').

Dressing and finishing aids

Hairsprays

Hairsprays contain a variety of chemicals with different functions. These may be dissolved in water or in alcohol. Some sprays contain **polyvinyl pyrrolidone**, or **PVP**, which helps to reduce the absorption of water from the atmosphere. Others include **plasticisers**, which make the hair more flexible, **cetrimide**, which helps in conditioning the hair and minimising static electricity, or **silicones** which add sheen to the hair. Finally, they may contain colouring, perfume and often preservatives.

To achieve a fine spray and an even distribution, hold the can upright, about 30 cm from the hair. (If you hold it closer you will wet the hair and loosen the set: sticky beads will form, and the hair will hang in strands. If you spray from too far away, most of it will miss the hair.) For a firm hold, spray into the roots. For a lighter hold, sweep your hand across the hair. You can always add a little more, but you can't remove it if you've applied too much.

HEALTH AND SAFETY

Some aerosol sprays contain CFCs (chlorofluorocarbons). These are the propellants that force the spray out of the can. It is now known that CFCs damage the ozone layer in the upper atmosphere. Sunlight contains ultraviolet (UV) light which can be harmful to the skin: the ozone layer protects us by absorbing most of this UV light.

CFCs are gradually being replaced by less harmful chemicals. Make sure that the hairsprays you use do not contain CFCs.

Other dressing aids

As you comb or brush hair, especially when it has just been dried, the friction produces **static electricity**. The hairs each carry a very small *positive* charge, causing them to fly away from each other. The brush or comb carries a very small *negative* charge, which attracts the positively charged hair. You can reduce the amount of static electricity by lightly touching the hair with your hand, which earths it. There are also dressing aids which may help: these include control creams, oils, gels and mousses.

These aids may be used for other reasons, too: to add gloss, to hold the hair, or to make combing smoother. **Emollients** or **moisturisers**, such as lanolin and olive oil, reduce water loss; **humectants**, such as glycerine, absorb moisture.

Dressing aids come in various forms, including aerosols. Some are applied to wet hair and others to dry hair. Always check the manufacturers' instructions before using them.

HEALTH AND SAFETY

Store hairsprays away from heat. They may explode if overheated.

Never use them near naked flames. They are flammable.

Never crush or burn used cans. Even when apparently empty, cans are still pressurised and can explode.

When spraying, protect your client's face and clothes. Chemicals may harm or irritate the eyes, especially if your client wears contact lenses.

Never try to unblock the spray with a pin or the end of a tailcomb – the can might explode.

To clean the spray head and prevent blockage, use alcohol or spirit. Check the manufacturer's instructions.

ASSIGNMENTS: SETTING AND DRESSING HAIR

A practical activity

Collect together information about setting for styling and dressing hair. Include styles for long, medium, short, thick, fine and coarse hair. Plastic jackets or pockets can be useful particularly if you intend to present them to your clients. A section on ornamentation would give added interest. Include photographs, sketches and magazine clippings, and cover the following information:

- a list of the different types of pincurl
- the effects of the different forms of pincurl
- methods of rollering, including the effects of differing roller sizes
- methods of finger waving, and the effects of growth patterns
- the questions you need to put to your clients
- how you determine direction for your hair styles
- how setting differs from blow-styling
- the important factors in setting hair
- an outline of the possible links with cutting and styling
- the problems that might arise in setting, and how you might resolve them.

For you to find out

Investigate the range of setting and dressing techniques. Use your practice blocks and models to determine the effects of them. Consider how, where and when each technique might be used. Try to capture the differences by sketching or photography. Include the following information and retain for your folder.

1. Examine different types of pincurl. Note the formation of the bases, how direction is determined, and how lift and volume might be achieved.
2. Examine the different types of roller and the techniques for their use. Note how lift or flatness is achieved.

3 Examine how finger waving is achieved. Note the natural hair pattern growth and its effect on wave direction.
4 Consider how setting differs from blow-styling, and the different effects achieved by each.

A case study

A client asks you to change from blow-styling to setting her hair. How would you deal with this request? Work through the following sequence, and record your answers for your folder:

1. What factors need to be considered? List them and discuss them with your client.
2. How do you determine whether setting is going to be satisfactory?
3. How do you present the techniques involved in setting, and what determines which need to be used?
4. How do you demonstrate the care required for the set style? Explore how the client will be able to manage it at home.
5. How do you present the range of setting and finishing products, and recommend the most suitable?
6. How do you deal with long, medium and short hair? What are the differences?
7. How do you secure long hair?
8. What dressing products are available? How do you present these to your client?
9. Outline the problems that you might encounter, and how you might resolve them.

PREPARING FOR ASSESSMENT

In preparing for assessment on setting and dressing hair the following checklist may be helpful. Check that you have covered, and understand these items:

- determining clients' requirements
- considering the important influencing factors
- agreeing with the client which setting and dressing techniques to apply
- understanding the differences between the different setting techniques and the different effects they produce
- applying setting techniques
- understanding the effects produced on the hair structure
- introducing a range of suitable products to your clients
- recognising the links with cutting and styling
- appreciating different types of hair dressings
- dealing with different hair lengths
- handling different hair textures, conditions and shapes
- recognising and dealing with problems that might arise
- applying relevant safety factors and precautions
- completing setting and dressing within acceptable time limits.

When you feel that you are ready, talk to your trainer and arrange a suitable time for your assessment.

CHAPTER 7

Perming, neutralising and relaxing/straightening hair

INTRODUCTION

LINO CARBOSIERO AT DANIEL GALVIN FOR L'OREAL

Permed hair

Perming is the term given to the physical and chemical processing of straight hair that will change it into curls or waves. There are various perming systems and procedures. Throughout history, people have experimented with their hair in attempts to make themselves more beautiful. Changing straight hair to curly, or curly hair to straight, have alternated in popularity for centuries. More recently there have been rapid developments in technique, and newer perming systems are regularly introduced. In the past sixty years there have been systems using heat, tepid and cold processes. Some have used electrical attachments and 'cooked' clients' hair for hours at a time. Your grandmother or your great-grandmother could probably tell you some strange tales of what she went through in her search for beauty!

In this chapter we will look at the methods that are currently being used in salons. The following are some of the topics we shall consider:

- perming principles
- perming – how it works
- preparation and planning
- examination and consultation
- tests to be taken
- sectioning and sub-sectioning
- techniques for winding the hair
- processing and development.

PERMING – PRINCIPLES

WELLA

Permed hair

Perming, also known as **permanent waving** or **curling**, is a technique for making straight hair curly. Some methods use warmth, but the most popular techniques, called cold perming (or **CPW**), do not. Unlike the curls produced by setting and blow-styling, the curls produced by perming really are permanent: the hair does not straighten out later when it absorbs water from the atmosphere. Hair grows, however, and new hair takes its natural form. So the waves and curls produced by perming gradually get further and further from the scalp as the hair grows. To keep the style, sooner or later the hair will need to be permed again.

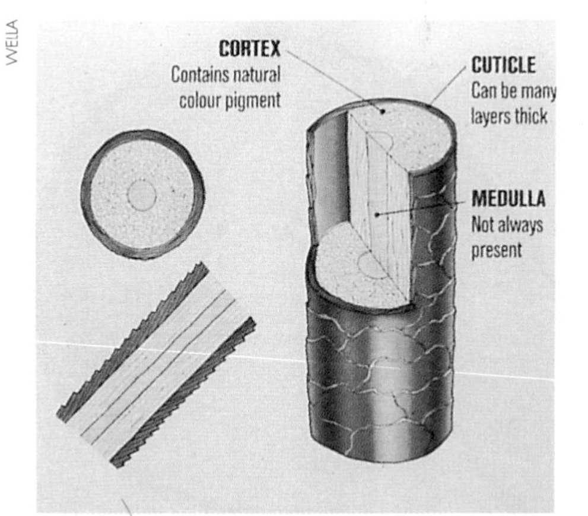

Cross-section of hair

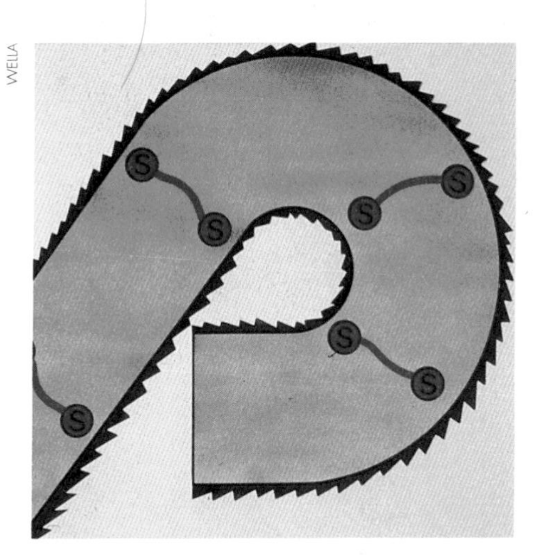

Disulphide bridges

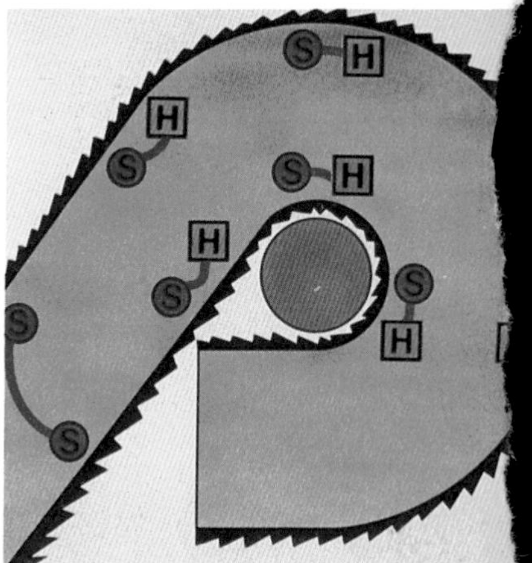

Reduction: breaking existing disulphi[illegible] bridges

Because perming really does make a permanent change to the hair, you cannot easily correct mistakes (as you can with blow-styling, for example). The process also involves various chemicals. It is therefore important that you make sure you understand what you are doing.

How perming works

Changing the keratin

Before going ahead with this section, re-read 'The chemical properties of hair' in Chapter 2 (pages 28–9).

Of the cross-links between the polypeptide chains of hair keratin, the strongest are the **disulphide bridges** that give hair its strength. Each disulphide bridge is a chemical bond linking two sulphur atoms, one in each of two polypeptide chains lying alongside each other. Each sulphur atom forms part of an amino acid unit called **cysteine**; the pair of linked units is called **cystine**.

During cold perming some of these bridges are chemically broken, converting each cystine into two cysteine units. The breaking of the bridges makes the hair softer and more pliable, allowing it to be moved into a new position of wave or curl.

Only about 20 per cent of the disulphide bridges need to be broken during a perm. If too many are broken, the hair will be damaged. You need to keep a check on the progress of the perm, and stop it at the right time. You do this by rinsing away the perm lotion and **neutralising** the hair. During neutralising, pairs of cysteine units join up again to form new cystine groups. The new cross-links thus formed hold the permed hair firmly into its new shape.

Changing the bonds

The hair is first wound on to some kind of **former**, such as a **curler** or **rod**. Then you apply perm lotion to the hair, which makes it swell. The lotion flows under the cuticle and into the cortex. Here it reacts with the keratin, breaking some of the c[illegible] between the polypeptide chains. This [illegible] g it to ta[illegible] the shape of the former. You [illegible] he hair, and allow it to

[illegible] part

Reducing agents

In the past, most cold perming lotions were alkaline, but these tend to roughen the cuticle. Newer lotions are acidic instead, and these are becoming popular.

Some perm lotions contain **ammonium thioglycollate**. This is environmentally damaging, and new perm solutions use other chemicals.

Oxidising agents

Hydrogen peroxide is the best-known oxidant. Others include sodium perborate, sodium percarbonate, sodium bromate and potassium bromate.

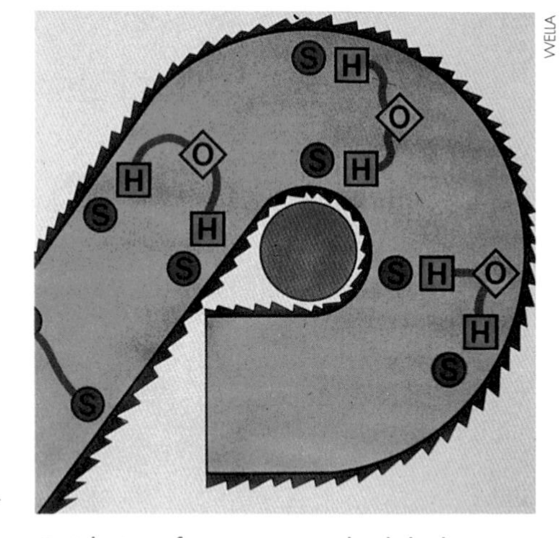

Oxidation: forming new disulphide bridges

PREPARING AND PLANNING THE PERM

The client

For the client a perm is a major step – she will have to live with the result for several months. She may not be familiar with the range of perms available: she will need you to explain what is involved in each and to help her decide which is the most suitable.

- There are several cold perms designed to curl straight hair. See the brochures produced by manufacturers.
- Acid perms are popular because their effects are gentle. Strongly alkaline perms can be too harsh: new forms are being developed.
- Not all perms contain ammonium thioglycollate: 'non-thio' perms tend to be gentler in their action.

Discuss your client's requirements. Find out what she is expecting from a perm, and determine whether this is the best solution.

- Consider the style and cut, togethe... client's age and lifestyle.
- Examine the hair and ... inflammation, d...

HEALTH AND SAFETY
Always bear in mind how your ...erm will affect the client's hair ...cture.

ACTIVITY
List all the factors that could influence your choice of perm.

ACTIVITY
List the different types of perming products, with notes on the main differences between them.

a perm. If there is excessive grease or a coating of chemicals or lacquer you will need to wash these out first. Previously treated hair will need special consideration (discussed later in this chapter).

- Analyse the hair texture. Carry out the necessary tests to select the correct perm lotion.
- Always read manufacturers' instructions carefully.
- Determine the types of curl needed to achieve the chosen style.
- If this is a regular client, refer to her record card for details of previous work done on her hair.
- Advise your client of the time and costs involved. Summarise what has been decided, to be sure there is no misunderstanding.
- Minimise combing and brushing, to avoid scratching the scalp before the perm.
- Ensure that a client record card is prepared.

ACTIVITY
On your practice block or collected hair samples (all of the same texture), use an alkaline perm on one part and an acid perm on another. Follow the directions for the use of each. Wind carefully; and apply the neutralisers properly. Compare the results.

Use pH papers to test each of your perm lotions. Which are acid and which alkaline?

ACTIVITY
In your work folder, list all the signs and symptoms of the hair and scalp diseases, states or defects that indicate that you should not carry out a perm.

Examination

It is important to make sure you choose the most suitable perm lotion, the correct processing time and the right type of curl for the chosen style. Consider the following factors.

- **Hair texture** For hair of medium texture, use perm lotion of normal strength. Fine hair curls more easily and requires weaker lotion; coarse hair is harder to wave and requires stronger lotion.
- **Hair porosity** The porosity of the hair determines how quickly the perm lotion is absorbed. Porous hair in poor condition is likely to process more quickly than would hair with a resistant, smooth cuticle (see page 29).
- **Previous treatment history** 'Virgin' hair – hair that has not previously been treated with chemicals – is likely to be more resistant to perming than hair that has been treated. It will

require a stronger lotion and possibly a longer processing time.

- **Length and density of hair** Long, heavy hair requires more perming than short hair because the hair's weight will pull on the curls. Short, fine hair may become too tightly curled if given the normal processing time.
- **Style** Does the style you have chosen require firm curls or soft, loose waves? Do you simply wish to add body and bounce?
- **Size of rod, curler or other former** Larger rods produce larger curls or waves; smaller rods produce tighter curls. Longer hair generally requires larger rods. If you use very small rods in fine, easy-to-perm hair, the hair may frizz; if you use rods that are too large you may not add enough curl. To check, make a test curl before you start.
- **Incompatibility** Perm lotions and other chemicals used on the hair may react with chemicals that have already been used – for example, in home-use products. Hair that looks dull may have been treated with such chemicals. Ask your client what products she uses at home, and test for incompatibility (see below).

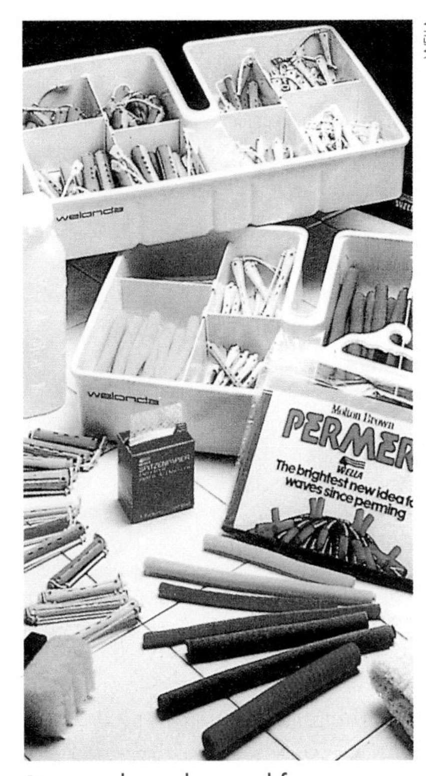

Perm rods, curlers and formers

Tests

- **Cleanliness** Check that the hair is clean. Dirt or grease will block the action of the perm, and the results may be straight rather than curly.
- **Elasticity** Stretch a hair between your fingers. If it breaks easily the cortex may be damaged, and perming could be harmful.

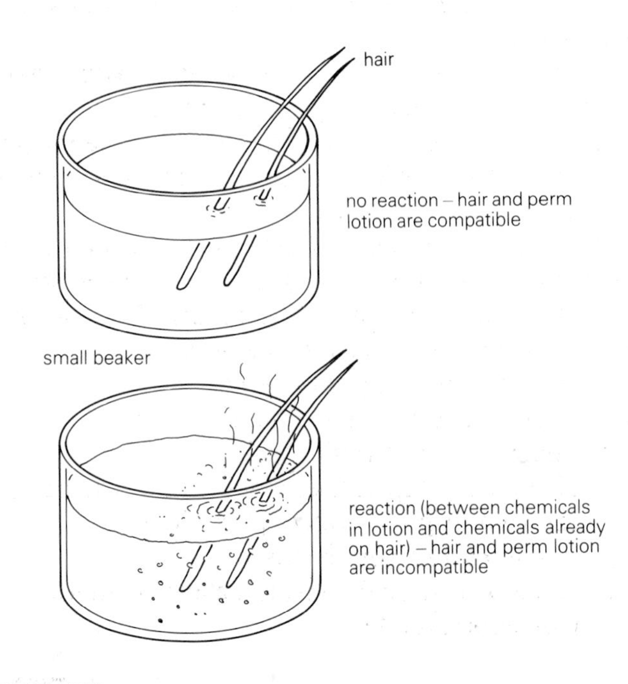

Incompatibility reactions

- **Porosity** Rub the hair between your fingertips to feel how rough or smooth it is. Rougher hair is likely to be more porous, and will therefore process more quickly.
- **Incompatibility** Protect your hands by wearing gloves. Place a small cutting of hair in a mixture of hydrogen peroxide and ammonium hydroxide. Watch for signs of bubbling, heating or discoloration: these indicate that the hair already contains incompatible chemicals. The hair should not be permed, nor should it be tinted or bleached. Perming treatment might discolour or break the hair, and might burn the skin.
- **Test curl** Wind, process and neutralise one or more small sections of hair. The results will be a guide to the optimum rod size, the processing time and the strength of lotion to be used. Remember, though, that the hair will not all be of the same porosity.
- **Processing** Unwind – and then rewind – rods during processing, to see how the curl is developing. If the salon is very hot or cold this will affect the progress of the perm: heat will accelerate it, cold will slow it down. When you have achieved the 'S' shape you want, stop the perm by rinsing and then normalising the hair.

HEALTH AND SAFETY
Before processing, check the salon temperature, because of its influence on the course of the perm.

ANDREW COLLINGE FOR TRESemmé

Permed hair

PERMING TECHNIQUE

Perming is a straightforward procedure – the more organised you are, the simpler and more successful it will be. Once you have consulted your client and made the necessary tests, you are ready to start.

Preparation

1. Protect your client and her clothes as necessary with a gown and towels.
2. Shampoo the hair to remove grease or dirt which would otherwise block the action of the perm lotion.
3. Towel-dry the hair. (Excess water would dilute the perm lotion, but if the hair is too dry the perm lotion won't spread thoroughly through the hair.)
4. Some perm lotions contain chemicals to treat porosity. If you are going to use a pre-perm lotion, apply it now. Make sure you have read the instructions carefully. Too much pre-perm lotion may block the action of the perm itself.
5. Prepare your trolley. You will need:
   - rods, curlers or formers of the chosen sizes
   - end papers, for use while winding
   - a tailcomb and clips, for sectioning and dividing
   - cottonwool strips, to protect your client
   - gloves, to protect your hands
   - perm lotion and a suitable normaliser (read the instructions carefully)

- a water spray, to keep the hair damp
- a plastic cap and a timer for the processing stage.

6 Check that your client's skin and clothing are adequately protected.

Sectioning

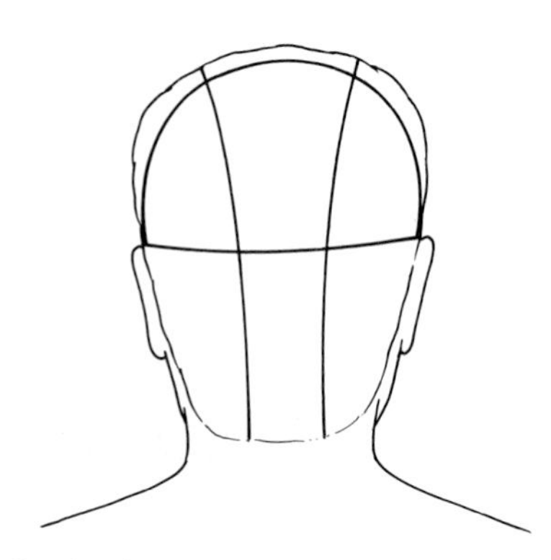
Sectioning

The first operation is to divide the hair into **sections**. This makes the hair tidier and easier to control. Done properly, sectioning makes the rest of the process simpler and quicker. If it's not done well, though, you will have to re-section the hair during the perm, and this may spoil the overall result.

Cold perm sectioning

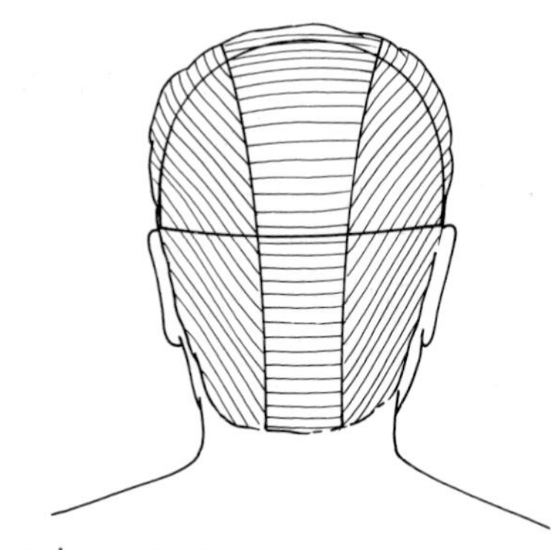
Sub-sectioning

1. Following shampooing and towel-drying, comb the hair to remove any tangles.
2. Make sure you have the tools you will need, including a curler, to check the section size.
3. Now divide the hair into nine sections, as follows. Use clips to secure the hair as you work.
   - Divide the hair from ear to ear, to give front hair and back hair.
   - Divide the back hair into lower, nape hair and upper, top back hair.
   - Divide the front hair, approximately above mid-eyebrow, to give a middle and two sides.
   - Divide the top section along the same lines, to give a middle and two sides.
   - Divide the nape section likewise, to give a middle and two sides.

TIP
Wear gloves from the beginning – it is inconvenient having to put them on later.

This is not the only way of sectioning a head of hair, but it is a good one to start with. When you have mastered this method you can try others.

Sectioning may seem cumbersome at first. Keep practising: it will get easier, and your movements will become quicker and neater. Don't be surprised if it all seems different again when you section a live head. It takes time to get used to the different lengths, textures and conditions of hair – and unlike a practice block, clients don't always stay still!

ACTIVITY
On a block, and later a model, practise sectioning techniques until you can work quickly and efficiently. Practise with the hair wet and with it dry. Your first attempts on a live head may be disappointing, until you are used to the client moving around and the different textures, lengths and conditions of hair.

Winding

Winding: taking a hair section

Winding is the process of placing sectioned hair on to rods, curlers or formers. There are various winding techniques, designed to produce different effects, but the method is basically the same in each case. In modern cold perming systems you need to wind the hair firmly and evenly, but without stretching the hair or leaving it in tension.

First practise winding wet hair on a block. It should be dampened with water rather than perm lotion, as this gives you more time. When you can wind a block in 40–60 minutes, move on to a live model. When you can do this in 20–30 minutes, you can try 'live perming' with perm lotion.

TIP

To gain control of hair ends, practise winding without using papers. These aids help to make winding quicker, but you still need good technique.

Method

1. Divide off a section of hair, of a length and thickness to match the curler being used.
2. Comb the hair firmly, directly away from the head. Keep the hair together, so that it doesn't slip.
3. Place the hair points at the centre of the curler. Make sure the hair isn't bunched at one side and loose at the other.
4. Hold the hair directly away from the head. If you let the hair slope downwards, the curler won't sit centrally on the base section: hair will overlap, and the curler will rest on the skin.
5. Before winding, make sure the curler is at an angle suited to the part of the head against which it will rest when wound.
6. Hold the hair points with the finger and thumb of one hand. The thumb should be uppermost.
7. Direct the hair points round and under the curler. Turn your wrist to achieve this. The aim is to lock the points under the curler and against the main body of hair – if they don't lock, they may become buckled or fish-hooked. Don't turn the thumb too far round or the hair will be pushed away from the curler and won't lock the points.
8. After making the first turn of the curler, pass it to the other hand to make the next turn. The hands need to be in complete control: uncontrolled movement, or rocking from side to side, may cause the ends to slip, the hair to bunch, or the firmness to slacken.

Winding the section on to the curler

Winding: securing the curler

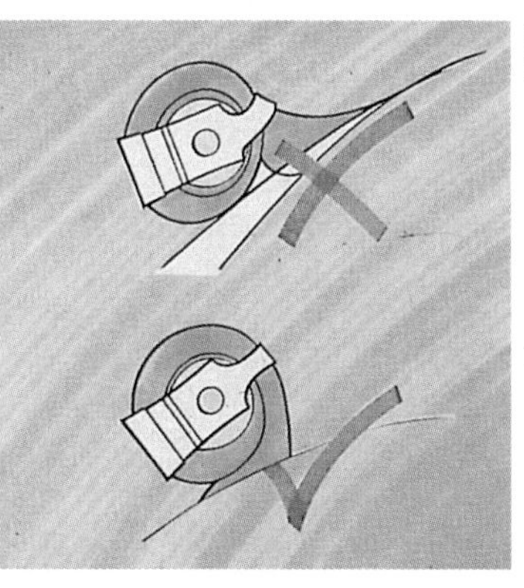

Winding: depth of section

Winding: width of section

9. After two or three turns the points will be securely locked. Wind the curler down to the head. Keep the curler level – if it wobbles from side to side, the hair may slip off or the result may look uneven.
10. At the end, the curler should be in the centre of the section. If it isn't, unwind it and start again.
11. Secure the curler. Don't let the rubber fastener press into the hair – it might damage it.

Winding techniques

There are various winding techniques, used to produce varied effects. The following are the most commonly used.

- **Spiral winding** The hair is wound from roots to points, around a variety of sticks, shapers, hair moulders or curlers of one shape or another. Triangular and square shapers have been used. The effects produced are mainly in the lengths of the hair, the root ends being less affected. This is probably the oldest form of winding. It is most effective, and most practical, with long hair.
- **Croquignole winding** This starts at the hair points and works down to the roots. This technique has been commonly used for years in cold perming. It is best used where the hair curl needs to be strongest at the points. (The term 'croquignole' comes from the old wigmaking trade.)
- **Directional winding** The hair is wound in the direction in which it is to be finally worn. This technique is suitable for enhancing well-cut shapes. The hair can be wound in any direction required, and the technique is ideal for shorter hairstyles.
- **Staggered winding** or **brick winding** The wound curlers are placed in a pattern resembling brickwork. By staggering the partings of the curlers, you avoid obvious gaps in the hair. It is suitable for short hairstyles.

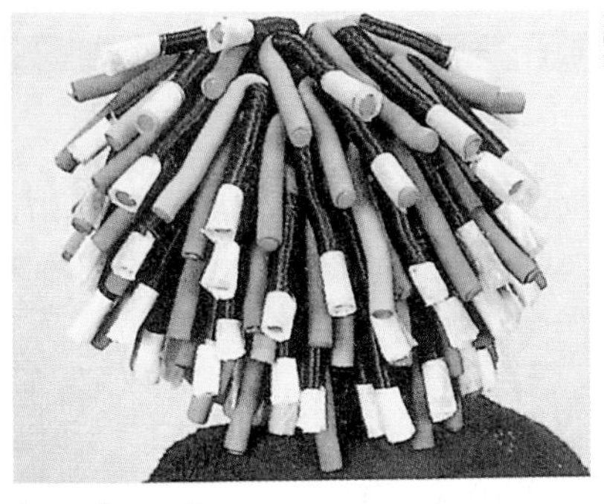
WELLA

Spiral winding

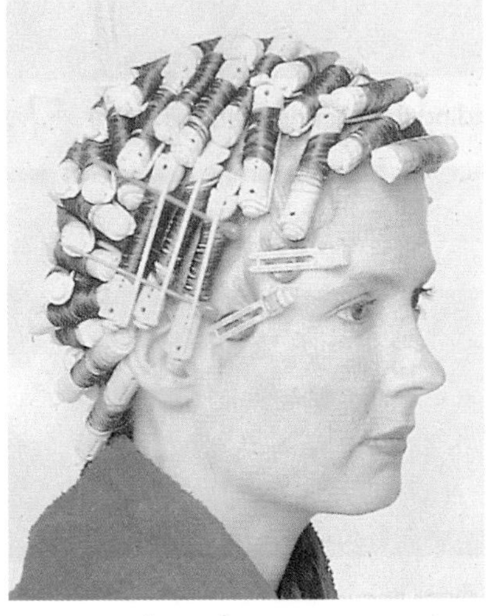
L'OREAL

Directional winding

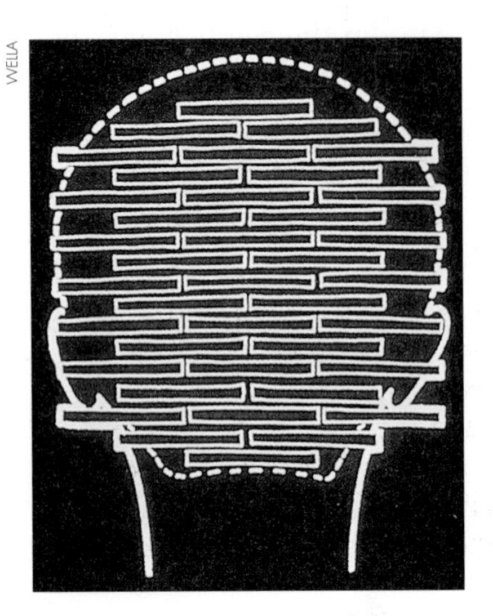
WELLA

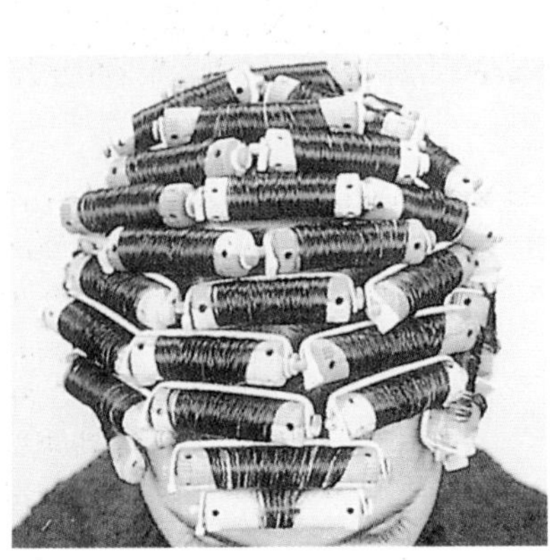

Staggered or brick winding

- **Weave winding** The normal-size section is divided into two and then the hair is woven. A large curler is used to wind the upper sub-section, and a smaller one is used for the lower sub-section. This produces two different curl sizes, giving volume without tight curls. Alternatively, one sub-section is wound and the other left unwound. With short hair this produces spiky effects.

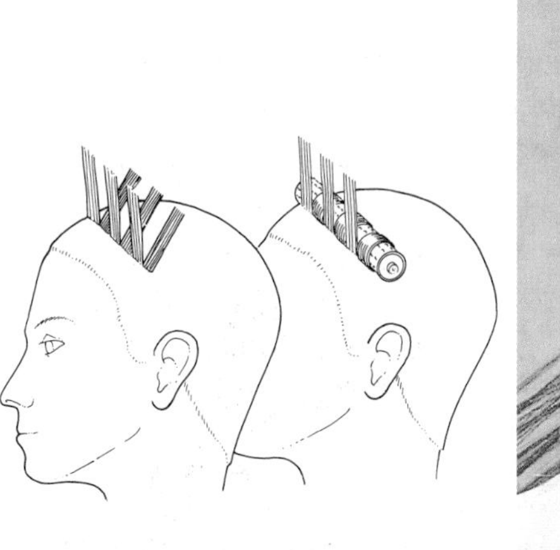

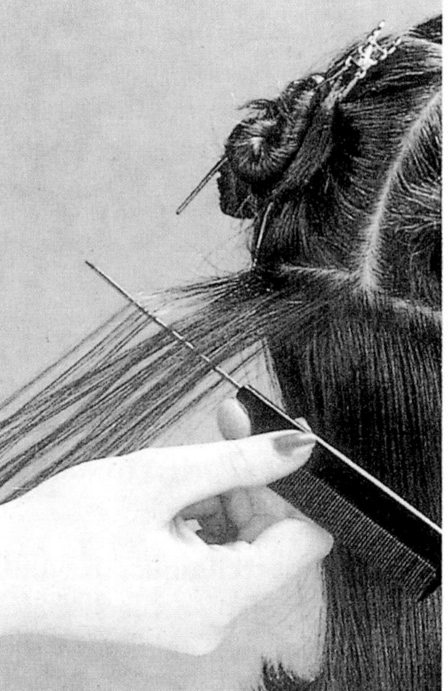

WELLA

Weave winding

- **Double winding** This technique consists of winding a section of hair halfway down on a large curler, then placing a smaller curler underneath and winding both curlers down to the head. This produces a varied curl effect.

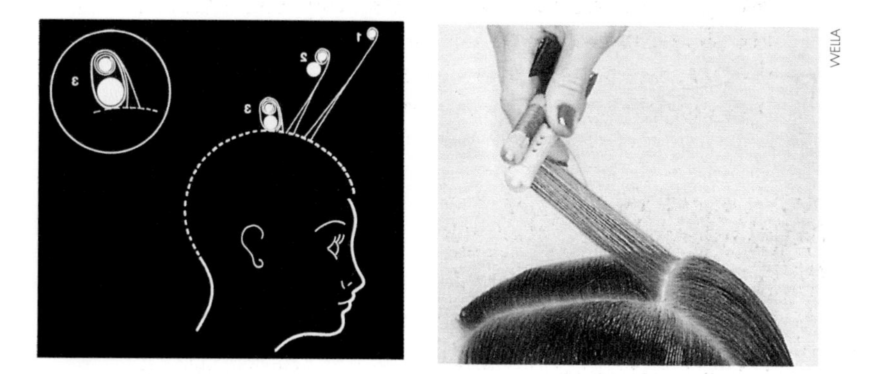

WELLA

Double winding

- **Piggyback winding** This is winding using a small and a large curler. The normal-size section is wound from the middle on to a large curler, down to the head. The ends are then wound from the points on to a smaller curler, which is placed on top of the large curler. This produces softly waved roots and curly points. Alternatively this technique can be used to produce root movement only by not winding the point ends.

WELLA

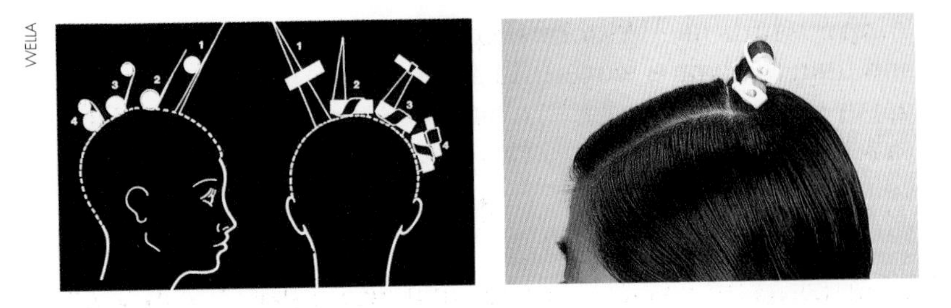

Piggyback winding

- **Stack winding** This is used where fullness of long hair is required, with little curl movement on top – it is ideal for bobbed hair lengths. The sections are wound close to the head in the lower parts; the upper sections are part wound only, at the points. This allows the curlers to stack one upon another.

CLYNOL

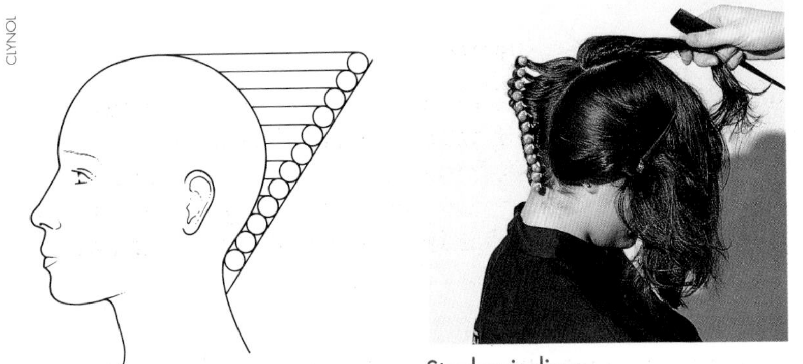

Stack winding

To appreciate the effects of different techniques of winding you need to experiment with them. Many professionals are continually trying out new approaches, sometimes with exciting results.

> **ACTIVITY**
> Using blocks, practise the different winding techniques. Process them as well, so that your are familiar with their effects before live perming.

Winding aids

- The **tailcomb** is useful for directing small pieces of hair on to the curler. Don't let the tail pass around the curler, as this causes unevenness and hair may slip out of the wound section.
- **End papers** or **wraps** are specially made winding aids. They ensure control of the hair when it is wound. Fold them neatly over the hair points (never bundle them). The wrap overlaps the hair points and prevents fish-hooking. For smaller or shorter sections of hair, half an end wrap is sufficient – a full one would cause unevenness. Other types of tissue may absorb the perm lotion and interfere with processing, and these are best avoided.

> **ACTIVITY**
> Try out different curlers, rods and winding shapes. Note the varied effects they produce.
>
> Practise the different curler positions for perming. Try these out on blocks or models to appreciate the differences.

ACTIVITY
On a practice block of sample hair cuttings, experiment with the effects produced by different faulty windings. This will help you to recognise and to avoid these effects.

- **Crêpe hair** is useful for holding the hair points when winding: it allows enough grip and prevents the ends from slipping. As with end papers, only a little should be used. Too much makes the hair bunch together.
- Many kinds of **curler** are suitable for cold perm winding. Plastic, wood, bone and china are amongst the materials used. Different colours are used to indicate size. The greater the diameter, or the fatter the curler, the bigger the wave or curl produced. The smallest curlers are used for short nape hair, or for producing tight curls. Most curlers are of smaller diameter at the centre: this enables the thinner hair points to fill the concave part evenly and neatly as the hair is wound. This is particularly useful with tapered hair. Clubbed hair should be evenly spread across the centre of the curler.

Processing and development

Perm lotion may be applied before winding (**pre-damping**) or when winding is complete (**post-damping**). Follow the manufacturer's instructions. Post-damping is perhaps more convenient: you can wind the hair without wearing gloves, and the time taken in winding doesn't affect the overall processing time.

HEALTH AND SAFETY
Cold perm lotions and neutralisers are potentially hazardous substances. Use them with care. Always follow the manufacturer's instructions for their use, and check with your salon's COSHH list of potential hazards (see page 280) for correct usage. Refer to the HMWA leaflet *Health and Safety in the Salon* and the Health and Safety Executive's *Completing COSHH Assessments.*

Applying the perm lotion

Most perm lotions come in an applicator bottle, ready to use. Others may need to be applied from a bowl, using cottonwool, a sponge or a brush. Read the instructions carefully before applying.

- Underlying hair is usually more resistant to perming. Apply lotion to these areas first.
- Keep lotion away from the scalp. Apply it to the section, about 12 mm from the roots.
- Don't overload the applicator, and apply the lotion gently. You will be less likely then to splash your client.

TRESemmé

WELLA

Perming products

- If you do splash the skin, quickly rinse the lotion away with water.

Processing time

Processing begins as soon as the perm lotion is in contact with the hair. The time needed for processing is critical. Processing time is affected by the hair texture and condition, the salon temperature and whether heat is applied, the size and number of curlers used, and the type of winding used.

- **Hair texture and condition** Fine hair processes more quickly than coarse hair, and dry hair than greasy hair. Hair that has been processed previously will perm faster than 'virgin' hair.
- **Temperature** A warm salon cuts down processing time; in a cold salon it will take longer. Even a draught will affect the time required. Usually the heat from the head itself is enough to activate cold perming systems. Wrap your client's head with plastic tissue or a cap to keep in the heat. Don't wrap the hair in towels: these would absorb the lotion and slow down the processing.

  Some perm lotions require additional heat, from lamps or dryers. Don't apply heat unless the manufacturer's instructions tell you to – you might damage both the hair and the scalp. And don't apply heat unless the hair is wrapped; the heat could evaporate the lotion, or speed up the processing too much.
- **Curlers** Processing will be quicker with a lot of small sections on small curlers than with large sections on large curlers. (The large sections will also give looser results.)
- **Winding** The type of winding used, and the tension applied, also affect processing time. A firmer winding processes faster than a slack winding – indeed, if the winding is too slack it will not process at all. Hair wound too tightly may break, close to the scalp. The optimum is a firm winding without tension.

TIP

Choose a winding technique according to the effects you require.

HEALTH AND SAFETY

Don't pack curlers with dry cottonwool. This would absorb the perm lotion; it would also put it in direct contact with the skin, causing irritation.

Mop up any surplus lotion on the skin, then use a barrier cream or place a water-dampened band of cottonwool to protect the skin. Don't let barrier cream get on to the hair, however, as this would spoil the process.

TIP

During processing, don't leave your client while you do something else. You might lose track of time or forget to check the curls. Besides, your client might become anxious.

ANDREW COLLINGE (PHOTO: JOHN SWANNELL)

JOY AGAR FOR L'OREAL

Permed hair

Testing curls during processing

As processing time is so critical, you need to use a timer. You also need to check the perm at intervals to see how it's progressing. If you used the pre-damping technique, check the first and last curlers that you wound. If you applied the lotion after winding, check curlers from the front, sides, crown and nape.

- Unwind the hair from a curler. Is the 'S' shape produced correct for the size of curler used?
- If the curl is too loose, rewind the hair and allow more processing time. (But if the test curl is too loose because the curler was too large, extra processing time will damage the hair and won't make the curl tighter.)
- If the curl is correct, stop the processing by rinsing.

Rinsing and neutralising

When processing is complete, leave the curlers in place while you rinse away the perm lotion. Use tepid water (not hot). Direct the spray head on to and between the rollers for several minutes to make sure all the lotion is removed. Long hair will require more rinsing than shorter hair.

After rinsing, blot the hair with towels and cottonwool to remove excess water. The hair is now ready for neutralising, which is described in the next part of this chapter.

This is the point at which to apply rinses or conditioners. Before doing so, however, check the manufacturer's instructions.

HEALTH AND SAFETY

Take care not to splash your client's face while rinsing. Even dilute perm lotion can irritate the skin.

ASSIGNMENTS: COLD PERMANENT WAVING

A practical activity

Collect together a range of hair samples, or use a suitable practice block. Try out different perming processes and techniques, such as handling the hair, sectioning and subsectioning, winding, using different formers and curlers, processing, developing and so on. Make a careful record of your results and retain it for your folder. Include the following:

1. Outline the processes of cold permanent waving.
2. Note how the different hair textures react.
3. Note the effects of different winding techniques.
4. Describe, and sketch, what happens to the hair structure during perming.
5. Describe the reduction process.
6. How does body/salon temperature affect perm processing?
7. List the precautions to be taken during perming.
8. List the problems that might arise during a perm, and how you would resolve them.

Make careful notes, and keep them in your folder.

For you to find out

Investigate the theory and practice of perming. Use your reference books and examine the history of perming. Take note of the development of the perming processes. Compare modern processes, and effects, with some of the earlier ones. Keep a record, crediting your sources. Answer the following questions:

1. What are acid perms and alkaline perms? What are tepid perms and hot perms? How do they differ from cold perms?
2. How do these differ from early hot perms?
3. What are the advantages and disadvantages of older perms?
4. What are the advantages and disadvantages of modern perms?
5. Why do you test for perm results?
6. What do you do if an incompatibility test proves negative? If it proves positive?
7. What do you do if a perm results in frizz, discoloration or straight pieces?
8. How do you determine the most suitable perm to use?
9. List the precautions that you should take when giving a perm.
10. What are the problems that might arise during perming, and how might you deal with them?

A case study

A client requests a cold perm. Her hair is fine, greasy and below shoulder length. Previous results at other salons have been unsatisfactory. How do you deal with this? Simulate the event, make careful and precise notes and retain them for your folder. Work through the following sequence:

1. Describe the client examination and discussion.
2. List the questions that you would ask. Include those that refer to past problems.
3. How would you select a suitable perm process? What are the chemical processes involved?
4. What tests might you make?
5. What determines the most suitable perm curler/former size?
6. How do you select suitable section sizes?
7. How do you know the correct tension to apply?
8. How do you know when the perm has 'taken'?
9. How should your client manage the new perm? What advice will you give?
10. What are the problems that might arise when perming? How do you deal with these?
11. List the precautions you should take.
12. You need to ensure that all information is carefully recorded. Describe how you would do this.
13. What fashion style have you decided to give your client? State why.

PREPARING FOR ASSESSMENT

In preparing for your assessment on cold permanent waving the following checklist may prove to be helpful. Check that you have covered and now fully understand these items:

- determining the client's requirements and needs
- explanation of the perming processes
- gaining the client's approval and agreement to proceed
- selecting suitable perm processes, with your client, for the results required
- assessing the type and condition of the hair, its length, and when it was permed last
- preparing the client for processing
- sectioning the hair appropriately
- determining curler sizes and type of winding to use
- using the correct techniques for the required style effects
- determining when the perm process should stop
- recording information accurately and legibly
- ensuring client satisfaction
- discussing details of after-care required.

When you feel that you are ready, talk to your trainer and arrange a suitable time for your assessment.

NEUTRALISING

KATHLEEN BRAY FOR CLYNOL PHOTO: IAN HOOTEN

Permed hair

INTRODUCTION

Whether or not a perm is satisfactory to the client depends in part, of course, on correct processing of the hair, but also on correct neutralising of the perm lotion after the correct period of time.

In this section we will look at the following topics:

- principles of neutralising
- how neutralising works
- choosing a neutraliser
- neutralising techniques
- what to do after perming.

NEUTRALISING – PRINCIPLES

Neutralising is the process of returning hair to its normal condition after perming. The word is a little misleading: chemically speaking, a 'neutral' condition is neither acidic nor alkaline (pH 7.0). In fact, healthy hair is slightly acidic.

How neutralising works

As described above, perm lotion acts on the keratin in the hair. The strongest bonds between the polypeptides are the disulphide bridges. Perm lotion breaks some of these, allowing the keratin to take up a new shape. This is how new curls can form.

What neutralising does is to make new disulphide bridges. If you didn't neutralise the hair would be weak and likely to break, and the new curls would soon fall out. Neutralising is an oxidation process – a process that uses oxidising agents such as hydrogen peroxide, sodium bromate and sodium perborate.

WELLA

Neutralisers

Choosing a neutraliser

Manufacturers of perm lotions usually produce matching neutralisers. These are designed to work together. If possible, always use the neutraliser that matches the perm lotion you've used.

A neutraliser may be supplied as an emulsion cream, a foam or a liquid. Always follow the manufacturer's instructions. Some can be applied directly from the container, others are applied with a sponge or a brush.

> **ACTIVITY**
> Try perm processing with one type of perm lotion on two or more hair samples or practice blocks. Use a different neutraliser for each. Note the different effects, if any.

> **TIP**
> Always check that you're using the right chemical. Because they are designed to match, the container for the neutraliser may look similar to the container for the perm lotion.

NEUTRALISING TECHNIQUE

Neutralising follows directly on from perming. Imagine that you have shampooed, dried and wound the hair. The hair is now perming, and you are timing the perm carefully and making tests to check whether it is complete. You will also be reassuring the client that she has not been forgotten! As soon as the perm is finished, you need to be ready to stop the process immediately.

Preparation

1. Gather together the materials you will need.
2. Make sure there is a washbasin free, preferably one where the client can put her head back to use it. (This makes it easier for you to keep chemicals away from her eyes.)

First rinsing

1. As soon as the perm is complete, move your client immediately to the washbasin. Make sure she is comfortable. Offer her hand towels or tissues in case any liquid trickles over her face.
2. Carefully remove the cap or other head covering. The hair is soft and weak at this stage, so don't put unnecessary tension on it. Leave the curlers in place.
3. Run the water. You need an even supply of warm water. The water must be neither hot nor cold. Check the pressure and temperature against the back of your hand. Remember that your client's head may be sensitive after the perming process.
4. Rinse the hair thoroughly with the warm water. This may take about five minutes. It is this rinsing that stops the perm process – until you rinse away the lotion, the hair will still be processing. Direct the water away from the eyes and the face. Make sure you rinse *all* the hair, including the nape curlers. If a curler slips out, gently wind the hair back on to it immediately.

L'OREAL

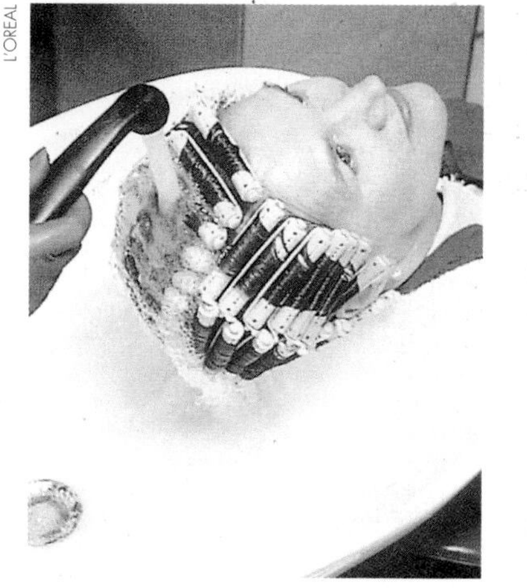

Neutralising: first rinse

L'OREAL

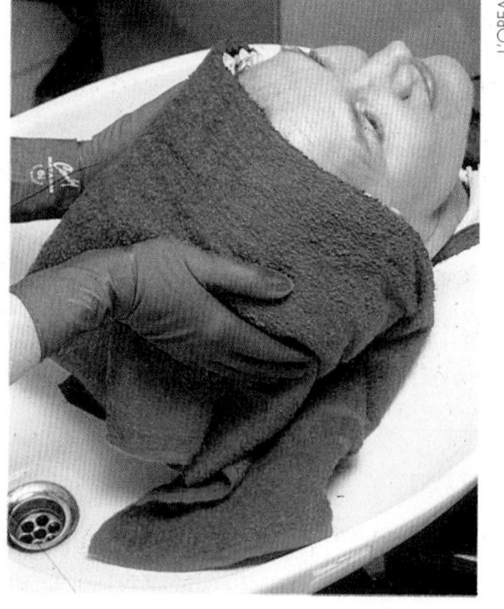

Neutralising: towel-drying the hair

Applying neutraliser

1 Raise your client to a comfortable sitting position.
2 Blot the hair thoroughly, using a towel or tissues. It may help if you pack the curlers with cottonwool.
3 When no surplus water remains, apply the neutraliser. Follow the manufacturer's instructions. These may tell you to pour the neutraliser through the hair, or apply it with a brush or sponge, or use the spiked applicator bottle. Some foam neutralisers need to be pushed briskly into the hair. Make sure that neutraliser comes into contact with all of the hair.
4 When all the hair has been covered, time the process according to the instructions. The usual time is 5–10 minutes. You may wrap the hair in a towel or leave it open to the air – follow the instructions.
5 Gently and carefully remove the curlers. Don't pull or stretch the hair. It may still be soft, especially towards the ends.
6 Apply the neutraliser to the hair again, covering all the hair. Arrange the hair so that the neutraliser does not run over the face. Leave for the time recommended, perhaps another 5–10 minutes.

L'OREAL

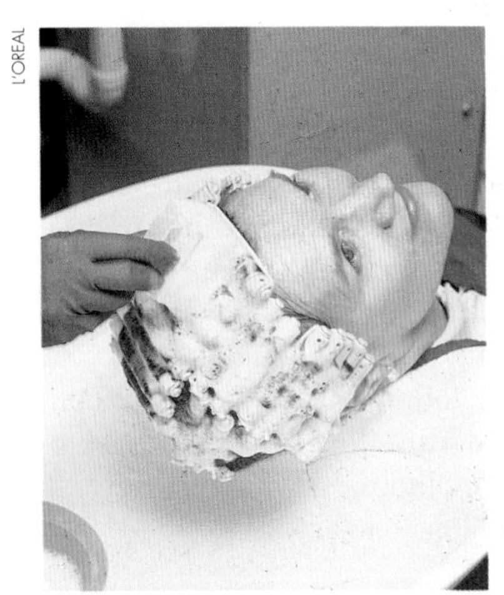

Neutralising: first application

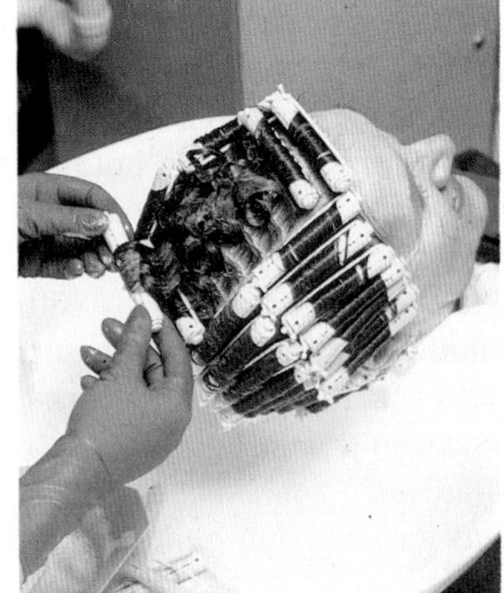

Removing curlers

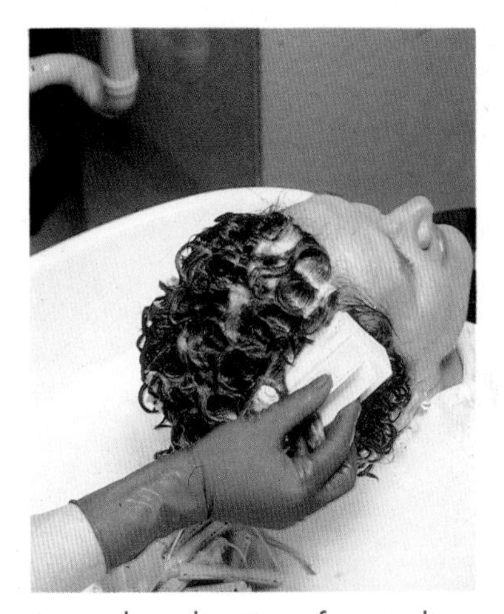

Second application of neutraliser

Second rinsing

1 Run the water, again checking temperature and pressure.
2 Rinse the hair thoroughly to remove the neutraliser.
3 You can now treat the hair with an after-perm aid or conditioner. Use the one recommended by the manufacturer of the perm and neutraliser, to be sure that the chemicals are compatible.

ACTIVITY

Wind several curlers and perm process them. Neutralise in the normal way. When unwinding, make a point of stretching some of them. Compare the result with others that were more carefully undone. Note the differences when the hair is dry.

TIP

After using the curlers, remove the end wraps. Rinse, dry and powder the curlers. This prevents the rubbers from becoming soft. Separate the curlers into different sizes and colours, ready for the next time they are used.

ACTIVITY

Collect together several hair samples. Wind and process each with perm lotion. Follow the manufacturer's instructions. Apply neutraliser to each sample. Process the neutraliser, allowing 5, 10, 15 and 20 minutes and longer. Compare the results. Record the effects produced by the different neutralising times.

ACTIVITY

With hair samples treated with perm lotion, try using different volume strengths of hydrogen perioxide in the neutraliser. Compare the effects.

L'OREAL

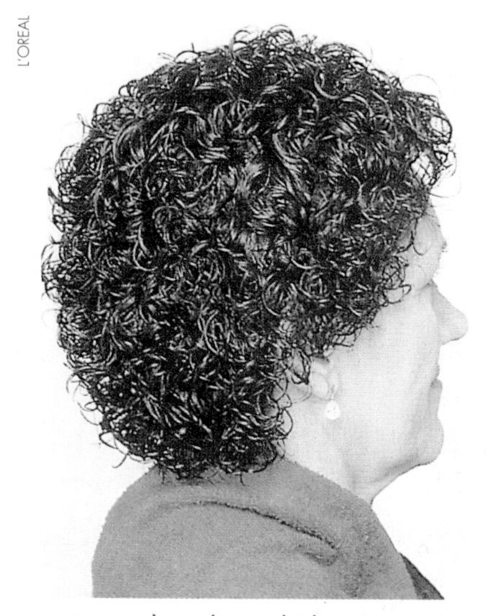

Hair ready to be styled

Successful neutralising

At the end of the neutralising process, you will have returned the hair to a normal, stable state.

- The reduction and oxidation processes will have been completed.
- Finishing aids or conditioners (antioxidants) may need to be applied to counteract the oxidants used.
- The hair will now be slightly weaker – fewer bonds will have formed than were broken by the perm. Special conditioners may be needed. If the cuticle is lifting or roughened, this too may be countered with conditioners.
- Record any hair or perm faults on the client's record card. Correct faults as appropriate.
- **Under-neutralising** – not leaving neutraliser on for long enough – results in a slack curl or waves.
- **Over-oxidising** – leaving the neutraliser on too long or using oxidants that are too strong – results in weak hair and poor curl.

The hair should be ready for shaping, blow-drying or setting.

SPLINTERS

SCHWARZKOPF

AFTER THE PERM

- Check the results of perming.
  - Has the scalp been irritated by the perm lotion?
  - Is the hair in good condition?
  - Is the curl even?
- Dry the hair into style.
  - Depending on the effect you want, you may now use finger drying, hood drying or blow-drying.
  - Treat the hair gently. If you handle it too firmly the perm may relax again.
- Advise the client on how to manage the perm at home.
  - The hair should not be shampooed for a day or two.
  - The manufacturer of the perm lotion may have supplied information to be passed to the client.
  - Discuss general hair care with your client.
- Clean all tools thoroughly so that they are ready for the next client.
- Complete the client's record card. Note details of the type of perm, the strength of the lotion, the processing time, the curler sizes and the winding technique. Record any problems you have had. This information will be useful if the hair is permed again.

Perming faults and what to do about them

Fault	*Action now*	*Possible cause*	*Action in future*
The perm is slow to process	Increase warmth but do not dry out; check the winding tension and the number of curlers	Winding was too loose	Wind more firmly or use smaller curlers
		The curlers were large, or too few were used	Use smaller curlers, and more of them
		The wrong lotion was used	Double-check labels on bottles
		The sections were too large	Take smaller sections
		The salon is too cold	The temperature should be comfortable
		Lotion was absorbed from the hair	Don't leave cottonwool on the hair
		Too little lotion was used	Don't skimp the lotion or miss sections
The scalp is tender, sore or broken	Apply first aid	The curlers were too tight	Don't apply too much tension when winding
		The wound curlers rested on the skin	Curlers should rest on the hair
		Lotion was spilt on the scalp	Keep lotion away from the scalp
		There was cottonwool padding soaked with perm lotion between the curlers	Renew the cottonwool as as necessary, or don't use it
		The hair was pulled tightly	Don't overstretch it
		The perm was overprocessed	Time perms accurately

Fault	*Action now*	*Possible cause*	*Action in future*
There are straight ends or pieces	Re-perm, if the hair condition permits*	The curlers or sections were too large	Take sections no longer or wider than the curler used
		Sections were overlooked	Check that all hair has been wound
		Too few curlers were used	Put curlers closer together
		The winding was too loose	Be a little firmer next time
		Lotion was applied unevenly	Take care to apply it evenly
There are fish-hooks	Remove by trimming the ends	The hair points were not cleanly wound	Comb the hair cleanly
		The hair points were bent or buckled	Place hair sections evenly on to the curlers
		The hair was wrapped unevenly in the end papers	Curl from the hair points
		Winding aids were used incorrectly	Take more care; practise winding
Hair is broken	Nothing can be done about the broken hair; after discussion with your senior or trainer, condition the remaining hair	The hair was wound too tightly	Wind more loosely next time
		The curlers were secured too tightly	Secure them more loosely next time
		The curler band cut into the hair base	Keep it away from the hair base
		The hair was overprocessed	Follow the instructions more carefully
		Chemicals in the hair reacted with the lotion	Test for incompatibility beforehand
The hair is straight	Re-perm, if the hair condition permits*	The wrong lotion was used for hair of this texture	Choose the lotion more carefully
		The hair was underprocessed	Time perms accurately
		The curlers were too large for the hair length	Measure the curlers Beforehand
		The neutralising was incorrectly done	Follow the instructions more carefully
		Rinsing was inadequate	Rinse more thoroughly
		Conditioners used before perming were still on the hair	Prepare the hair more carefully
		The hair was coated and resistant to the lotion	Check for substances that block the action of perm lotion: shampoo if necessary
The hair is frizzy	Cut the ends to reduce the frizziness	The lotion was too strong for hair of this texture	Assess texture correctly; select suitable lotions; read manufacturers' instructions
		The winding was too tight	Practise and experiment to avoid this
		The curlers were too small	Choose more suitable curlers
		The hair was overprocessed	Time perms accurately
		The neutralising was incorrectly done	Follow the instructions more carefully

Fault	Action now	Possible cause	Action in future
		There are fish-hooks	Avoid bending hair points when winding
The perm is weak and drops†	Re-perm, if the hair condition permits*	Lotion was applied unevenly	Apply lotion more evenly
		The neutraliser was dilute	Follow the instructions more carefully
		Neutralising was poorly done	Be more careful
		The hair was stretched while soft	Handle the hair gently
		The curlers or sections were too large	Use more curlers
Some hair sections are straight	Re-perm, if the hair condition permits*	The curler angle was wrong	Wind correctly
		The curlers were placed incorrectly	Wind correctly
		The curlers were too large	Use smaller curlers
		Sectioning or winding was done carelessly	Practise before perming again
The hair is discoloured	Tone the hair to correct this	Metal in the tools or containers reacted with the lotion	Test for incompatibles beforehand
		Chemicals coating the hair reacted with the lotion	Check for substances that block the action of perm lotion; shampoo if necessary

* Don't re-perm the hair unless its condition is suitable. For example, you should not re-perm if the hair is overprocessed. Conditioning treatments, cutting and careful setting and styling may help. Discuss the problem with your senior or trainer.

† Before attempting to correct this fault, make sure that the hair is not overprocessed. Dampen the hair to see how much perm there is.

ASSIGNMENTS: NEUTRALISING

A practical activity

Using several hair samples – hair that has been through the cold permanent waving process and is ready to be neutralised – try out different ways of neutralising. Note the different effects produced, and record them for your folder. Carry out this assignment systematically using the following procedures:

1. Without rinsing the hair sample, apply the neutraliser and time as the instructions direct. Note the effects produced when the hair is still wet and again when it has been dried.
2. Using another permed hair sample, rinse the hair but do not apply any neutraliser. Note the effects when it is wet and when it is dry.
3. On a third permed hair sample, omit both rinse and neutraliser. Note the effects both wet and dry.

4. To a fourth sample, apply rinses and neutraliser as directed by the perm manufacturer. Note the effects wet and dry.
5. Retain these four samples and compare the results when the hair has dried out. Then check again after 12, 24 and 48 hours.
6. List and try out different types of neutraliser, with varying times of application. Compare the results.
7. Repeat these experiments using hair of different textures.

Make sure that you have a correctly permed and neutralised sample with which to compare your results.

For you to find out

Investigate the chemical processes of applying neutraliser to a variety of perms, from both a theoretical and a practical point of view. Use your textbooks, the manufacturers' instructions and your practical experience. Retain your record for your folder, crediting your sources of information. Answer the following questions.

1. Outline the chemical process of cold permanent waving neutralising. Use diagrams where possible.
2. What are the effects of neutralising hair of different textures?
3. What are the effects of temperature on neutralising?
4. What would you do if you spilt the last batch of neutraliser?
5. Why should the hair be moved gently after neutralising?
6. What processes can you apply after completing the neutralising process? Describe what these do to the chemical structure and state of the hair.

A client has returned to complain of services received at your salon. Describe the following:

- the action or actions you would take
- how you would record what the client has told you
- the questions you would need to ask
- what you would do if you could not deal with the problem yourself
- what you could do to calm an angry or upset client.

A case study

Your client recently had a cold permanent wave at another salon. She did not consider the result to be satisfactory. The hair was slightly curly or wavy in parts but mostly straight otherwise. How would you deal with this situation?

Make notes of what you would say and do. List the questions you would ask, and the order in which you would ask them. Retain notes for your folder. Here are some procedures you should carry out:

1. Try to determine why the hair was not successfully treated at the other salon.

2. Find out whether the client returned there to complain, and what the outcome was.
3. State what you think might have caused the unsatisfactory results.
4. State what you think would have been successful.
5. Determine, and agree with your client, what should now be done.
6. Determine whether the hair is in a fit state for further treatment.
7. Record the results of your discussion with your client, and what you have agreed with her that you will carry out.
8. How would you record this information?
9. Add any further information you feel applies.

PREPARING FOR ASSESSMENT

In preparation for assessment on neutralising the following checklist may be helpful. Check that you have covered and now fully understand these items:

- assessing whether the perm process is complete before the application of neutraliser
- the reasons for using the correct neutraliser (and the need for checking instructions) and the different chemicals used
- the reasons for rinsing the hair thoroughly and removing excess moisture
- applying the neutraliser evenly, timing accurately, and removing as directed
- understanding the effects of neutraliser on the hair structure
- understanding neutralising as part of the perm process
- being aware of problems that may occur, and knowing how to deal with them and when to refer to senior staff
- understanding the health and safety requirements (see Chapter 13).

When you feel that you are ready, talk to your trainer and arrange a suitable time for your assessment.

JACKIE HENRY AT A CUT ABOVE

NICK JONES, HAIR DESIGN

Straightened hair

INTRODUCTION

Straightening and relaxing processes have always, in one form or another, been applied to hair. Throughout hairdressing development, people with very tightly curled hair have wanted less curly or smoother looks. Most early straightening processes were physically based and temporary in their effects, but today's chemical techniques can produce effective and permanent results.

In this section we will look at the application of methods currently used in salons for straightening and relaxing hair. The following are some of the topics discussed:

- consultation, examination and preparing the client
- testing for suitability of product
- products available: their advantages and disadvantages
- important influencing factors
- methods of straightening and relaxing hair
- how straightening/relaxing works – one- and two-stage methods
- dealing with re-growth
- problems that might arise and how to deal with them.

Relaxing or **straightening** hair is a process of removing curl or wave, wholly or in part. Clients with naturally very curly, kinky or frizzy hair may want it looser, softly curled or straight. Then their re-growth may need periodic straightening.

Preparation

In addition to the normal preparation of your client, her hair and the tools/materials required, you should double-check the following for this service:

- determine your client's needs
- determine your client's hair type (curly or wavy) and hair texture (fine, medium or coarse)
- check whether your client's hair is 'virgin' (chemically untreated) hair; if so, it may be more resistant to straightening
- closely examine the hair and scalp for signs of poor condition or disease
- if contra-indications are present, then refer to your seniors so a decision can be made

HEALTH AND SAFETY
In all relaxing or straightening processes you must take great care to prevent damage to your client's hair or skin. You must ensure that she is adequately protected throughout.

- agree with your client exactly what is to be done, about how long it will take, and what it will cost
- check that she is comfortable and remains so throughout the service.

Tests

Always make tests on your client's hair to ensure that it is in a suitable state for relaxing and straightening, particularly when dryness, brittleness or breakage of the hair are evident. The following tests are recommended:

- a test cutting, to check the likely result of the intended process
- elasticity check, to determine the hair condition
- porosity check, to determine the rate of absorption
- testing a strand, to check on process development
- incompatibility test, to detect the presence of metals.

Products, tools and equipment

Product knowledge is essential. Whatever you decide to use, you must be familiar with it. You must study the manufacturer's instructions for use before your client arrives, or before you attempt to apply the product. (This also applies to your tools and equipment.) You should only decide on the most suitable strength of chemical product after:

- the consultation with your client, and making sure you know her wishes and requirements
- checking to determine whether your client is taking any prescribed medication, and if she has any allergies
- examining her hair and scalp condition
- the results of the relevant tests are known
- checking with a salon senior or specialist (proceed only after agreement is reached)

LUSTER

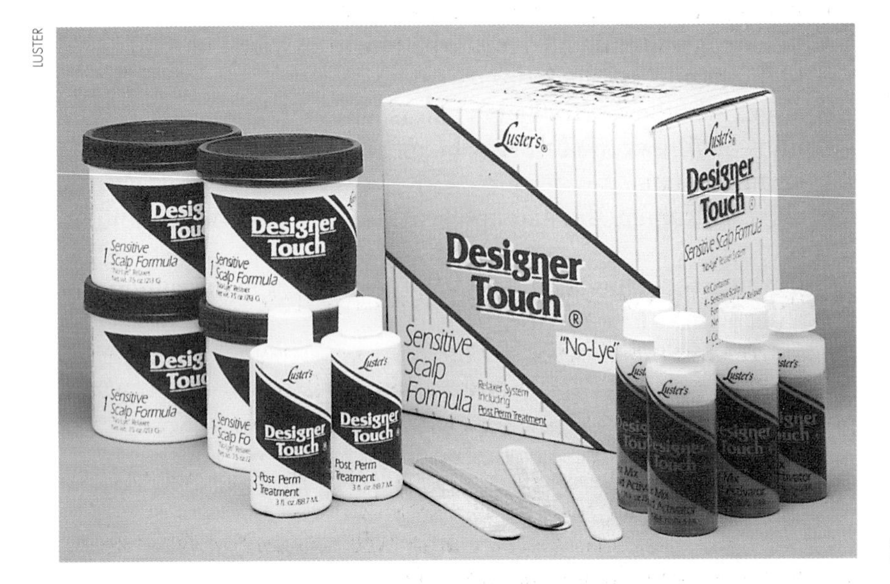

Straightening products

TIP

New products are being launched all the time. Always check with the manufacturer's instructions, particularly for processing times suitable for the different hair textures and types (European, African, Asian and so on – see page 31).

- ensuring products are in stock, to avoid disappointing your client
- deciding whether the hair is fine, medium, coarse, thick, thin, porous or resistant (coarse hair requires the longest processing time, and fine hair the shortest; grease or heavy chemical build-up on hair can block the relaxer product; hair that has been previously bleached, permed, straightened or relaxed can be very receptive and may process very fast)
- noting any other helpful information.

You can begin the relaxation process once you have considered the following factors:

- whether the hair is in a suitable condition for processing (for instance, a rough cuticle could indicate patchy porosity, which would be likely to affect the result)
- the salon temperature – a hot salon could speed processing, a cold one could delay process time
- the hairstyle required after the hair has been relaxed or straightened; your client's head and face shape and hair growth patterns (see page 88); if her hair is to change from very curly to very straight, she may need guidance from you about managing it afterwards and about home maintenance products.

RELAXING/STRAIGHTENING METHODS AND PROCEDURES

HEALTH AND SAFETY
Repeated combing, particularly with hot combs, can cause hair to break.

HEALTH AND SAFETY
Always check the temperature of a heat appliance to ensure your client does not get uncomfortably hot.

Most of the methods of curling hair can be used to relax hair. See page 113 for details of the chemistry involved. As with curling, relaxing/straightening hair may be temporary or permanent.

Temporary or physical relaxing/straightening

The temporary methods of relaxing or straightening hair include the following:

- placing large rollers in wet hair and drying
- wrapping wet hair around the head and drying
- using heated rollers
- using heated irons or tongs
- blow-drying or stretching
- using hot combs
- applying hot brushes.

TIP

When rollering long hair, take care to avoid tangling it.

Permanently straightening/relaxing hair

The permanent methods are chemical ones. These involve the use of strong chemicals and must be used with care. The types of chemical relaxers/straighteners currently available include:

- ammonium thioglycollate-based lotions, made for looser-curled hair, such as European-type hair
- specially made creams, also ammonium thioglycollate-based, intended specifically for Afro hair

- creams or gels based on sodium hydroxide 'lye' or caustic soda, made for Afro-Caribbean clients
- creams or gels based on calcium hydroxide, called non-lye products, made for tightly curled hair and a wide range of hair textures
- creams based on ammonium and sodium bisulphites, which are slower-acting and kinder to the hair, also suitable for a range of hair textures.

Important differences between these products are:

- the strengths – how much of the active chemical is present: this varies considerably and affects the process speed
- the pH – the degree of alkalinity; the higher the alkalinity, the stronger the product
- the contact time (length of processing) required.

In general, do not apply a degree of heat that would accelerate the chemical process and damage hair or skin. Some newer products, however, specifically recommend a certain amount of applied heat.

Some products require that adequate **basing** – the application of protective gels or creams to the skin around the hairline and ears – is made before the relaxing process commences.

HEALTH AND SAFETY
Do not press hair that is in poor condition. Wait until it has been conditioned.

TIP
The terms 'hard press' and 'soft press' are used to describe the amount of curl reduction imposed on the hair. In **hard press**, most of the curl is removed; in **soft press**, about half the curl is relaxed.

Relaxing/straightening methods

The following is an outline of a suggested application method using ammonium thioglycollate derivatives, but this should not be used in place of the manufacturer's instructions.

1. Section the hair into four: centrally from forehead to nape, and laterally from ear to ear (see diagram).
2. Apply the basing product.
3. Subdivide the nape sections into smaller ones.
4. Apply the straightener/relaxer cream, gel or lotion, avoiding the skin. Do not go closer than 12 mm from the scalp.
5. Comb the hair gently. Use a comb with widely spaced teeth. Some manufacturers advise you to wait till the hair has softened before combing.
6. Do not continually comb the hair when it is soft. Treat it gently at this stage – it can easily break. Leave the hair as straight as the client requires.
7. Processing time depends on the product and the hair. Softly curled hair relaxes quickly. Kinky hair takes longer. It is safest to monitor continuously throughout the process. Do not exceed the manufacturer's recommended time for processing.

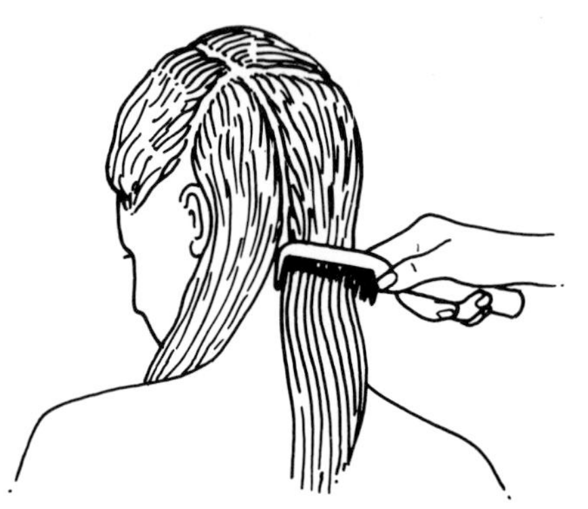
Sectioning hair

HEALTH AND SAFETY
Chemical relaxers/straighteners are made for specific hair types – for example, for Afro, tightly curled hair. There are other, gentler, products which are designed for use on curly European hair only.

LUSTER

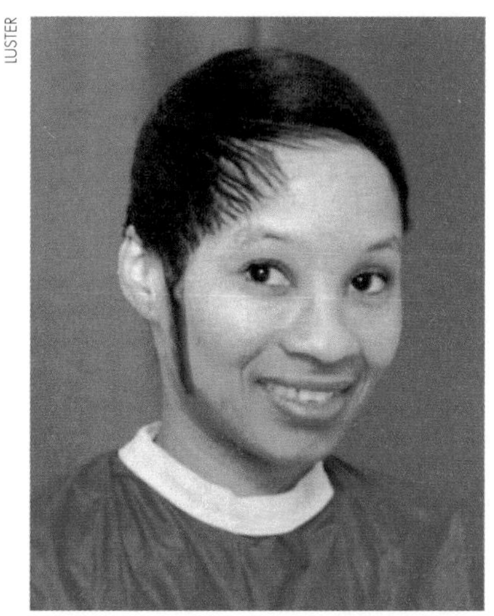

Relaxer has been applied and is allowed to process

LUSTER

The hair has been cut and styled for the finished effect

8 When processing is complete, you may apply neutralisers. Neutralisers vary; some are based on hydrogen peroxide. Whichever product is used, it must thoroughly cover the area treated.

9 After final rinsing and conditioning with moisturisers or other products, the hair may be styled.

> **HEALTH AND SAFETY**
> Always follow the manufacturer's instructions for the use of chemicals and products. Check with your salon's COSHH list of potential hazards (see page 280) for the correct usage.

Relaxing/straightening hair: how it works

'Straightening' and 'relaxing' are both terms that have been and are used to describe curl and wave reduction. Both can produce temporary and permanent effects.

- **Temporary effects** are physical effects.
- **Permanent effects** are chemical effects.

The chemistry of hair **straightening** with a thioglycollate derivative is a two-step process, similar to cold permanent waving (page 137). The disulphide bridges in the cysteine links between the keratin chains of the hair are reduced (broken) by the action of the ammonium thioglycollate in the straightening cream/gel/lotion. This softens the hair, which can then be moulded into its new straighter shape. This is followed by neutralisation, which is an oxidation process – reaction with oxygen. Cysteine groups pair up again to form cystines, and the disulphide bridges re-form in new positions.

The chemistry of hair **relaxing** relies on the use of other chemicals, such as sodium hydroxide. Sodium hydroxide breaks down the disulphide bonds in hair by **hydrolysis** – that is, the breakdown of a substance by, and with, water. Cystine groups are separated into cysteines, and sulphonic acid is also formed; continued processing produces lanthionine – another amino acid – and other single sulphur links. The hair softens and relaxes, tight curls are loosened, and the hair can be moulded into a straighter shape. When a sufficient degree of straightness is

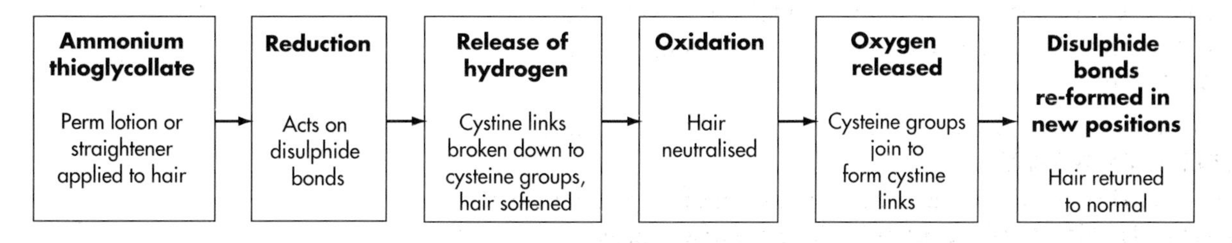

Straightening hair: two-stage reduction and oxidation

SPLINTERS
SPLINTERS

Straightened hair

reached the hair is shampooed with an acid-balancing shampoo, which returns to its normal acid state. No oxidising neutraliser is used.

This one-step chemical process differs from the straightening and perming processes using ammonium thioglycollate reduction followed by oxidation. It is very important to vet closely the subsequent use of other chemical processes on the chemically relaxed hair because the basic nature of the hair has been changed. No disulphide bridges are now present, so further reduction processes should not be used.

NICK JONES, HAIR DESIGN

Dealing with re-growth

Since hair grows approximately 12 mm (½ inch) each month, within a few weeks after relaxing/straightening very curly hair will begin to show itself above the scalp. This will need to be processed if the client wishes to continue with straightened or relaxed hair. When applying a process to the re-growth – called **retouching** – you must take care to avoid the scalp; make sure it is based well where required.

NICK JONES, HAIR DESIGN

HEALTH AND SAFETY

Overlapping previously chemically treated hair must be avoided in order to avoid breakage. Protective creams are available, but must be used with great care.

ACTIVITY

Contact your salon's wholesalers and manufacturers for information about the different types of relaxing and straightening processes available. Collect this together and keep it in your folder, not only for your own use but also for others for whom you may soon become responsible. You can thus constantly update your knowledge of newer relaxer products which are proving to be 'kinder', milder and less damaging to the hair.

HEALTH AND SAFETY
If allowed to remain too long in contact with the hair, all relaxers may have a depilatory action – they may remove the hair completely. Use a timer, and make sure that all processes are accurately timed.

Relaxing/straightening faults and what to do about them

Problems	*Possible cause*	*What to do*
Hair breakage before relaxing	Poor dressing, or results of previous relaxing methods; poor condition	Do not relax hair; wait till improved; refer to your senior/ trainer
Hair breakage after relaxing	Overpressing, or relaxers too strong, or poor normalising	Condition if possible refer to your senior/ trainer
Bald areas	Traction baldness due to poor relaxing or overprocessing	Do not relax hair; avoid tension, and treat gently
Sore scalp	Harsh treatment (e.g. combing) or sign of disease, or relaxers too strong or left too long	Do not relax hair; wait till improved; refer to your senior/ trainer
Discoloration or pink colour	Metals present, or wrong relaxer used, or overprocessing	Test and check; recondition; colour rinse; avoid using further chemicals
Hair too curly	Not relaxed enough, or wrong method chosen; or not normalising sufficiently	Condition the hair; choose the correct method, and relax again, after two weeks if the condition permits

ASSIGNMENTS: STRAIGHTENING AND RELAXING HAIR

A practical activity
Using suitable hair switches or lengths of hair, experiment with the different hair-straightening processes. (Alternatively, special models can be arranged on which to practise these techniques.) First collect together information from product knowledge sessions, visits to hair and trade shows, wholesalers and manufacturers and so forth. Make careful notes of your results, credit your sources, and include the following information:

1. List the questions that need to be put to your client.
2. Discuss your client's requirements.
3. Note any contra-indications.
4. Determine what products have been used previously.

5. Examine, and discuss with your client, the condition and texture of her hair, and a suitable choice of straightening process.
6. Apply tests as required.
7. Outline the chemical effects on the hair structure of both one-stage and two-stage processes.
8. Note the differences between the various techniques for straightening hair.
9. List the important influencing factors.
10. Outline the precautions to be taken.
11. List the problems that could arise and how you would deal with them.

For you to find out

Investigate the variety of information sources dealing with straightening and relaxing hair that are available to you. Use your trade journals, textbooks, wholesalers, manufacturers, videos and group training sessions for information. Collect facts and figures, credit your sources, and make precise notes to retain in your folder. Then answer the following questions:

- List the permanent and temporary methods of straightening hair.
- Outline the effects produced.
- Why are consultations and hair tests necessary?
- What advice do you give for client after-care?
- How often should straightening be applied?
- What are contra-indications? How do you deal with them?
- Outline one method each of physical and chemical straightening.
- What is 'virgin' hair?
- How do you deal with re-growth?
- What causes hair breakage? How would you deal with this if you noticed it on your client?
- Collect copies of manufacturers' instructions. Make sure that you read them and understand how to use their products.

A case study

A client requests a hair straightening or relaxing process. How would you deal with this if the hair was

- naturally very curly?
- previously permed?
- wavy, and in poor condition?

Work through the following sequence:

1. Consult the client and determine what treatments the hair has previously undergone.
2. Determine the client's exact wishes and requirements.
3. Assess whether these are suitable and attainable.
4. List the questions that you need to ask.
5. Agree with the client what is to be done.

6 What methods would you suggest for naturally very curly hair?
7 What would you do, and what would you say to your client, if the test results indicated that treatment should not be applied?
8 When should a client be referred for a second opinion?
9 How do you ensure the products you use are suitable for your client's hair and skin?
10 Why should manufacturers' instructions be strictly followed?
11 What after-care do you recommend to your client?

PREPARING FOR ASSESSMENT

In preparing for assessment on straightening and relaxing hair the following checklist may be helpful. Check that you have covered and now fully understand these items:

- straightening/relaxing methods, temporary or permanent, physical or chemical
- the effects of these processes on the hair and skin
- dealing with various hair lengths, hair and skin conditions, and previously treated hair
- choosing between one- and two-stage processes
- selecting the most suitable processes to achieve the client's satisfaction
- following manufacturers' instructions for their product use
- listing problems that could arise and dealing with them
- recording client information confidentially and legibly
- understanding such terms as 'hard press', 'soft press' or 'basing'
- dealing with style requirements after straightening.

When you feel that you are ready talk to your trainer and arrange a suitable time for your assessment.

CHAPTER 8

Colouring hair

INTRODUCTION

VIDAL SASSOON

ANDREW COLLINGE FOR TRESemmé

Coloured hair

The history of hair colour, together with colour used for the face, body, nails and clothes, has been a long and varied one. The social and religious reasons for the use of colour make an interesting study. Many people use colour to convey their individuality, to keep up with fashion, to enhance their appearance, or just to feel better about the way they look. All kinds of natural and artificial materials have been used. The early hair colourist was a master at creating colours from a variety of substances, sometimes with what we would now consider to be harsh, artificial and startling effects.

The application of dyes to enhance appearance and hair styling has been closely tied to the developments in chemistry and cosmetic manufacturing. The range of hair cosmetics produced now is probably wider than ever before, yet is often taken for granted. Products have improved considerably over the years: their quality and effects are now of a high standard. You need to have equally high standards in their application and use.

In this chapter we will look at the application of currently used methods of colouring hair. The following are some of the topics covered:

- the colours around us
- natural hair colour
- hair colorants
- choosing colour
- synthetic colour
- colour tests
- adding temporary colour
- adding semi-permanent, quasi-permanent and permanent colour
- other colouring techniques
- successful colouring
- bleaching – removing natural colour
- bleaching techniques
- bleaching the whole or part of the head.

WELLA

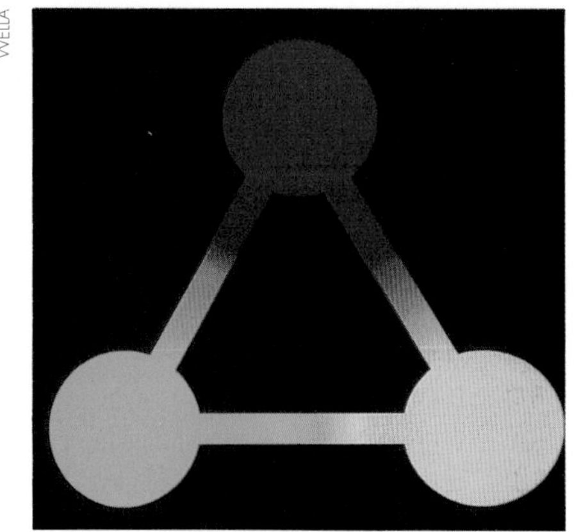

The colour triangle

WELLA

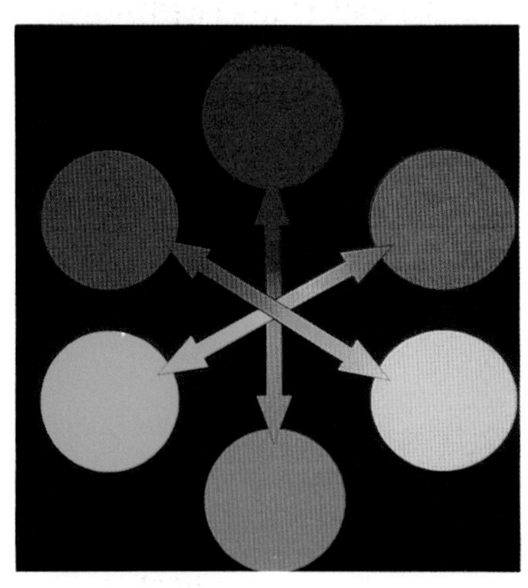

The colour circle

WELLA

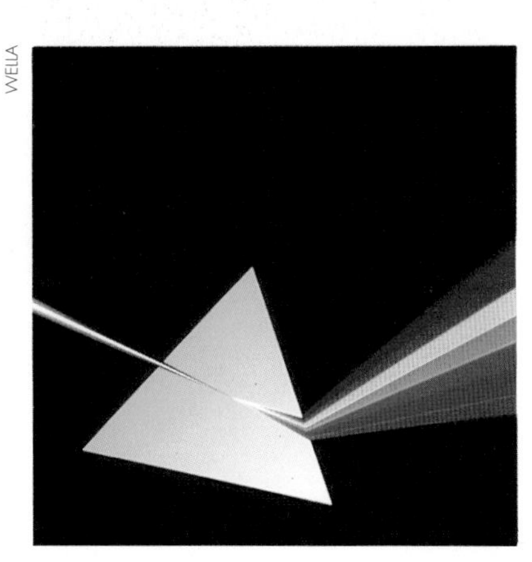

The colour spectrum from visible light

COLOURING – PRINCIPLES

Basic colouring

We are surrounded by colour. Look around the salon – at clothing, make-up, nail varnish, accessories, pictures, decor and packaging. Hair too can be colourful. Its colour can contribute to the overall style as much as its cut and finish. .

It is hard to define colours – words like 'chestnut' and 'blonde' describe them but are not at all precise. This chapter introduces the International Colour Chart and examines some basic facts about colour.

Seeing colour

When you look at an object, what you are actually seeing is light reflected from it. White light is really a mixture of many colours – that is why sunlight reflected by falling rain can produce a rainbow. A white object *reflects* most of the white light that falls upon it; a black object *absorbs* most of the light falling on it. A red object reflects the red light, and absorbs everything else.

Hair colour depends chiefly on the **pigments** in the hair, which absorb some of the light and reflect the rest. The colour that we see is also affected by the light in which it is seen, and (to a lesser extent) by the colours of clothes worn with it.

Mixing colours

The colours of the pigments in *paints* arise from three **primary colours** – red, blue and yellow. Pairs of these give the **secondary colours** – purple, green and orange. The various other colours are made from different proportions of the primary colours. White and black can be added to vary the **tone** of the colour.

The primary colours in *light* are different – red, green and blue. (These are the three colours used in a colour television set.) The secondary colours are yellow, cyan and magenta. The many colours in 'white' light can be separated by a glass prism or by raindrops: we see the **spectrum** of colour from white light as red–orange–yellow–green–blue–indigo–violet.

Hair colour

As discussed in Chapter 2 (page 31), the **natural** or **base colour** of hair depends on melanin pigments within the cortex of the hair. **Eumelanin** colours the hair black or brown; **pheomelanin** colours it red or yellow. The colour you see therefore depends on the amounts and proportions of these pigments. If the hair contains no pigment at all, it is white or blonde. (The pale yellow in this case is due to the keratin, not to pigment.) A young child's blonde hair may get darker later as more melanin is produced.

Some people never have any pigment in their hair, a condition known as **albinism**. Such people usually have no colour in the eyes or skin either. Sometimes there is just a little colour present: this condition is called **partial albinism**.

With age, or following stress, pigment may no longer be produced. Hairs already on the head will be unaffected, but new ones will be white. The proportion of white hairs among the coloured ones gradually increases, and the hair appears to go 'grey' – however, there aren't any actual grey hairs. 'Greyness' is often expressed as a percentage. For example, '50% white' means that half the hairs on the head are white, and half are their original colour.

Describing hair colour

- The **depth** of colour refers to how light or dark the colour is: this depends on the intensity of the pigments within the hair.
- The **tone** is the colour that you see – the combination of pigments that gives the overall colour. 'Warm' shades, such as gold or auburn, have more pheomelanin; 'cool' shades, such as ash, cendre, matt or drab, have less.

Visual aids

The **International Colour Chart (ICC)** offers a way of defining hair colours systematically. Even here, though, charts may vary between manufacturers. Take note of the way each manufacturer describes the different colours.

Shades of colour are divided and numbered, with black (1) at one end of the scale and lightest blonde (10) at the other. **Tones** of other colours (0.01–0.9) are combined with these, producing a huge variety of colours. Charts are usually arranged with shades in rows down the side and tones in columns across the top. To use them, first identify the shade of your client's hair: that row of the chart then shows the colours you could produce with that hair. For example, if your client has light brown hair (shade 5) and you tint with an orange tone (0.4), the result should be a light warm brown (5.4). The possibilities are almost endless, as these examples indicate:

- to produce ash shades, add blue
- to produce matt shades, add green
- to produce gold shades, add yellow
- to produce warm shades, add red
- to produce purple or violet shades, add mixtures of red and blue.

Hair colourings

Hair colourings, or **colourants**, may be grouped according to how long they remain on the hair:

- temporary colourings are applied as hair lotions, creams, mousses and the like
- semi-permanent colourings are applied as hair creams and rinses
- quasi-permanent colourings are applied mainly as creams
- permanent colourings are applied as tints.

WELLA

DEPTHS	
1/0	Blue Black
2/0	Black
3/0	Dark Brown
4/0	Medium Brown
5/0	Light Brown
6/0	Dark Blonde
7/0	Medium Blonde
8/0	Light Blonde
9/0	Very Light Blonde/Lightest Blonde
10/0	Extra Light Blonde/Pastel Blonde

Depths

WELLA

TONES	
/0	Natural
/1	Ash
/2	Cool Ash
/3	Honey Gold
/4	Red Gold
/5	Purple
/6	Violet
/7	Brunette
/8	Pearl Ash
/9	Soft Ash

Tones

WELLA

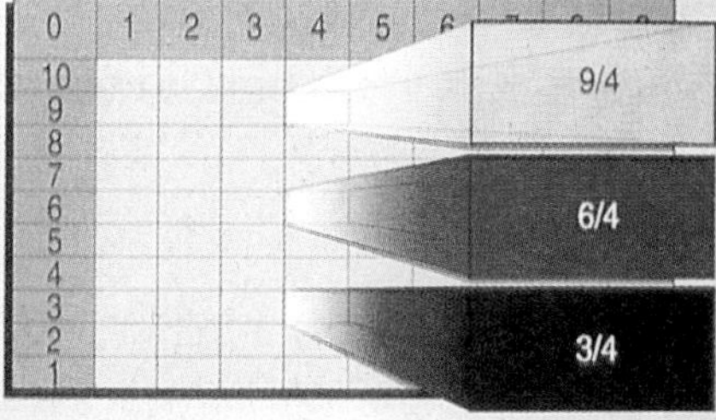

Depths and tones

TRESemmé

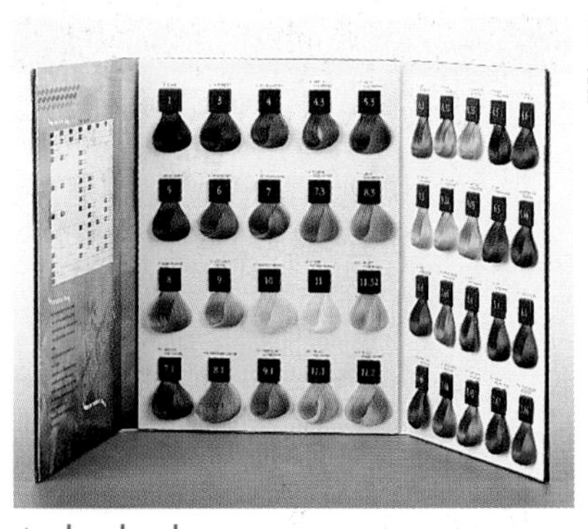
A shade chart

SCHWARZKOPF

WELLA

Hair colouring products

There are many different colouring products, developed from a variety of materials including vegetable extracts and minerals.

Vegetable colourings

These are made from the flowers, stems or barks of various plants.

- **Henna**, or **Lawsone**, is made from the powdered leaves of the Egyptian privet. It is used to add red colour to hair.
- **Camomile**, made from the flowers of the camomile plant, has a yellow pigment. It is used to add yellow to light hair, thereby brightening the hair. It colours the surface only.
- **Indigo**, made from the leaves of the indigo plant, gives a blue-black colour. When mixed with henna in different proportions it produces a variety of shades.
- **Walnut**, made from the outer shell coverings, yields a yellow-brown dye. It is a surface, non-penetrating colourant.
- **Quassia**, made from the bark of a tree, is often used with camomile to produce a useful colourant which brightens hair.

Other substances, including sage, sumach, oak bark, cudbear and logwood, have been used for their varied shades and effects.

HEALTH AND SAFETY
Compound henna is incompatible with modern colouring and perming materials. Don't confuse it with vegetable henna.

Vegetable and mineral colourings

These are mixtures of vegetable extracts and mineral substances. One of the commonest was **compound henna** – vegetable henna mixed with metallic salts. This surface colourant is no longer used in salons.

Mineral colourings

These are divided into two groups: metallic dyes and aniline derivatives.

Metallic dyes are surface-coating colourings. They are variously known as reduction, metallic, sulphide and progressive dyes. They are not commonly used in the salon, but are occasionally found in 'hair colour restorers'.

JINGLES

HEALTH AND SAFETY
Metallic dyes are incompatible with modern hairdressing materials. Always make tests before using bleach, oxidation tints or cold perm neutralisers with them.

Aniline derivatives are made from compounds found in crude oil, as are many chemicals used in cosmetics and medicines. These synthetic organic dyes, often known as **'para' dyes**, include *para*-phenylenediamine and *para*-toluenediamine. These dyes penetrate the cortex of the hair as small molecules. They are then treated with an oxidising agent such as hydrogen peroxide. This makes them combine into larger molecules which remain 'trapped' in the cortex: shampooing cannot wash them out.

You can use these aniline dyes both to lighten the melanin and to tint the hair at the same time.

TIP

Each type of colouring has its own set of instructions for application. Follow these carefully.

ACTIVITY

Collect together your own examples of vegetable colourings.

Using hydrogen peroxide

Hydrogen peroxide is one of the most commonly used oxidising agents. It can be mixed with cream or with liquid tints. The mixture appears colourless at first, but darkens on exposure.

With a modern tint and hydrogen peroxide, the mixture first penetrates the cuticle. In the cortex, the natural pigment is bleached, and the colourant is oxidised. The tint becomes 'locked' within the cortex. (Note that peroxide is needed even when you are making the hair *darker* – not to lighten the natural pigment, but to fix the tint in the cortex.)

To lighten the natural hair colour ('colour up') two or three shades, use a higher strength of hydrogen peroxide. To take the natural colour 'down' to a darker shade ('colour down'), use a lower strength. The percentage strength to use is determined by the manufacturers' instructions, the colour of the hair to be lightened or darkened, and the hair's porosity. (See the table of hydrogen peroxide dilutions on page 197.)

Pre-lightening is necessary when the natural colour is to be changed to a very light shade. Mixtures of hydrogen peroxide and ammonium hydroxide (or other bleaching agents) may be used. Modern colourings lighten several shades, but cannot by themselves lighten to the very pale tones.

Pre-softening is a technique used on resistant hair. Dilute hydrogen peroxide and ammonium hydroxide are applied, not to lighten the colour but to soften the cuticle. This makes it easier later for the colourant to penetrate the hair.

HEALTH AND SAFETY

Dyes or tints such as these may cause a skin reaction. Carry out a skin test before applying them.

Always follow the manufacturer's instructions for the use of peroxide products. Check with your salon's COSHH list of potential hazards (see page 280) for the correct usage.

ACTIVITY

In your styling book, list the different colour products available. Collect examples from journals and magazines.

CHARLES WORTHINGTON FOR L'OREAL

Tinting aids

The activation of colouring processes can be aided by the use of steamers, accelerators or rollerballs. The applied heat causes the hair to swell and the cuticle to lift. This makes it easier for the colourant to enter the cortex, and may halve the processing time.

Steamers, accelerators and rollerballs allow tint applications to be made on hair regardless of its length, even though the hair may vary in its porosity between the roots and the points. The heat distribution allows even processing throughout the hair length. Colour application must not be delayed, however, or the result may be uneven.

Choosing colour

The choice of colour depends on the following important factors:

- **The client's requirements** Think about your client's age, lifestyle, job, fashion and dress sense, the colours she wears (both clothing and make-up), and the effects she would like to see. Younger clients may want bright colours or black. Older clients may wish to disguise the fact that their hair is going grey. In general, choose colours from a natural range that blend with the natural colour – avoid bright, harsh colours that contrast with it.
- **The natural hair colour** The client's base colour depends on the amounts and relative proportions of melanin, eumelanin and pheomelanin, and on the percentage of white hair present.
- **The client's skin colour** In nature the colour of the skin tends to blend with the colour of the hair. You are altering that balance, so be careful. A deep red tint would clash with a ruddy complexion, for example; blonde, cool tints would look odd against oriental and warm, dark skins. The amount of melanin in skin increases when the skin is exposed to sunlight, so the skin darkens – this is what we see as a **tan**. (The production of extra melanin is the body's defence against the ultraviolet light from the sun. Too much UV light may cause skin problems, including cancer.)
- **The hair texture** The coarseness or fineness of the hair affects the absorption of colouring chemicals. In general, fine hair will tint more rapidly than coarse hair.

TIP

If in doubt between two shades, always choose the lighter one – it is easy to add extra colour if required, but harder to remove unwanted colour.

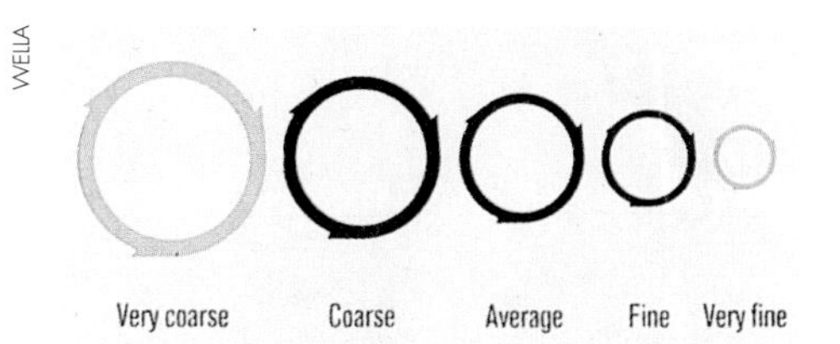

WELLA

Hair textures

ACTIVITY

Collect pictures from magazines showing hair colours worn with clothes of various colours. Which look most attractive? Why do some hair colours look more suitable with clothes of particular colours? A photograph album of hair colourings that you have used is helpful in planning colour treatments – and teaching others, when you become a senior!

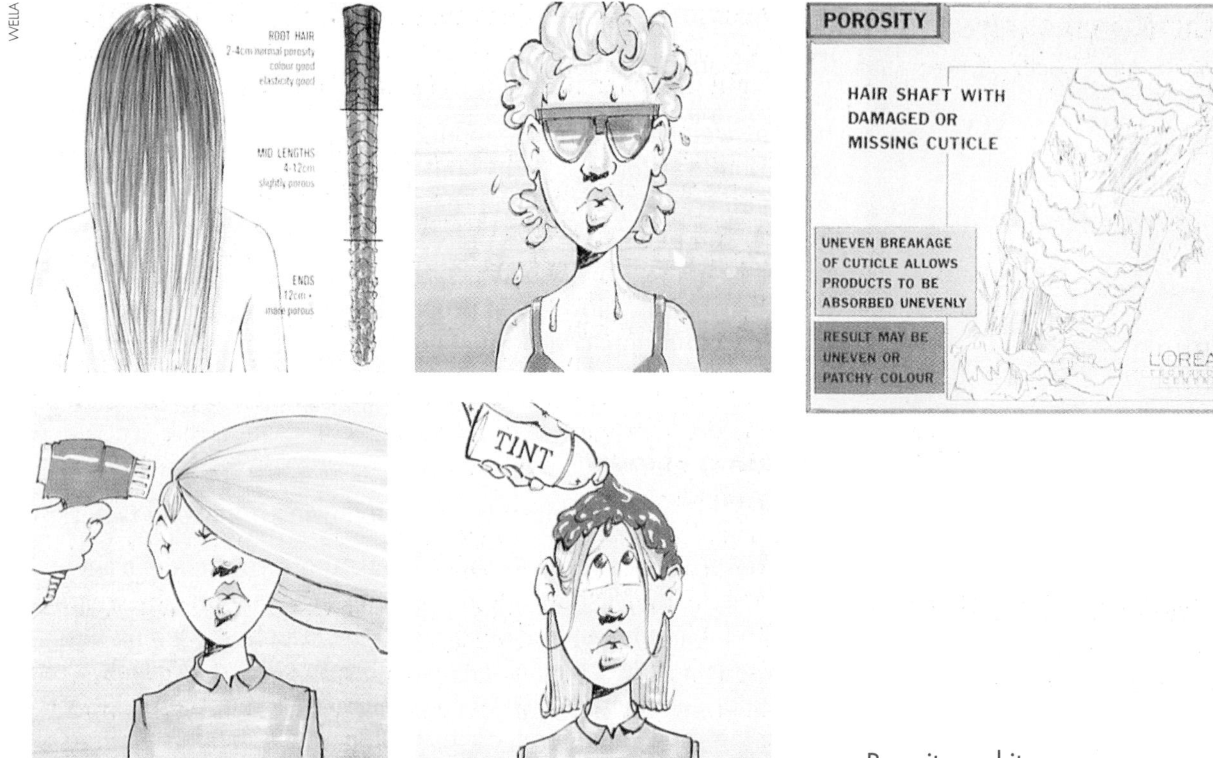

WELLA

L'OREAL

Porosity and its causes

- **The condition and porosity of the hair** Porous hair will absorb tints quickly, and porosity depends on the general condition of the hair. Hair with a smooth cuticle absorbs less tint. Uneven colour may result.
- **The colouring product used** Tests on the hair will indicate which products may be used. This will affect the range of colours available to this particular client. For example, tests may show that it is safe to use a light, temporary colouring, but there is no point in using it on dark hair – it wouldn't show.
- **The shade of colour sought** This too may influence the suitability of various products. A white-haired client, for instance, may want to have a slight tone added. In this case a temporary or semi-permanent colouring might be best, in a colour such as silver, pewter, blue or violet. Lighter colourings will be preferable to heavy, darker ones; they will match the skin colour better.

TIPS

Remember to consider lighting when choosing colour.

Apply colour quickly in order to achieve evenly coloured hair. Delay may lead to blotchy effects.

The client consultation

Your client may ask many questions about colour. What colour would be best for her? How can that colour be achieved? How long will it last? How much will it cost? How will it affect the hair? Is her hair suitable? You need to be ready with answers to such questions on all aspects of hair colouring before you start work on your client's hair.

VIDAL SASSOON

HEALTH AND SAFETY
Rushed work is rarely, if ever, efficient.

- Discuss the client's ideas about colouring, considering the style and how colour may enhance it. Are there factors that might influence the choice of colour, such as the client's lifestyle?
- Examine the hair for previous colouring, perming and other chemical treatments. What is its natural colour?
- Analyse the state of the hair and consider the effects of colouring treatments on it. Determine the hair's condition, porosity and elasticity.
- Refer to the client's record card, if available.
- Decide what sort of colouring to carry out, and agree with your client on the product you will use. Refer to a colour chart to make sure you really are agreed about the colour.
- Advise your client how long the process will take and how much it will cost.
- Carefully read the manufacturer's instructions for each product you are going to use.
- Prepare your client with a gown and other coverings. Make sure all clothing is protected.
- Keep brushing and combing to a minimum – if you scratch the scalp, you will make it sensitive to the chemicals you will be using.

TIP
Colour choice must be appropriate to the client's hairstyle.

Tests

Strong chemicals are involved in hair colouring and bleaching. If misused, these could damage the hair or skin. The following are tests you should carry out, most before you start, one during processing.

Most permanent colourings contain chemicals that irritate certain skin types. This is usually stated on the label. Always test the skin 24–48 hours before applying such colourings, so that you know how the skin is likely to react. Don't assume that a product is safe just because it has been used on this client before. A skin reaction may develop even after regular use.

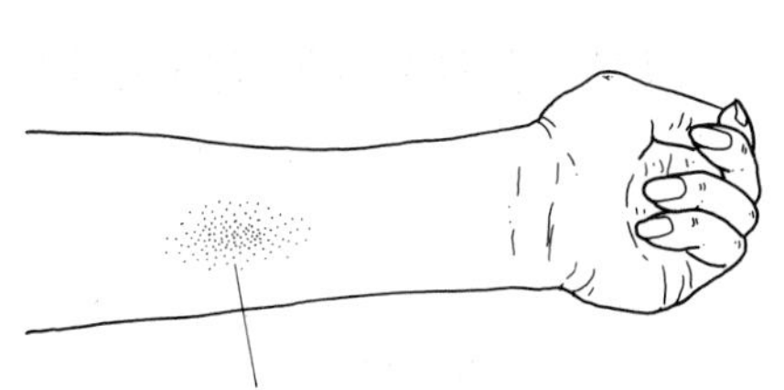

Skin test for an allergic reaction

- **Skin test** A test to find out whether the client's skin reacts to chemicals in the permanent colourings you are going to use (see below). It is also known as the **predisposition test**, **patch test** or **Sabouraud–Rousseau test**. The method is as follows:

  1. Mix a little of the tint to be used with the correct amount and strength of hydrogen peroxide.
  2. Clean an area of skin about 8 mm square, behind the ear or in the arm fold. Use spirit on cottonwool to remove the grease from the skin.
  3. Apply a little of the tint mixture to the skin. Allow it to dry.
  4. Cover the tint patch with collodion, which protects it.
  5. Ask your client to report any discomfort or irritation that occurs in the next 24–48 hours. Arrange to see the client at the end of this time so that you can check for signs of reaction.

TIP
Some clients are sensitive to chemicals in tints – the tints may cause an allergic reaction on first use. Other clients may become allergic later. You must make a skin test *each time* you use a tint.

Ask whether the client is allergic to anything else, such as washing-up liquid, make-up or certain foods. If she is, she is more likely to react to tinting products.

6 If there is a **positive response** – *any* skin reaction, such as inflammation, soreness, swelling, irritation or discomfort – do not use this colouring treatment. *Never* ignore the result of a skin test. If a skin test showed a reaction and you carried on anyway, there might be a much more serious reaction: this might affect the whole body, and it might for example lead to dermatitis. If there is a **negative response** – no reaction – you can carry out the treatment proposed.

- **Colour test** A test for the suitability of a chosen colour, the amount of processing that will be required, and the final colour that will result. Apply the tint or bleaching products you propose to use to a cutting of the client's hair.
- **Porosity test** A test to indicate how fast chemicals will be absorbed. Rub the hair between your fingertips – is the cuticle smooth or rough? The rougher the cuticle, the more porous it is, and the faster it will absorb chemicals.
- **Elasticity test** A test for hair strength. Pull a hair between your fingers. Does it stretch and spring back? If the hair breaks easily it may be that the cortex is damaged, in which case chemical processing might cause it to break.
- **Incompatibility test** A test for chemicals already on the hair. Use gloves to protect your hands. Place a sample of hair in a mixture of hydrogen peroxide and ammonium hydroxide. If the mixture bubbles, heats up or discolours, you should *not* apply a tint – to do so would cause hair loss and skin damage.
- **Strand test** A test during processing, to check progress (see page 184). If the colour is uneven or insufficient, further processing or more tint is required.

Colour care

- Make sure that clothes, both yours and your client's, are always fully protected by gowns and towels.
- Confirm the client's requirements by showing her colour charts and illustrations.
- Select the appropriate colour product, tools and equipment required for the process.
- Always follow the manufacturer's recommendations, particularly when preparing and mixing products.
- Isolate any hair that is not to be coloured.
- Ensure that the colour change takes into account the client's wishes, influencing factors and the results required.
- Use colouring techniques that prevent products dripping and spreading unnecessarily.
- Remove colourants effectively, by thorough rinsing on completion of the colouring process.
- Make notes of any problems you encounter. Refer them to your senior as soon as possible.
- Complete record cards by noting all details clearly and accurately including the final results achieved.

Temporary hair colouring products

TRESemmé

COLOURING TECHNIQUE

Temporary hair colourings

Temporary colourings remain on the hair only until they are washed off. They do not penetrate the hair cuticle, nor do they directly affect the natural colour. They merely coat the surface of the hair. Some colourings may nevertheless be absorbed if the hair is porous and its condition poor. Temporary colourings are supplied as setting lotions and creams, coloured hairsprays and lacquers, hair colour crayons and paints, glitterdust, mousses and gels. Many contain **'azo' dyes**.

There are several advantages to temporary colourings:

- the colour effect is only temporary
- a wide range of colours is available
- the colourants are easily removed, by washing
- hair condition is improved
- subtle toning can be applied to grey, white or normal hair
- fashion effects can be used on bleached hair
- no skin test is required.

Types of temporary colouring products

- **Setting lotions and creams** are popular forms of colouring. The colour is usually carried in a setting agent, which gives 'body' to the hair. No mixing or dilution is required. The colourant is applied with a sponge or brush, or directly from the container. It may be distributed throughout the hair by light frictioning with the fingers. Towel-dry the hair before applying the lotion or cream, to prevent dilution.
- **Coloured hair lacquers** are temporary colourings that may be sprayed on to dry, dressed hair. Based on shellac, lacquers coat the hair cuticle, and can be removed by brushing and washing. There is a restricted range.
- **Coloured hairsprays** are made in liquid or powder form, and in various colours. They are used on dry, dressed hair. These are based on plastics: they coat the cuticle and are also easily removed by brushing and washing. Some contain metallic colourings; silver and bronze are popular, for example.
- **Hair colour crayons and paints** are mainly for theatrical effects. They are particularly useful for highlighting a dressing for the stage or for television.
- **Glitterdust** is made from shining, coloured metal dust. When sprinkled on the hair, it produces a twinkling effect. Gold and silver are commonly used. The effects are temporary and ornamental.
- **Coloured mousses and gels** are popular forms of temporary colouring with advantages similar to those of coloured setting lotions. They are able to colour and condition hair, and add extra 'hold'.

HEALTH AND SAFETY

Take care when using metallic colours on blonde, white or bleached hair – the hair may discolour.

Remove metallic colourings thoroughly before carrying out any oxidation process, such as bleaching.

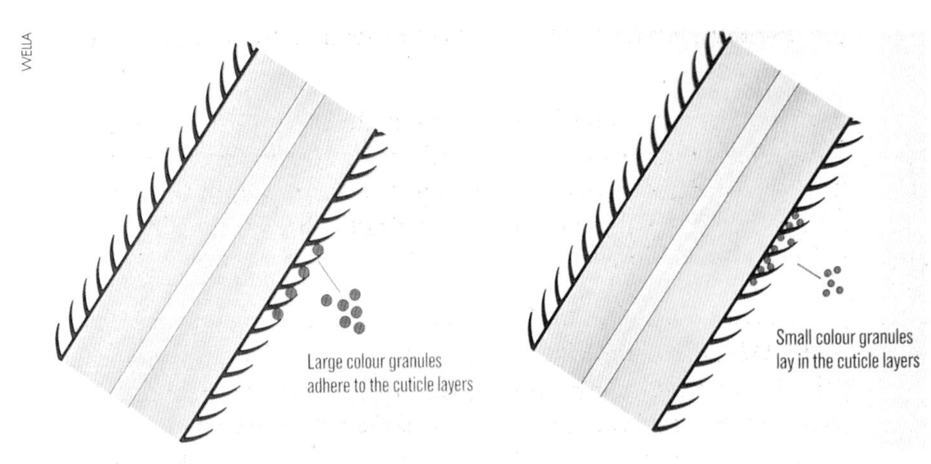

Temporary hair colouring

Temporary hair colouring

Semi-permanent colourings

Semi-permanent colourings are made in various forms and normally require no mixing, unlike some temporary rinses and permanent colourings. However, you should always check the instructions before using any commercial product.

Semi-permanent colouring is deposited in the cuticle and outer cortex. It remains in the hair longer than temporary colourings do. The colouring gradually lifts each time the hair is washed. Some last through six, seven or eight washes. Semi-permanent colourings are not intended to cover a large percentage of white hair, but they nevertheless do so to a greater extent than do temporary colourings.

The colour range is varied, but you need to choose carefully. A black rinse on white hair, for instance, will not produce a pleasing result. Timing and development are affected by salon temperature, and by the hair's texture and porosity. Heat and poor hair condition may speed absorption.

Semi-permanent colourings have several advantages:

- They are more effective and longer-lasting than temporary colourings.
- A larger colour range and choice is available.
- Root re-growth is less noticeable, as the colour lifts anyway by the time contrasting hair has grown.
- Natural hair colour is not affected, either directly or chemically.
- Skin tests are not usually required (but always check the instructions before you start).

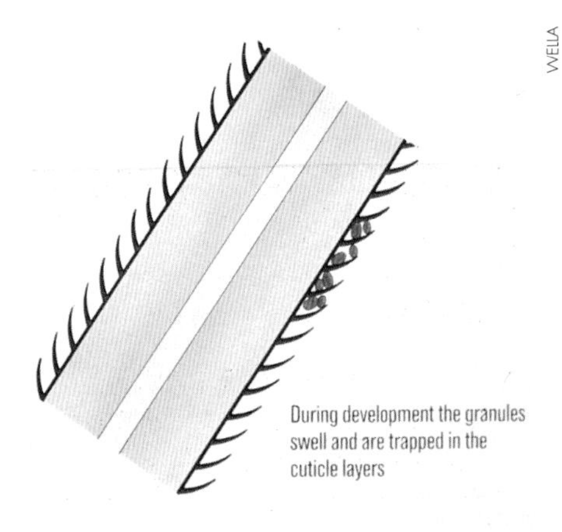

Temporary hair colouring

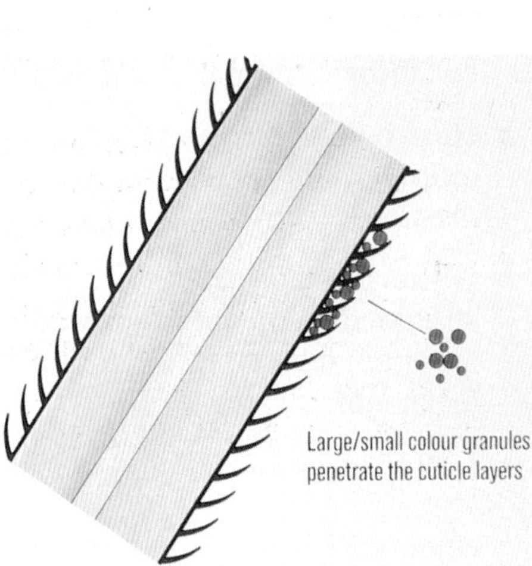

Semi-permanent hair colouring

Semi-permanent hair colouring product

- foaming agents within the colourants help to prevent colour dripping.

Semi-permanent colourings may be made from nitrodiamines, nitrated aminophenols and picramic acid. These are collectively known as **'nitro' dyes**. The pigment molecules penetrate the cuticle and enter the cortex, but are gradually removed by subsequent washings.

HEALTH AND SAFETY

Some permanent colourings may be diluted or mixed to produce varied semi-permanent effects. These products *do* contain substances that are known to be skin irritants. Carry out skin tests first. Mixtures of this type should be made only on the manufacturer's recommendation.

Adding semi-permanent colour to hair

Preparation

TIPS

Check that the colour in the container is the right one – it's easy to mix up the tints!

Check that the container isn't damaged. Air can oxidise the tint and make it useless.

TIP

Always measure quantities of chemicals carefully and mix them thoroughly following the manufacturer's instructions.

1. Check the scalp for cuts, sores, or any abnormalities that may be aggravated by chemicals in the colouring.
2. Use suitable protective coverings to protect both yourself and your client.
3. Wash the hair with a suitable shampoo, preferably one made for pre-colouring. (Some semi-permanents contain a detergent and require no pre-shampooing.)
4. Remove excess water to prevent colour dilution.
5. Comb through the hair to remove any tangles.
6. Isolate and protect parts of the hair that are not to be coloured.

Application

1. Apply the colouring using a sponge, a brush, an applicator bottle, or by pouring it direct from the container, according to the manufacturer's instructions.
2. Apply it evenly, and leave the hair loose to allow free circulation of air. This helps even development. Large hair sections may be taken. (When *tinting*, small sections must be taken.)
3. Do not apply heat without first covering the hair. A plastic cap may be useful, to prevent the colouring drying out, which would adversely affect colour development.
4. Remove any skin stains with spirit or stain remover. Barrier creams help to prevent skin staining.
5. Time the process, following the manufacturer's recommendations.
6. Remove surplus colouring by thorough rinsing, but without further washing.

Quasi-permanent colourings

These colourings are nearly permanent – they last for longer than the semi-permanent colourings do, but not as long as the true permanent colourings. Strictly follow the manufacturer's instructions for their use.

Permanent colourings

A wide variety of **permanent colourings** is now available. They are used to cover white hair and most natural colours, and to produce other natural colours as well as fashion and fantasy shades. Modern colourings are made in cream, semi-viscous and liquid forms. Most need to be mixed with hydrogen peroxide: this oxidises the hair's natural pigment and combines the small molecules of synthetic colouring into much larger molecules. This process is called **polymerisation**. Without hydrogen peroxide the synthetic colouring would rapidly be lost again.

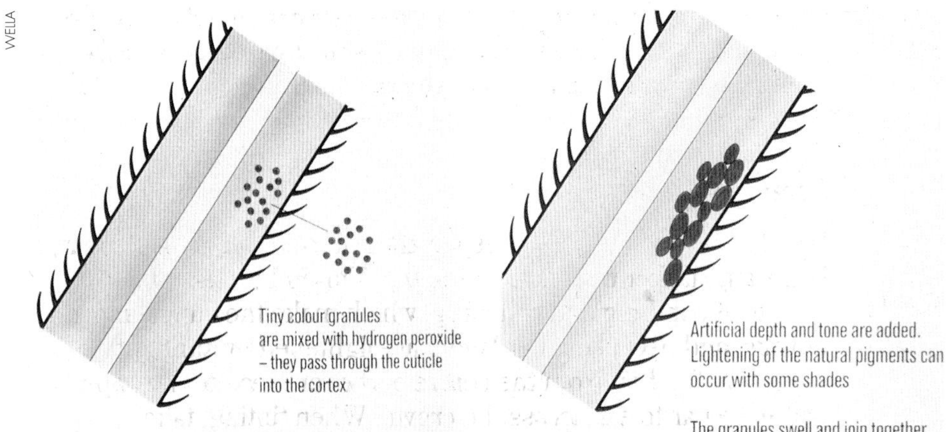

Permanent hair colouring

Tinting is the process whereby the synthetic colouring penetrates the hair cuticle, and is absorbed into the cortex. There it is oxidised and remains permanently fixed. The natural colour is bleached at the same time. Although the colours are permanent, the choice of product and the rate of hair growth affect how long the colour lasts. The condition of the hair also affects this: hair with damage to the cuticle (which can be caused by the effects of weather) will lose the colour more rapidly.

PENETRATION OF COLOUR

TEMPORARY COLOUR

LARGE COLOUR MOLECULES LODGE BETWEEN CUTICLE SCALES

SEMI-PERMANENT COLOUR

COLOUR MOLECULES ARE SMALL ENOUGH TO PENETRATE CUTICLE AND OUTSIDE EDGE OF CORTEX

PERMANENT COLOUR

VERY SMALL MOLECULES CAN PENETRATE INTO CORTEX AND GROW ON DEVELOPMENT

L'OREAL

Penetration of colour

Adding permanent colour to hair

Preparation

Before colouring a client's hair you must make the usual preparations: consulting with the client, agreeing what is to be done, and making the necessary tests (see pages 177–8). Examine the hair and skin thoroughly for signs of poor condition or inflammation. When you carry out the skin test – 24–48 hours before processing – don't forget to take a cutting of the client's

TRESemmé

Permanent hair colouring product

TIP

Make sure that any hair not to be coloured is isolated – for example, carefully sectioned and wrapped in foil or tissue.

hair so that you can make colour tests. Unless you know exactly what products have been used on the hair previously, test for incompatibles such as metallic dyes. The results of these tests will then be available when the client returns for the actual tinting.

Gather together everything you will need:

- protective coverings, both for you and your client
- barrier cream to protect the skin around the hairline
- rubber gloves
- glass measures and hydrogen peroxide, for mixing the tint
- a dish and an applicator
- a tailcomb and clips, for sectioning
- cottonwool, to soak up excess tint
- the chosen tint or tints.

HEALTH AND SAFETY

Tints contain strong chemicals. Unless you are using the tint as a toner after prebleaching, always apply tint to dry, unwashed hair. Shampoo washes away the natural oils which protect the hair and skin from the chemicals in the tint. It also stimulates the skin, bringing blood to the surface and increasing the risk of skin reactions.

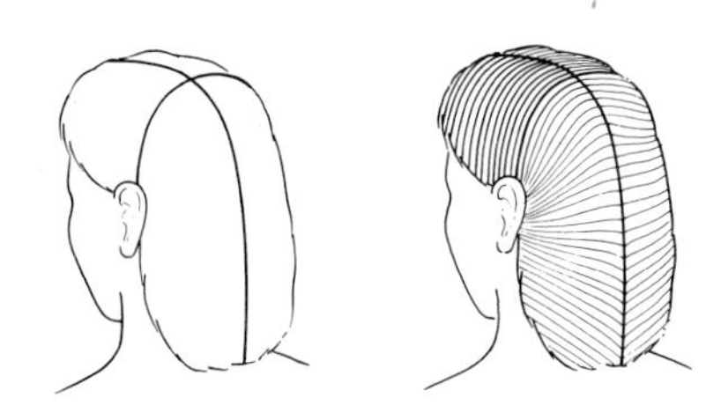

Hair sectioning

Sectioning

Hair lower down the head, especially hair covered by other hair, is usually darker than that on the top. This is because of the effects of combing and brushing, which make the cuticle more porous, and because outer layers are lightened by sunlight.

Section the hair from the centre of the forehead to the nape, and from ear to ear across the crown. When tinting, take subsections about 6 mm wide, starting from the nape.

Mixing the tint

Don't mix the tint until you're ready to start tinting! Once mixed, it needs to be used immediately.

Mix the tint carefully, measuring amounts accurately. If the proportions are wrong, the result may not be as you intended. Add the peroxide to the tint gradually, to make sure the mixture is smooth.

Application

1. Place the tint bowl near your client, to minimise the risk of dripping tint on her or on the floor.
2. The method of application depends on how runny the tint mixture is. Cream tints are best applied with a brush. Carefully lay the tint on to the subsection and leave it: don't scrape it off again. With practice you will judge how much to put on. Liquid or semi-liquid tints can be applied with a sponge, an applicator, a dispenser or directly from the bottle.
3. If the tint is thick, work with small subsections. The thinner it

is, the larger the subsections can be, because it will penetrate more quickly. The applicator brush often gives the best control.

4. Work swiftly and methodically, from the nape upwards.
5. Distribute the tint evenly, covering each subsection. Too little tint will produce varied colour; too much will be wasteful.

ACTIVITY
Using samples of hair of one base colour, apply different shades of tint. Assess the results.

Processing: colour development

Monitor and time the processing from the point when all of the hair has been treated. Timing must be accurate. Too short a time will cause **underprocessing** – the tinting will be incomplete and the colour won't be as you intended. Too long a time may cause **overprocessing** – the shades produced may be too dark. You may be able to use steamers or accelerators to speed up the processing. Check the manufacturer's instructions.

When you think processing may be complete, carry out a **hair-strand colour test.**

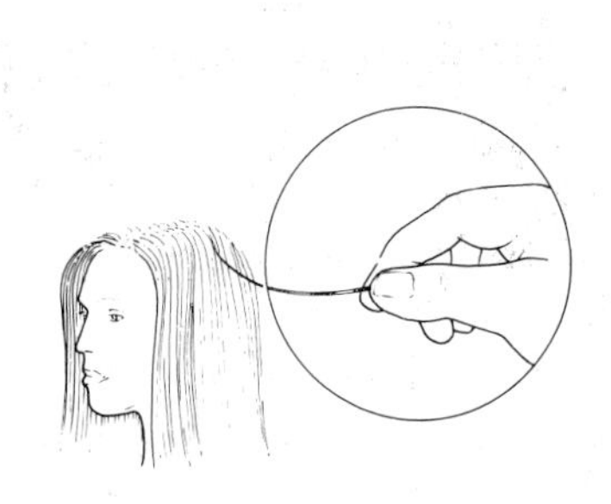

The hair strand colour test

1. Most colouring products just require the time recommended by the manufacturer. Check the instructions.
2. Rub a strand of hair lightly with a paper tissue or the back of a comb, to remove the surplus tint.
3. Check whether the colour remaining is evenly distributed throughout the hair's length. If it is even, remove the rest of the tint. If it is uneven, allow processing to continue, if necessary applying more tint.
4. If any of the hair on the head is not being treated, you can compare the evenness of colour in the tinted hair with that in the untinted hair.

Removing surplus tint

Some tints can be removed by adding a little water, lightly massaging the hair, and rinsing. Others may require shampooing. Don't ruffle the hair at this stage or it may get tangled.

If there are any **skin stains**, apply a little tint directly to the

ACTIVITY
Collect together four or five dark brown hair samples. Apply tint to them. Time them differently: the first for 5 minutes, the next 10 minutes, the third 15 minutes and so on. At the end of the time, rinse the hair sample. When they are all processed, compare the different colour effects produced by the different timings.

Repeat the process with mid-brown or light brown hair.

HEALTH AND SAFETY
Always follow the manufacturer's instructions for the application of chemicals and products. Check with your salon's COSHH list of potential hazards (see page 280) for the correct usage.

TIP

When using dry heat, don't dry the hair too quickly. If the colourant is dried out too soon, it may be ineffective.

TIP

Always note the salon temperature. If the salon is warm, processing could be faster; if it is cool, processing could be slower. If the client is sitting near a heater or in a cold draught, then part of the head could be processed differently from the rest.

stain to soften it. Then rinse the skin thoroughly. Don't let the stain remain on the skin for long, as the colour will deepen.

While the hair is wet the colour will look darker. Towel-dry the hair and the true colour will be easier to assess.

Further colouring techniques

Virgin hair

Hair that has not been tinted or otherwise chemically treated before will vary in lightness and porosity along its length. The mid-lengths are usually the most resistant to tinting, and so they take the longest. The hair points are naturally lighter and more porous, because they are the most exposed to wear and weather. The roots are closest to the head, heat from which activates the tint.

For the first tint, therefore, use this special method:

1. Begin by applying tint to the mid-lengths (the main part of the hair).
2. Then apply tint to the hair points (the last 25 mm of the hair tips).
3. Finally, apply tint to the roots (the 12 mm nearest the scalp).

First time (virgin) application

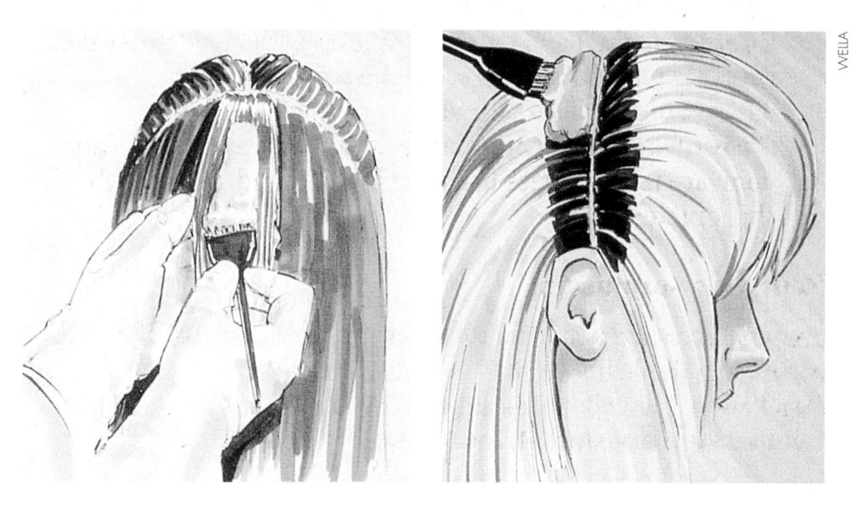

WELLA

L'OREAL

Re-growth tinting

Re-growth tinting

Re-growth tinting is the process of tinting just the hair that has grown since the tint was applied last time. Tint is applied to the root ends only, not to the mid-lengths or points. It is then processed and rinsed in the usual way.

With some tints you can add a little water and comb the colourant through the rest of the hair after processing. This dilutes the tint and maintains an even colour throughout the hair, correcting any lifting that has occurred.

Tinting lighter or darker

With modern oxidation tints it is possible to lighten or darken the natural hair shade. As usual, you need to plan the final colour, taking into account the starting colour, the texture and condition of the hair, and so on.

To darken the hair, you will need a darker tint and not too much hydrogen peroxide. To lighten it, more peroxide will be needed to oxidise the pigment in the hair. If the client wants the hair lightened by many shades (from black to light blonde, for example), you will need to prebleach it.

> **TIP**
>
> Don't repeatedly comb *undiluted* tint through the hair after a re-growth tint. This would spoil the final colour and damage the hair.

Resistant hair and greying hair

Some hair resists tint, usually because the cuticle isn't porous. With experience you will learn to recognise this just by feeling the hair – rough hair is more likely to be porous. Hair is likely to tint easily in certain conditions:

- if has recently been permed
- if it usually takes a perm quickly
- if it curls easily and tightly
- if it has previously been coloured
- if it has been bleached
- if it is dry.

It is likely to be resistant:

- if it takes perms slowly
- if it soon drops out of curl
- if it has a smooth surface (a tightly packed cuticle)
- if it is greasy or lank
- if it is covered with chemicals or a metallic coating.

White hair is sometimes resistant, but often it is *more* porous than pigmented hair. If there are white patches, tint them last of all, especially if you are using warm shades such as red.

If necessary, pre-soften the hair by applying a diluted mixture of hydrogen peroxide and ammonium hydroxide. This will cause the cuticle to lift, making the hair more porous.

Competition and fantasy colouring

This involves the application of colourants to produce a variety of special effects. The results may not be natural or suitable for normal wear: some **competition colours** are good examples of wearable colours, others are harsh and garish as a fashion or style requirement. **Fantasy colours** are more extreme, with vivid and startling colour blends.

Lighting plays an important part in colour effects and needs to be considered when planning the overall effect. Lighting has effects in the salon, as well as on competition colourings. Some of these are as follows:

- Blue light, produced by some types of fluorescent tube, tends to neutralise the warm red effect of hair colour.
- Yellow light, as from bare electric bulbs, adds warmth to hair colour and tends to neutralise blue or ash effects.
- Whiter 'daylight' lights show a truer hair colour than ordinary artificial light (tungsten bulbs).

> **TIP**
>
> Your product knowledge and experience will enable you to use your initiative. This means interpreting the client's wishes, and taking into account all the factors that affect the colouring process. Until you are qualified, however, always check first with your seniors.

Colours planned for special competitions can look unexpectedly different if the lighting has not been considered. In the salon the client's hair colour should be planned to fit the lighting in which the hair is to be seen. For example, the hair of a typist working most of the day under a blue fluorescent light will look greenish if it has been coloured (or left) yellow.

ACTIVITY
You need to be clear about the different kinds of colouring – bleaching, temporary colour, semi-permanent colour and permanent colour. Make a list of these; then, in each case, say:
- which parts of the hair are affected
- the normal processing time
- how long the colour is expected to last
- what are the effects on the hair structure.

ACTIVITY
Where possible, take colour photographs of successful colourings. Keep them in folders or your styling book.

TIPS
First make your own assessment of the colouring process you will use. Then check with your supervisor. Recognise the limits of your own authority.

Remember to note down every step of the colouring process applied to your client.

Successful colouring

Precautions

Certain precautions need to be taken when using colour or colouring products:

- Always carry out a skin test 24–48 hours before tinting. (This is recommended by most manufacturers.)
- Make other tests, for hair colour and incompatibles.
- Examine the hair and scalp for disease, inflammation or abnormalities. Avoid adverse skin reactions and the aggravation of existing problems.
- Choose colours wisely. Wrong colour applications will undermine your client's confidence.

JINGLES

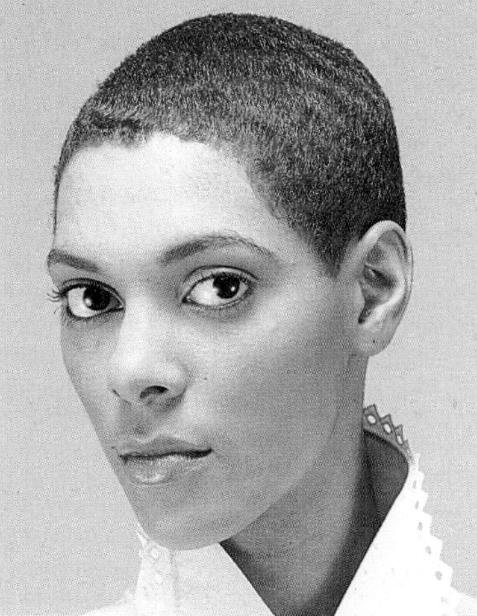

SPLINTERS

TIP
When colouring curly or wavy hair, take smaller sections for control. Comb sections as smooth as possible to ensure even coverage.

- Check applicators before use. Clean and replace all tools and materials after use. Any remaining tint could discolour light or blonde hair.
- Do not try to make temporary colourings do the work of permanent ones. Use products as intended by their manufacturers.
- Use reliable products, correctly stored and carefully maintained. Poor-quality products result in loss of time, effort and money – and clients.
- Measure quantities accurately. Never rely on guesswork.
- Avoid the use of metal containers, or hair discoloration may result.
- Avoid harsh rubbing and hair ruffling when pre-shampooing or removing colourants.
- Protect your hands and skin by using rubber or plastic gloves.
- Remove surplus water before tinting, to avoid dilution of colour.
- Keep hair colourants away from the eyes. Never use scalp hair colourants on eyebrows or eyelashes: special, non-irritant preparations are made for these.
- Check the numbers on the tubes or bottles with the numbers on their containers. It is easy to put a tube in the wrong box!
- Use correct dilutions of colourants and correct volume strengths of hydrogen peroxide.
- Constantly monitor and time the colour process.
- Work methodically and efficiently: this will produce confidence in the client, and good results.
- Remove stains from clothes immediately, using clean water. If allowed to remain they may become more difficult to remove.
- Ensure that all information is carefully recorded on the client's record card.

TIP

When applying colour to previously chemically processed hair (for example, relaxed, bleached or permed hair), allow for uneven porosity. Parts may readily absorb colour and other parts may resist it. Colour-fill to even out the absorption.

Colouring hair: problems, faults and corrections

Fault	*Possible causes*	*Correction*
Colour patchy or uneven	Insufficient coverage by tint Tint poorly applied Poor colour mixing Sections too large Overlapping (colour build-up in parts) Underprocessing (full colour did not develop) Spirit-based setting lotion used (some colour removed)	Spot-tint the light areas
Colour too light	Insufficient colour in chosen shade Peroxide strength too low for full colour development Peroxide strength too high, causing bleaching; insufficient colour oxidised Underprocessing Hair in poor condition/too porous to hold colour	Choose a darker shade Check peroxide strength Check peroxide strength Colour fill Recondition
Colour fades after two or three shampoos	Bleaching effects of sun Hair treated harshly (e.g. brushing, sand) Hair in poor condition/too porous Underprocessing	Recondition before next colour application Process correctly; do not repeatedly comb the colour through
Colour is too dark	Chosen shade too dark Overprocessing Hair in poor condition/too porous Hair coted with incompatible chemicals	Use chemical hair colour reducer or stripper (see page 200), as recommended by manufacturer
Colour is too red	Peroxide strength too high If prebleached, wrong neutralising colour chosen, or hair not bleached light enough Colour development incomplete	Apply matt or green colour to neutralise
Hair has discoloured	Hair in poor condition/too porous Undiluted tint repeatedly combed through hair Hair coated with incompatible chemicals If green, may result from blue ash on yellow base, or from metallic salt reaction If mauve, may be due to presence of incompatible chemicals	Correct green with contrasting colour (beware of producing dark brown) Correct mauve with contrasting colour, or remove with special colour reducer
Colour coverage is good except for white hairs	Hair resistant	Presoften, or use lighter shade with higher-strength peroxide
Hair is resistant to tint generally	Cuticle is closely packed Underprocessing Chosen colour unsuitable Materials poorly mixed or poorly applied	Presoften Choose colour carefully Time development correctly Check for correct mixing and application
Scalp irritation or skin reaction	Hair not washed clean, tint still present Peroxide strength too high Hair badly combed, tint poorly applied Client allergic to tint chemicals	Give no treatment, but wash hair thoroughly Advise client to visit her doctor Notify salon's insurance company

BLEACHING – PRINCIPLES

How bleaching works

A **bleach** is a chemical used to lighten the colour of hair. To be effective, bleach needs a ready supply of oxygen. In hairdressing the most common source of this oxygen is **hydrogen peroxide**, a colourless, oily liquid. In practice, peroxide is used in solution in water.

Hydrogen peroxide (H_2O_2) is an **oxidant**: it readily reacts to produce a lot of oxygen. Because it is so reactive, peroxide needs to be stabilised by other chemicals (such as sulphuric acid or phosphoric acid) and stored carefully. To allow the peroxide to work you need to counteract these stabilisers. This is done by mixing it with ammonium hydroxide or (for powder bleaches) sodium acetate or ammonium carbonate. These 'activate' the peroxide.

When you use bleach you mix it with peroxide diluted to the appropriate strength (see page 197). The bleach now begins to work. The hair swells and the cuticle lifts, allowing the bleach to penetrate the cortex. Here oxygen released from the peroxide reacts with the natural hair pigments, making them colourless.

Eumelanin is the pigment that makes the hair black or brown. As the melanin bleaches, the pheomelanin becomes more noticeable. This is the pigment that makes the hair red or yellow. As bleaching proceeds, the hair becomes lighter and lighter, changing through a range of shades – from dark brown, perhaps, through a warm red, to a very pale yellow. The shades and the final colour depend on the proportions of eumelanin and pheomelanin in the hair.

At some point, the hair stops getting lighter. Some very light brown and blonde hair easily reduces to light shades without **toning** (see page 197). With darker hair, though, the final colour after bleaching may still be somewhat yellow. To make it white or platinum, you will need to neutralise any remaining yellow with a toner, usually a violet one.

ANDREW COLLINGE (PHOTO: JOHN SWANNELL)

Bleached hair

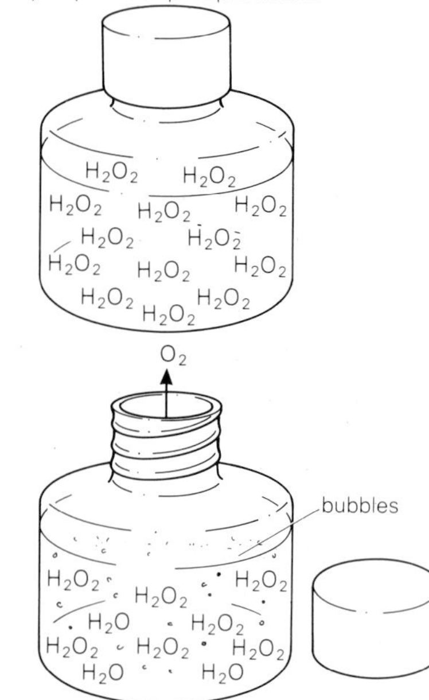

Stabilised hydrogen peroxide

Overbleaching

Bleaching is a precise process. Too much bleaching will destroy the structure of the hair. Before starting, always process a strand of hair to see how light it will become.

There are several reasons why **overbleaching** may occur:

- using peroxide solution that is too strong
- processing the hair for too long
- overlapping hair sections
- combing bleach through previously bleached hair
- bleaching hair that is in poor condition and too porous.

Additionally, if you use a strong peroxide solution and a dryer, the dry heat may increase the speed at which oxygen is produced. This can cause overheating and overprocessing of the hair, making it likely to break.

WELLA

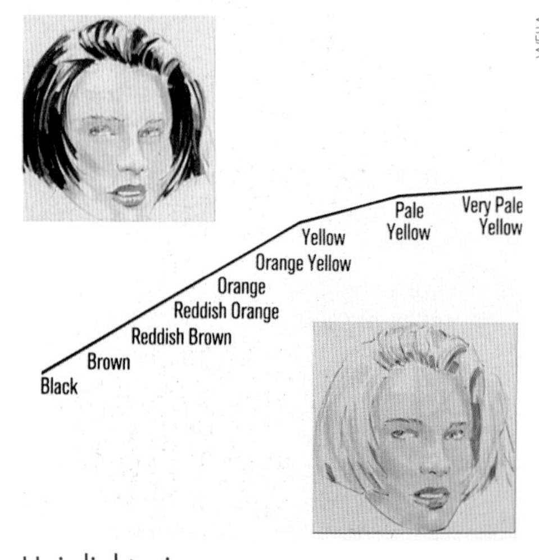

Hair lightening

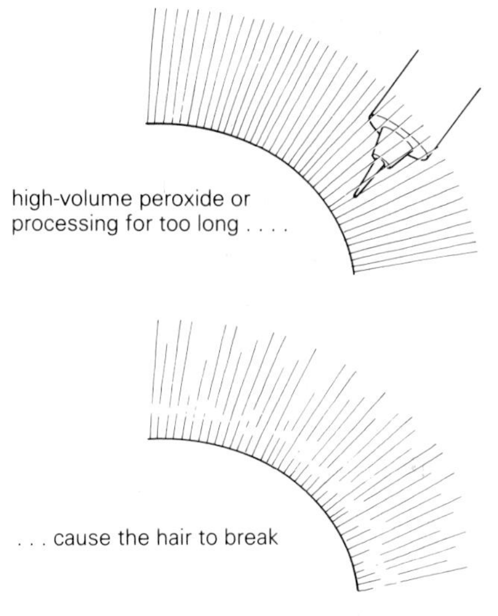

Overbleaching or lightening

Even if it doesn't actually break, overbleached hair may become spongy, very porous and unevenly coloured. Further colouring, toning or perming become difficult; so does hair management generally. When wet, overbleached hair may resemble chewing gum. The effects of blow-styling and other processes will not last. Even a little tension will break the hair. If the hair gets into this state, you must condition it before processing it chemically in any other way.

Natural bleaching

Sun, wind, sea, sand and chlorinated water affect hair in the same way as a peroxide bleach. Sun and wind dry and lift the cuticle. Brushing, if sand is present, roughens the cuticle. Hair that has previously been bleached is particularly prone to such effects. Hair liable to be exposed to strong **sunlight** is best kept covered; hair exposed to **sea** or **chlorinated water** should be rinsed as soon as possible.

HEALTH AND SAFETY
Be careful never to use too strong a solution of peroxide. A milder solution applied for longer is kinder to the hair than a stronger one applied for a shorter time.

HEALTH AND SAFETY
Strong peroxide solutions can easily burn skin and damage hair structure. Protect yourself and your client.

Choosing a bleach process

The client

When a client asks for a bleach process, discuss what she has in mind. You can bleach the whole head, part of the head, or the hair tips only. Or you can make streaks in the hair. Consult with your client as you would for a tint (see page 176).

Explain to your client that bleaching, like other chemical processes, affects the condition of the hair. Once you've bleached it your client will need to take special care of the hair at home and return to the salon regularly for further treatment. There will be additional costs in maintaining the effects of bleaching.

Bleaches

Bleaches are supplied as liquids, oils, creams, gels, emulsions, powders and pastes. Each of them needs to be mixed with an oxidant – usually hydrogen peroxide.

- **Liquid bleach (simple bleach)** is basically ammonium hydroxide (or 'ammonia'). 1 ml of ammonium hydroxide is mixed with 20–50 ml of hydrogen peroxide. The proportions needed depend on the shade required. If there is too much ammonium hydroxide, the bleach will redden the hair. This mixture lightens the hair by up to three shades.
- **Oil bleach** is usually a slightly thicker liquid, containing ammonium hydroxide and sulphonated oils or a thickener.

WELLA

Hair bleaching/lightening product

HEALTH AND SAFETY
Always follow the manufacturer's instructions for the application of chemicals and products. Check with your salon's COSHH list of potential hazards (see page 280) for the correct usage.

Several types are made. These too are mixed with hydrogen peroxide. They lighten by up to four shades.

- **Cream, emulsion and gel bleaches** are thicker substances which contain alkalis (usually ammonium hydroxide), thickening agents, **boosters** or **activators** (which provide additional oxygen), conditioners and other materials. They are mixed with hydrogen peroxide or some other oxidant, and can lighten the hair from dark to light or very light blonde.
- **Powder and paste bleaches** are made from magnesium carbonate and sodium carbonate. These too are mixed with oxidants, such as hydrogen peroxide, sodium bromate or sodium perborate. The mixture is a creamy paste – probably the thickest of bleach mixes. Ammonium hydroxide or ammonium carbonate is added. These bleaches can lighten hair from dark to very light.

Nowadays the cream or emulsion bleaches and the powder or paste bleaches are the most popular, as these offer a range of lightening.

JINGLES

Bleached hair

TIP

There is a simple relationship between volume strength and percentage strength:

10 volume = 3 per cent
20 volume = 6 per cent
30 volume = 9 per cent
40 volume = 12 per cent

Using hydrogen peroxide

Hydrogen peroxide may be purchased in the form of a liquid or a cream. It is supplied in different strengths, described in one of two ways. The **volume strength** refers to the amount of oxygen that the peroxide can produce. For example, 1 litre of '30 volume' peroxide would produce 30 litres of oxygen. The **percentage strength** records how much of the peroxide solution is peroxide, the rest being water. For instance, in 100 g of '9 per cent' or '9%' peroxide there would be 9 g of peroxide and 91 g of water. The strength can be measured with a **peroxometer**.

TIP

Keep hydrogen peroxide in a securely sealed bottle, in a dark cupboard, to retain its strength.

BLEACHING TECHNIQUE

Bleaching all of the hair (virgin hair)

Preparation

- Consult your client, examine her hair and scalp, analyse the condition of the hair and so on, as for tinting (page 176).
- Make a skin test 48 hours before you plan to bleach the hair, to check your client's reaction to any toner that may be used after bleaching.
- Make a test cutting to assess possible results. (You can do this when you make the skin test.)
- Make sure that your client is fully protected with appropriate gowns, towels, and so on.

ACTIVITY

Find out how samples of light hair (of the same natural shade) can be bleached using different strengths of bleach.

- If the hair is greasy or lacquered, shampoo it.
- Prepare the tools, equipment and materials so that they are at hand and ready for use.
- Use a barrier cream to protect the client's hairline.
- Wear protective gloves or barrier creams to protect your hands.

Sectioning

1. Section the head of hair into four. Subdivide it into smaller sections as work progresses. Liquid bleaches penetrate easily, so large sections may be taken (about 9–12 mm). For oil bleaches sections should be smaller (about 6–9 mm); for cream and paste bleaches smaller still (about 6 mm or less). As a general guide, use larger sections for thin bleaches and smaller sections for thick bleaches. Hair quantity, too, helps to determine the best section size.
2. Clip the hair well away from the section you are working on.
3. Work methodically, to avoid missing any part of the hair.

Application

Bleach application: short and long hair

1. Mix the bleach so that it is fresh – do not leave it standing.
2. Apply the bleach mixture to the darkest areas first. These are usually around the nape.

   With long hair (approximately 140 mm or more) apply bleach to the mid-lengths first. Leave about 25 mm of the hair tips, and 12–25 mm of the roots, without bleach. Allow the mid-lengths to begin to develop; then apply bleach to the hair tips. When these start developing, apply bleach to the roots. Completely cover all of the hair. This method takes account of the faster development at the roots, due to the heat of the head, and the porosity of the points.

   With short hair (approximately 140 mm or less) apply bleach to the mid-lengths and the ends together. Leave about 12–25 mm of the root ends without bleach. When the mid-lengths and points start to develop, apply bleach to the roots. This method allows for the hair points not being porous.
3. Avoid overlapping previously bleached or overporous areas. Overlapping could cause overbleaching.
4. Keep on applying bleach, working up to the crown area. Complete the application by working on the sides and the top front.
5. When application is complete, check around the hairline, particularly around the ear, for full coverage.
6. Make sure that hair is not packed down. This would prevent air circulating, and slow down processing.

ACTIVITY
Apply bleach to some hair samples of different colours. Leave to process for varying times. When developed, rinse the hair. Compare the different degrees of lightness produced by the different times of processing.

Processing

1. Remember that bleach starts developing – releasing oxygen – from the moment it is applied.
2. Carefully time the bleach process. Manufacturers give

approximate times, but the process is different for every client.

3 Make a hair strand colour test from time to time, to check development. Hair looks darker when wet and while you are removing bleach from the hair strand: it will look lighter when it dries.
4 If you let the bleach dry out, development will cease.
5 Don't apply heat. This would release the oxygen too fast, resulting in little bleach action.
6 As soon as the strand test indicates the level of lightness required, remove the bleach. Delay at this stage could result in overbleaching.

TIP

Steamers and accelerators supply moist heat and can halve processing times. They may also be used to even out development.

Bleach removal

1 Use tepid water only. Rinse the bleach from the hair. The scalp may be sensitive, so treat it gently.
2 The hair cuticle may be raised, roughened and easily tangled: take care.
3 When the hair has been thoroughly rinsed, you may apply special conditioners, antioxidants or acid balancers to normalise it.
4 Comb the hair correctly – from the points – before blow-styling, setting and shaping it.

Re-growth bleaching

After two or three weeks newly grown hair will become visible. This re-growth will require bleaching if the colour is to be even.

1 Refer to the client's record for an indication of the development time.
2 Apply the bleach to the re-growth only. Do not allow it to overlap previously bleached hair.
3 Allow processing to continue until the regrowth is bleached to the same level as the rest of the hair.
4 Remove the bleach carefully.
5 Use conditioners, balancers and the like to return the hair to as near normal as possible.

JOHN JENKINS FOR L'OREAL

Highlights

REGIS

Lowlights

Bleaching or colouring some of the hair

The following are some of the terms used to describe bleaching or colouring part or parts of the hair: slicing, tipping, blending, streaking, weaving, frosting, highlights, lowlights, polishing, brightening, shimmering and scrunching. **Highlighting** refers to shading parts of the hair with bleach or tint. **Lowlighting** refers to parts of the hair being tinted with subtle shades. These techniques can be used most effectively to enhance hair shape and style.

- It is usually more effective to lighten small pieces than large, chunky ones.

L'OREAL

Re-growth to be bleached

Bleach has been applied to the re-growth

Processing

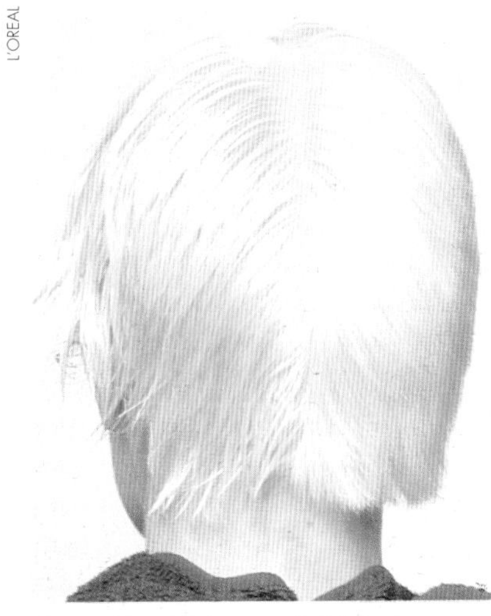

L'OREAL

Completed re-growth bleach

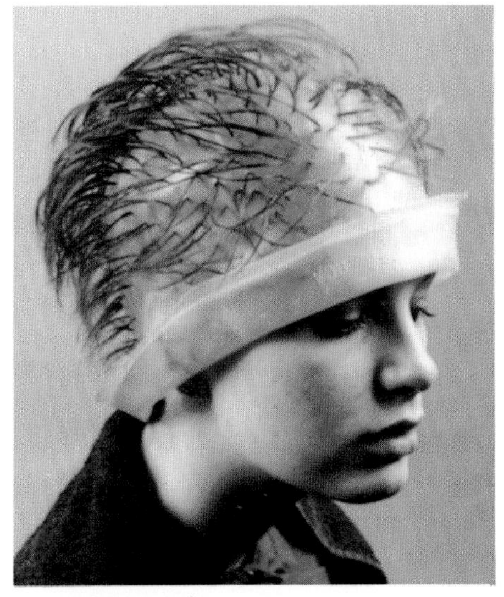

Hair streaking using a cap

- You can use the more prominent parts of the head to highlight a shape or dressing.
- You can use toners to produce varied coloured effects. These may blend with the client's natural colour, or contrast with it.

There are various methods of part bleaching or colouring. Especially popular is the use of streaks of lightened hair. Below are two methods of part bleaching.

Streaking

This can be done using a cap.

1. Pull sectioned strands of hair through holes in the plastic cap. (The holes must be carefully positioned.) The cap prevents the bleach running on to other parts of the hair.
2. Apply bleach, using a brush or an applicator.
3. Do not allow the hair to dry out. This would interfere with the bleaching process.
4. You may use a steamer or an accelerator.

Alternatively, you can use foil:

1. Section small groups of hair strands. Weave or zigzag them so that the hair does not form clumps of lightened or coloured areas.
2. Wrap the sections in aluminium foil, making small packets. The foil retains the heat produced by the oxidants, and the required degree of lightness is reached quickly.
3. Secure the root ends of the strands tightly, to prevent the bleach from running on to them.
4. No heat is necessary. (If you *did* apply heat, the bleach might 'bubble' and run, producing unwanted yellow patches on the roots.)

CLYNOL

Part bleaching using foil:
Application (*far left*)
Processing (*left*)

Bleach wraps or **packets** are now made. These are specially designed to cover small sections of hair, or woven hair sections. They seal the hair securely so that the bleach does not run.

There are many other techniques for lightening and bleaching, producing a wide range of effects. Manufacturers of bleach products often suggest methods of use.

L'OREAL

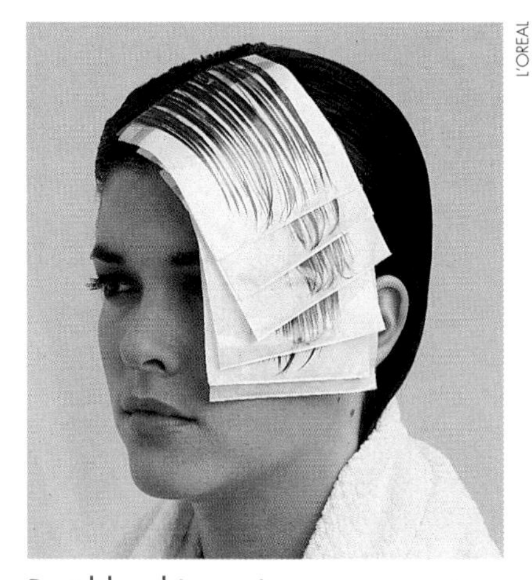

Part bleaching using wraps

Tinting back on bleached hair

It is easy to tint bleached hair back to a 'natural' colour: it is easier to darken than to lighten. As a woman ages, her skin and hair colour fade. Resist a client's requests for the 'natural' colour of twenty years ago – the result would probably be too dark. Two or three shades lighter is more likely to be suitable.

If the hair has porous parts, **colour filling** or **prepigmentation** is necessary. A base colour in the hair helps other colours to fix more evenly. Red is commonly used. Aim for a warm shade. Ashen, drab and matt shades may show slightly green. Cut off porous ends to allow a normal application.

Successful bleaching

Precautions

- Examine the hair and scalp. If there are cuts and abrasions or signs of disease, don't carry out chemical processing.
- Test the hair for condition, porosity and tensile strength.
- Apply bleach materials evenly, at the correct strength.
- Never overbleach by overlapping, or by processing too long.
- Never bleach hair coated with metallic or compound hair colourings.
- Do not allow the bleach to dry. If you do, oxidation will stop.
- If there is any yellow in the hair after bleaching, apply neutralising shades.
- On yellow hair, blue colourings or toners may produce green. Test first.

- Metallic tools and containers may be spoilt if you spill bleach on them. This in turn may cause hair discoloration. Use glass or china containers and measures.
- Never bleach hair that is in poor condition or porous. Overlapping in this case causes the hair to break.
- Never mix or apply lighteners or colourings without first checking the manufacturer's instructions.
- Thoroughly remove all traces of bleach materials.
- Recently bleached hair needs to be treated carefully.
- After bleaching, normalise the hair with special conditioners or acid rinses. (The oxidants in bleaches leave the hair somewhat alkaline.)
- As soon as the bleach has been removed, comb the hair. Comb from the points to the roots. Comb gently, avoiding unnecessary tension.
- To produce light shades, bleach in stages. When possible, use low peroxide strengths.

Hydrogen peroxide – diluting to the required strength

Strength of peroxide as supplied (%)	*Peroxide (parts)*		*Water (parts)*		*Strength of peroxide produced (%)*
30	3	+	2	→	18
30	2	+	3	→	12
30	3	+	7	→	9
30	1	+	4	→	6
30	1	+	9	→	3
18	2	+	1	→	12
18	1	+	1	→	9
18	1	+	2	→	6
18	1	+	5	→	3
12	3	+	1	→	9
12	1	+	1	→	6
12	1	+	3	→	3
9	2	+	1	→	6
9	1	+	2	→	3
6	1	+	1	→	3
3	1	+	2	→	1

TONING

Toning is the process of adding colour, usually to lightened hair. A variety of pastel shades may be used on very light bleached hair. The toner colour range includes beige, silver, rose and others. Toners give subtle effects. The lightest toners can only be used on the lightest bleached hair. If you use them on dark hair, the colour effect will be lost. Remember that colour added to colour always produces a slightly darker shade.

You can mix colours together to produce a wide range. Here are a few examples:

TIP

When tinting, bleaching or toning, always check the salon temperature. You must take this into consideration when monitoring and timing processes.

- red on green produces brown
- red on yellow produces orange
- blue on yellow produces green
- blue on red produces violet
- violet and orange may be used to neutralise green
- blue may be used to neutralise orange
- violet may be used to neutralise yellow.

The final colour depends both on the depth of the starting hair colour, and on the shades of toners.

Toners may be temporary, semi-permanent or permanent colourings in a dilute form. There are also specially made toners for use on lightened hair. These are used like permanent colourings.

JOHN CARNE FOR L'OREAL

Toned hair

Application and processing

The mixing of toners depends on the type used. Those mixed with peroxide need low strengths only. If you use higher strengths you may cause patchy results and porous hair.

Toners are applied in the same way as permanent colourings. Some are poured on to the hair and lightly massaged. All need to be evenly applied, taking into account any porous areas.

Development and processing depends on the product used. Aniline-derivative toners require 20–45 minutes. Other toners require several applications – colour is only gradually built up in the hair.

HEALTH AND SAFETY
Always make skin tests before applying toners.

TERENCE RENATI

Coloured hair

Toning: problems, faults and corrections

Fault	*Possible causes*	*Correction*
Uneven colour	Poor application Section too large Incorrect mixing	Spot bleach areas as necessary Recolour Prepare a new bleach mixture, combining the ingredients slowly and thoroughly
Dark ends	Under- or overbleached ends Toner too dark Toner overprocessed Remains of dark tint	Rebleach Remove; use lightener Time accurately Remove and tone
Too yellow	Underbleached Base too dark Wrong toner used Wrong bleach	Bleach lighter Try stronger bleach Use violet Use a different bleach (*not* an oil bleach)
Too red	Underbleached Too much alkali Wrong toner used	Rebleach Use blue bleach (*not* an oil bleach) Use green, matt or olive

Fault	*Possible causes*	*Correction*
Dark roots or patches	Poor bleach application	Rebleach, evenly
	Toner too dark	Remove; use lightener
Roots not coloured	Underbleached	Bleach again
	Undertimed	Apply full timing
	'Drippy' toner	Apply cream (*not* liquid)
	Unclean or coated	Clear and re-apply
Colour fade	Overporous	Correct the condition
	Harsh treatment	Advise on hair care
	Exposure	Keep hair covered
	Overprocessed	Comb through only with diluted colour
Hair breakage	Overprocessed	Correct the condition
	Incompatibles	Test
	Harsh treatment	Advise on hair care
	Sleeping in rollers	Demonstrate the effects
Discoloration	Underprocessed	Correct development
	Exposure	Condition hair and cover it
	Home treatments	Test and advise
Green tones	Incompatibles	Test
	Blue on yellow	Use warm or red shades
	Too blue ash	Use violet
Too orange	Overprocessed	Apply blue/ash
	Pigment lacking	Add blue pigment
Too yellow	Underprocessed	Add violet
Hair tangled	Overbleached	Use antioxidants
	Poor washing	Use correct movements
	Over-rubbing	Use gentle actions
	Backcombing	Reduce and demonstrate
Inflammation	Skin reaction	Seek doctor's advice
	Torn scalp	Seek doctor's advice
	Disease	Seek doctor's advice
Irritation	Skin reaction	Seek doctor's advice
	Harsh treatment	Seek doctor's advice
	Disease	Seek doctor's advice
Colour not taking	Overporous	Recondition
	Poor condition	Recondition
	Pigment lacking	Prepigment
	Lacquer build-up	Remove excess
Colour build-up	Overporous	Recondition
	Poor condition	Recondition
Hair 'stretchy'	Overprocessed	Treat carefully
	Very porous	Correct the condition
	Very poor condition	Correct the condition
Hair breaking	Overprocessed	Treat carefully
	Overlapping	Correct the condition; restructure
	Combing through too much	Always dilute the tint
	Incompatibles	Test

DECOLOURING

Decolouring is the removal of colour from the hair – specifically, the removal of synthetic colourings using special **colour reducers** or **strippers**.

- Oxidation tints may be removed by **reducing agents**. (Sodium bisulphite and sodium formaldehyde sulphoxylate are two examples.) Most manufacturers make special colour reducers for their products. Whenever possible, use colour stripper of the same make as the colourant.
- Avoid using oxidants. These tend to help the colour to penetrate, rather than remove it.
- Compound henna, vegetable and mineral dyes can only be removed by special colour reducers. Don't use hydrogen peroxide: it is incompatible.
- Remove temporary and semi-permanent colourings by repeated washing and the application of spirit.

HEALTH AND SAFETY

Take care to follow the manufacturer's instructions when using decolourants. Never mix products – always use decolourant of the same make as the colour that is to be removed.

Application and processing

To remove oxidation dyes and 'para' aniline-derivative dyes from the hair:

1. Wash and dry the hair.
2. Mix the correct colour remover – check the instructions.
3. Apply decolourant to the areas to be lightened. Use a brush or a special dispenser.
4. Allow the reducer to act, preferably uncovered and without heat. Processing usually takes 10–30 minutes. With some products, processing can be speeded by covering the hair with a plastic cap and placing it under a warm dryer, steamer or accelerator. Follow the manufacturer's instructions.
5. When developed, remove excess chemicals by washing. Normalise the hair. (If you don't do this thoroughly, you will have to repeat the decolouring.)
6. When the decolouring process is complete, make a **'peroxide' test**. This is to check that no synthetic pigment remains. Any remaining synthetic colour will oxidise later and darken again in two or three days. The 'peroxide' test shows whether the decolouring process has been effective. If the hair darkens after testing, remove all chemicals from the test, then re-apply the decolourant. It may take several applications to strip all of the unwanted colour.

Recolouring after decolouring varies according to the products used. In general, do not use any chemical process immediately after decolouring. With some products, however, immediate recolouring is recommended. Perming may be safely carried out, preferably at least a week after decolouring. Where possible perming should be applied *before* decolouring. Consider the lightening action of some neutralisers.

ASSIGNMENTS: COLOURING HAIR

A practical activity

Collect together all the information available on colouring hair from your varied sources, including wholesalers and manufacturers. Try out on blocks or models the various techniques of hair colouring. Satisfy yourself that you are able to follow the instructions given by your trainer, and by the manufacturer. Knowledge of your test results, the effects of synthetic colour on natural colours, the processes of tinting and bleaching, will be invaluable to you. Carefully record them for your file. Note the textures of the hair tested, the time it took, the resultant colour and any problems that arose. Then answer these questions:

1. What is colour? What is 'natural' hair and skin colour?
2. List the different terms that apply to hair colourings, and their meanings.
3. Outline the different hair colouring processes and the main differences between them.
4. List the range of available colourants, and the main differences between them.
5. Outline the chemical effects of colourants on the hair structure.
6. How do you retain information on hair colouring services?
7. List the problems that might arise and how you would deal with them.
8. List the items of information required for your assessment.

For you to find out

Investigate your sources of information regarding natural and synthetic hair colouring cosmetics. Consider too the fields of make-up, nail care and clothes design, as well as the balance between colours worn and various forms of lighting in the different situations. Then answer the following questions:

1. Why it is important to consider the colours your client wears? What do you consider to be suitable colours?
2. How do the colours of clothes interact with hair colour under different forms of lighting?
3. Collect sample colours and lay them out in different arrangements. Try to include different colour combinations of hair, clothes and accessories.
4. List the hair colours used for colour toning.
5. List the tests used for hair colouring, bleaching and toning.
6. List the possible causes, faults and problems that could arise when colouring, bleaching and toning, and how to resolve them. Describe future action that should be taken.
7. List the precautions to be taken when colouring hair.
8. Define polymerisation, and describe the process.

A case study

Imagine that a client is requesting an unsuitable hair colour.

With the help of your colleagues, prepare yourself for the day when this happens to you. Simulate the possible occurrence in advance by working through the following sequence:

1. Consider your client's request. Give your reasons for thinking that it is unsuitable.
2. Offer a suitable alternative. Justify your reasons for recommending this course of action.
3. List the questions you would ask the client.
4. Describe what requires to be done, and agree with the client exactly what is to be done.
5. Describe the various colouring/bleaching/toning processes and their likely effects.
6. Explore the need for after-care. Explain what the client is required to do and determine whether it is practicable.
7. List the important influencing factors.
8. Discuss recolouring and regrowth.
9. Outline the needs for different hair textures and conditions, and varying hair lengths.
10. Explain the various methods of part colouring/bleaching/toning.
11. Summarise the different times required for different colouring processes, and the costs to your client.

PREPARING FOR ASSESSMENT

In preparing for assessment on colouring hair the following checklist may be helpful. Check that you have covered and now fully understand these items:

- assessing the state of your client's hair and scalp
- selecting and applying relevant hair and skin tests
- determining the previous treatments that your client's hair has received
- selecting suitable colours and colourants
- applying colourants as intended by their makers
- monitoring, processing and timing developments of processes
- effectively isolating hair not to be coloured
- effectively removing colourants
- applying suitable conditioners and antioxidants
- dealing with problems that might arise
- accurately recording all details of applied processes.

When you are ready for assessment, talk to your trainer and arrange a suitable time.

CHAPTER 9

Barbering

SCWARZKOPF

INTRODUCTION

Barbering is the art of cutting and shaping hair. The word 'barber' derives from the Latin word *barba*, meaning beard. Nowadays the word refers to someone skilled in the art of cutting and shaping hair and beards, including shaving and other treatments. In short, the term 'barbering' applies to all the work carried out by men's hairdressers – or gents' hairdressers, or tonsorial artists – all names for those we now know as men's hair stylists or simply barbers.

Over the years, some people have tried to merge women's and men's hairdressing. The word 'unisex' often appeared on salon signs. But the division between the work covered by women's and men's hairdressers remains. Much of the work is common to both but many still wish the two sides to be treated differently. The choice is with each individual. You will be able to study both women's and men's hairdressing, and to specialise in one or the other, or to offer both, as you think fit.

The topics discussed in this chapter include:

- cutting facial hair
- facial hair fashions
- cutting men's hair
- cutting techniques
- wet and dry cutting
- cutting with or without partings
- layering
- fringes
- method variations.

CUTTING FACIAL HAIR

CLIENT CONSULTATION

TIP
When cutting a client's beard, consider the basic shape of his head and his hairstyle.

Re-read Chapter 2, 'Client care', especially pages 14–19, much of which applies to barbering work.

- Consult and communicate with the client to assess his requests, wishes, requirements or needs.

Examples of beard shapes

- Talk with him about the growing of a beard, a moustache or sideburns, their maintenance and their suitability.
- Explain the requirements of dealing with the shaping of facial hair.
- Examine any existing beard carefully and note its structure (whether it is coarse or fine, curly or straight, dense or sparse).
- Note the existing hairstyle. Make sure that the hair of the head and face complement each other in their balance, shape and so on.
- Consider a beard with or without a moustache, or retaining the moustache only.
- Discuss the sideburns (sideboards or side whiskers), which may be part of the facial or the head hair, or a blend between both.
- Confirm what is to be done, and carry out the work agreed.

Preparation

- Cover and protect all your client's clothes.
- Make sure that your client is sitting comfortably, and that his head is positioned so that the chin and beard area can be closely examined, and worked on.

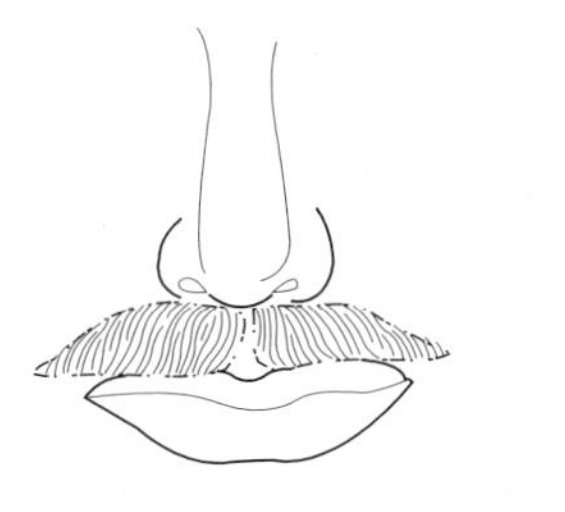
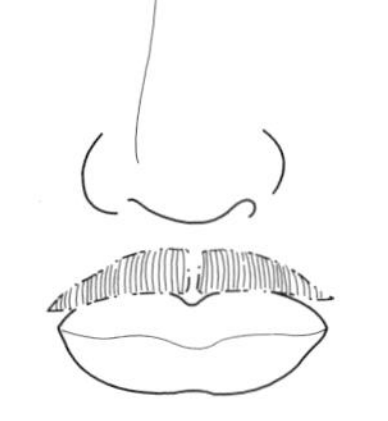

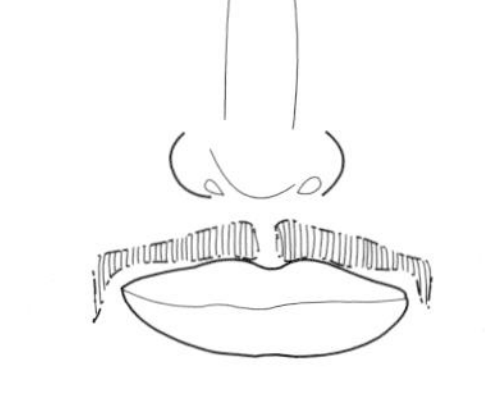

Examples of moustache shapes

- Protect your client's eyes by covering with tissue or pads of cottonwool. Hair, particularly coarse hair, is likely to fly in all directions when cut, and can be potentially dangerous.
- If your client's beard is long and unruly, untangle it by careful combing.
- Confirm the beard shape to be styled. Be careful with named styles: a name may mean quite different things to you and your client.
- Use pictures (photographs or sketches) to confirm styles and shapes.

Interpretation of your client's wishes

This requires your considered advice, guidance and initiative. You must take all the relevant factors into account.

TOOLS

The tools used for cutting beards and moustaches are usually lighter and smaller than those used for cutting the hair of the head, whether women's or men's. Some hairdressers find smaller scissors more accurate and precise for the delicate shapes and patterns required. Clippers, particularly electric clippers, razors and small combs and brushes are all commonly used. It may be necessary to shave part of the face to emphasise some beard and/or moustache styles.

CUTTING TECHNIQUE

The following are among the most commonly used techniques for cutting facial hair.

- **Scissor over comb** – lifting the hair sections and cutting the hair straight across. This technique is often used to attain graduation. When cutting beard and moustache, only very small amounts of hair need to be lifted by the fine end of a comb. Use the tips of the scissors, and always angle them to avoid cutting the lower lip.

- **Clipper over comb** is a common alternative. This is particularly useful on fuller beards with thicker hair. Either graduation or level lengths can be attained with this technique. Smaller clippers, which are more precise and adaptable, are generally more successful than large ones.

- **Razoring** is often carried out with open razors with unguarded blades. But safety razors, with a protective guard, and a variety of electric razors are both useful and common.
- **Freehand** scissoring – removing hairs with scissor tips by taking small, slicing movements.
- **Combing** and **brushing**, using a variety of combs and brushes, is employed to deal with the texture and density of hair. Small neckbrushes are used to keep the face free of loose hair cuttings, and small beard brushes to direct, control and shape. Mirrors are also required, and are used to reassure your client as work progresses.

Outlines

Where part of the face is covered by hair it may be necessary to outline the shape. This may be achieved by cutting the hair surrounding it with close-cutting clippers, or removing the hair completely by shaving; a dry electric shaver can be used. This emphasises the beard shape. Patterns and movements of shaving (see Chapter 10) can be applied, but smaller, lighter and carefully angled movements are usually required.

TIP

Support the scissors with your forefinger to ensure accuracy, precision and safety.

FACTORS INFLUENCING THE CHOICE OF STYLE

As with styling head hair of both men and women, it is important to determine the most suitable beard, moustache or sideburn shape to work to. The following are some of the critical factors to consider:

- the distribution of the facial hair
- the density (thickness) of the facial hair: sparse hair does not lend itself to thick, full beards, while dense growth patterns allow many shapes
- the hairstyle and the beard shape: ideally they should be balanced
- the shape and size of the face in relation to facial hair forms: a large face can take a fuller moustache, a smaller face can take a thinner, smaller one
- the size of the upper lip: wide lips will take a variety of shapes, small ones can only take thin, small designs
- a small nose can be accentuated by a tiny moustache and a compact beard
- hair growth patterns, such as hair whorls – these need to be followed rather than ignored; it is better to 'go with the flow' than against it
- facial features, such as the size and position of the ears, or whether spectacles are worn
- small scars, blemishes, defects or disfigurements: these should, wherever possible, be made less noticeable
- continuity of line, centralising the shapes, determining how the shapes 'look'.

TIP
Consider your client's reasons for wearing facial hair before you begin to cut.

FACIAL HAIR FASHIONS

Throughout the years fashions in beards, moustaches and side hair, as with hairstyles, costumes and accessories, have varied. Some reliably re-appear time and time again. The full set – a full beard without shaven parts – has often proved popular. The full sideburns sported by some individuals have a degree of popularity too. And there are as many beard shapes as there are men to wear them.

There are social and religious reasons for the wearing of facial hair, as well as personal ones. Small scars and disfigurements can be easily hidden under a beard. In times of war many servicemen had their beards and head hair completely removed, mainly for convenience and for hygienic reasons. Between the wars a wide variety of fashions for all facial and head styles re-appeared, ranging between the very long and the very short. Since the introduction of the safety razor, and subsequently that of a variety of very efficient electric razors, many men have chosen to remain cleanshaven, wearing neither beard nor moustache.

CUTTING A BEARD

TIP
Use hand or electric clippers, or special liners, for outlining shapes.

1. Having decided with your client what needs to be done and what shape the beard is to be, you can arrange protective towels, tissues and eyepads.
2. If not already done, comb the beard thoroughly, disentangling where necessary.
3. Begin by removing the straggling hairs at and above the neck and collar line. Avoid cutting too high at this stage. Use the scissor over comb technique, or clippers.
4. Then, working on your client's right side, begin to cut the hair using the scissor over comb technique. Most beards graduate to a point at the chin, so the hair that is cut shortest should be at the sides of the face. If there are to be no exaggerated sideburns, they will be part of the head hair

Cutting a beard:
(a) Before

(b) Removing hair with clippers

(c) Finishing with fine clippers

(d) Lining moustache with clippers

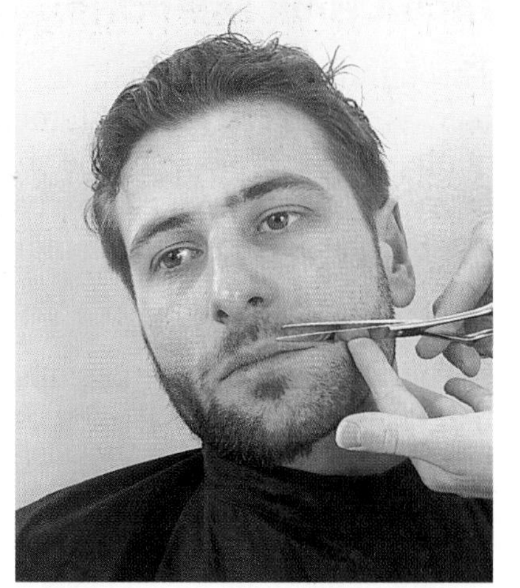
(e) Lining moustache with scissors

(f) One side completed

shape, and you should either shape them before you begin to cut the beard, or shape them at this stage.

5 Graduate towards the chin, leaving the hair slightly longer than required.
6 Repeat this on your client's left side, making sure that the centre of the beard aligns with the nose and the middle of the upper lip.
7 The centre of the beard can then be trimmed and shaped as required. Graduated, continuous lines are usually the most acceptable. A line that continues into the sideburns and hairstyle looks attractive, and is more likely to be suitable.
8 Taking small cuts rather than large, gradually building up the shape, will be more successful.
9 The moustache is usually cut last. Outline the shape required. Cut along the upper lip with carefully guided scissor tip movements or with the clippers.
10 With the fine end of the comb, commence with small cutting movements centrally. Where the comb cannot reach continue cutting freehand. Take slicing cuts rather than pincerlike movements with the scissor points.
11 Graduate the hair down and along as dictated by the moustache shape required.
12 Areas around the beard and moustache may require shaving (see Chapter 10).
13 It may be necessary to graduate the shaving line and blend it with the skin.
14 Allow your client to see your completed work, and discuss any aftercare that may be required.
15 To keep the beard and moustache looking smart, it will be necessary to retrim periodically. A salon appointment can be made for this, or the client may feel able to do it himself, at home. This partly depends on how difficult the shape may be to deal with, and how quickly your client's hair grows.

HEALTH AND SAFETY

Always protect your client's eyes from flying hairs. Ensure that your own are kept safe too: use goggles.

TIP

Your guides to cutting a beard (ears, for instance) must be symmetrically placed.

ASSIGNMENTS: CUTTING FACIAL HAIR

A practical activity

Collect together information on beards, with or without moustaches, and sideburns. With your colleagues simulate situations that you may encounter when dealing with clients. Remember to make clear notes and retain them for your folder. Consider the following:

1. Discuss with your clients the reasons for wearing beards.
2. List the questions you need to ask.
3. List the questions that your client might ask you, and how you would answer them.
4. Outline the selection of a suitable beard style for your client.
5. Consider the different beard hair textures – tight curly, wavy, straight – and the different lengths.
6. List the important factors influencing the selection of a style.
7. Discuss how the beard should be maintained, including how often it requires cutting.
8. Use photography, cine film or video taping.
9. Consider the tools to be used and list the reasons for using them.
10. List the precautions to be taken.
11. Describe the problems that may arise, and how you would deal with them.
12. List the evidence that you will require for assessments.

For you to find out

Investigate the traditional patterns of beards, moustaches and sideburns, and the variety of shapes and styles that exist. Try to get illustrations of them. Use libraries, history books and museums, in addition to trade journals past and present. Record your sources of information and retain in your folder. Include your answers to these questions:

1. How do you describe the shapes of beards, moustaches and sideburns with your clients? Do you use sketches, diagrams and photos?
2. Describe the tools and equipment that you might use. How would you discuss these with your client?
3. False beards are often made in boardwork. How would you use these when discussing beard shapes with clients?
4. Compare the effects of the beard shape alone, with or without a moustache, with or without sideburns, and how it combines with the hairstyle (which is usually cut first).
5. How do you protect your client and yourself from short, sharp, flying hairs? List the precautions to be taken.
6. Consider the wearing of moustaches or sideburns without a beard. Why might a client choose a style of this kind?
7. List the cutting techniques you would use for facial hair. Include your reasons for using them.

A case study

Your client is requesting information and advice on growing a suitable beard. His head hair is cut very short. How would you deal with this? Simulate this situation with your colleagues. Make notes, and retain them for your folder. Consider these points:

1. Discuss the need for an overall effect.
2. List the questions that need to be put regarding suitability of hairstyle before determining what beard, moustache and sideburns would be required.
3. Consider the time factor required for growing the head hair and beard.
4. Determine the hair growth patterns, and how this will affect the hair and face style.
5. Consider how face shapes affect suitability of head and facial hairstyles. What factors should be considered?
6. Outline the after-care required and the cost and time needed for carrying out the work required.
7. Carefully record the stages of meeting this client's requests.
8. If on return the client expresses dissatisfaction at the results achieved to date, what would you say? List the points that you would make.

PREPARING FOR ASSESSMENT

In preparing for assessment on cutting facial hair the following checklist may be helpful. Check that you have covered and fully understood these items:

- discussing clients' requests
- consulting and advising clients
- agreeing with clients a suitable shape and style
- determining hair quality, quantity, density, texture and growth patterns
- selecting correct tools and combination of techniques
- advising on growing beards, moustaches and sideburns
- cutting beards, moustaches and sideburns
- adapting styles to facial shapes
- giving the client confidence by communicating throughout the service
- dealing with problems as they arise
- precise recording of work carried out
- achieving client satisfaction
- discussing after-care and maintenance required.

When you are ready for assessment, talk to your trainer and arrange a suitable time.

KERRY HAYDEN FOR WELLA

CUTTING MEN'S HAIR

INTRODUCTION

Short layered looks, with different necklines, are worn by most men and many women. To achieve such a look, precise movements and accurate cutting angles are required. With the shorter styles the hair is too short to hide mistakes, so great care is necessary. Dressing is minimal and the styles rely on sharp definition and perfection of detail.

There are subtle differences between women's and men's styles. This is largely dictated by the differences in hair distribution, neckline patterns, facial hair and other characteristics. Pretty, fussy styles are not required by most men, while the decidedly shorter men's styles are generally not required by women (although fashion may dictate otherwise). Masculine and feminine looks are areas of study which, for those of you who intend to become expert, cannot ignore. Moreover, client consultation may reveal special considerations which need to be applied to your cutting.

TIP

Read Chapter 5, 'Cutting and styling hair', before going further.

PREPARATION

Prepare your client so that he will be comfortable and well protected throughout the cutting process (see page 84). Cutting short layered styles will involve a lot of small, sharp, spiky hairs which need to be kept constantly cleared. Be careful that you do not expose yourself to flying hairs: position yourself so that your face is not in line.

Decide, with the help of your client, what needs to be done and which techniques you are going to use, and in particular whether you will cut the hair wet or dry.

Examination of hair and scalp

While you are making your initial examination of your client's hair and scalp, note the texture of the hair. If it is coarse and tightly curled, you will need stronger combs to stretch the hair out from the hair before cutting, and firmer movements will need to be applied. The density of the hair is important: if it is abundant, styles with varied hair length are possible. Sparse hair, particularly if it is fine, requires a great deal of attention and expertise. If finely textured hair has to cover sparse areas of the head, it will have to be longer than hair of coarser texture. The amount, type and distribution pattern of hair are all important too. Younger men may have distinctly higher forehead hairlines than women of similar age. Thinning crowns and decreasing density of

ACTIVITY

Arrange a visit to a local art and design studio. Make careful notes of anything you see that will help you in styling hair.

hair marks many male patterns, though these are not usually seen in women until much later in life. Take this into consideration when designing and cutting hairstyles specifically for men and women. Hair growth, at a rate of about 12 mm each month, is more noticeable with shorter layered styles. To keep them tidy, regular trimming is essential.

INTERPRETATION OF YOUR CLIENT'S WISHES

Understanding the wishes and requirements of your clients is important. Creatively interpreting their needs and wants is a major part of hairstyle design. Clients of different age groups, careers, lifestyles and social positions require separate consideration. Factors such as practicality, suitability and the client's ability to cope with his hair are matters which you must not overlook. The final designs will be influenced by other considerations too – the amount of hair, its distribution, its texture and so forth. Unless all these are taken into account mistakes, and eventually a dissatisfied client, can be expected. By carefully and creatively interpreting your client's requirements from the beginning, you will be able to achieve professional results.

Short layered hairstyles can range from skin-cropped heads with 'coconut' crown shapes and forms to full, soft 'uncut' looks which are perhaps more acceptable to a greater proportion of your clients. A whole range of styling effects can be produced, from the once-traditional 'short back and sides' to longer, natural, more sculptured layered shapes. Named styles are fashionable from time to time. Some of these names, such as the various crew cuts, the 'DA' or duck-tailed shapes, have passed into the general vocabulary. Always make sure exactly what your client means if he names a style: it may be completely different from your idea of that style! Discuss with your client in detail what shape he wants, and apply it as agreed.

TIP

The principles of hairstyle design apply equally to men's and women's styling.

VIDAL SASSOON

ACTIVITY
With your colleagues, take turns at acting as a stylist, or a client, and go through the consultation process for a new cut hairstyle. Notice how different stylists adopt different approaches.

TIP
Remember that heavy fringes used with the intention of hiding bald areas can do the opposite and make them more obvious. Careful angling and placing of the hair in line with the style is usually more effective.

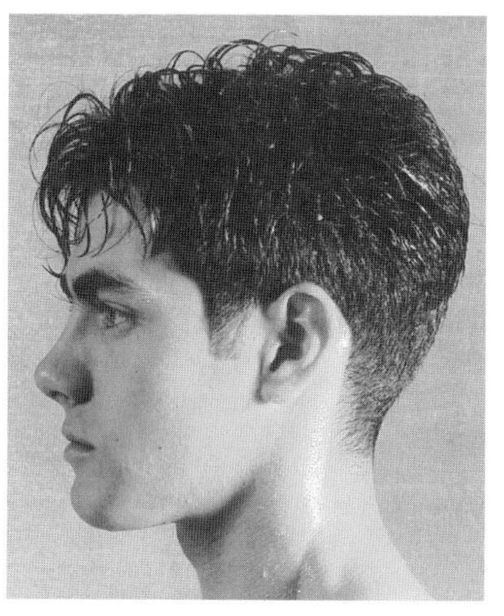

JOHN PHELPS

Outlines

Many short, layered cuts are graduated at the sides and nape (clipper contoured). The necklines, the front hairlines and the sides are emphasised and require careful attention.

Natural necklines in men are usually less well defined than in women and need to be outlined. Women generally have softer, natural napelines which do not usually need defining. The more natural the napeline, the softer and less severe will be the look. The deeper are the cuts made into the hairline, the harsher and starker the look becomes.

The napeline can be of a variety of shapes – V-shaped, tapered, round, square and so forth. These can be achieved by shaping with the electric clippers, or shaving the outlines. Traditionally shaving was carried out with open-bladed razors. Now electric shavers or safety razors can be used. Often outlining is done with the points of the scissors. Softer, graduated lines are to be preferred to blocky, blunt effects. The precise outline must be determined by the style required.

The shaping of front hair into a **fringe** (see page 220) can produce various acceptable effects on the chosen style. In many men, the front hairline recedes to some extent, however, due to male pattern baldness. This affects the choice and range of fringe shape. Think carefully about this before cutting the hair.

In men, the side hairlines, sideburns or sideboards bridge the hairstyle and beard shape. These need to fit, and care must be taken in shaping them. Lining the hair above the ears and along the sides of the nape is usually carried out with the scissor points or with inverted clippers. (In women there is little if any hair below the cheek bone at the side of the face. Recent styles have required shaping what little hair there is into points, and other forms.)

ACTIVITY
When you compile your men's style book, include notes on style design. Use pictures (rough sketches, detailed drawings or photographs), as appropriate. You may wish to use your book when consulting with clients, so consider the format carefully.

Cutting with or without partings

Partings in a hairstyle can be used to produce a variety of effects. Central partings divide the hair mass and can help to make a heavy head of hair look 'tamer'. If the hair is distributed evenly and symmetrically, it becomes more manageable. Side partings can be used to divert attention from a prominent point, such as a large nose or unlevel ears; they can carry the eye of the viewer away from the unwanted 'look'. Changing hair fashions affect the way in which partings are used, and many styles or dressing have no partings at all. Before attempting to cut, experiment by combing the hair to lie in different directions. Part the hair in several ways, diagonally, short or long, straight or angled. Longer lengths of hair or fuller effects may be required at the sides.

Ears

The ears, which in some people are not placed symmetrically, may be large or small, or irregular in shape. They may protrude from the head too noticeably and need to be considered, particularly when changing to a shorter hairstyle.

At this point you should also note whether your client uses spectacles or a hearing aid, and take these into your deliberations.

Between you and your client you will be able to decide exactly what look is required, and you will then have a basis on which to decide how the work is to be carried out.

Hair type

If your client's hair is very curly, do remember that it will coil back after stretching and cutting. Wavy hair, if cut too close to the wave crest, can be awkward to dress since it will tend to spring out from the head. Very fine straight hair will easily show cutting marks or unwanted lines if the sections are not divided and sectioned accurately, of if too large sections are taken. Tapering and thinning will encourage any tendency for the hair to curl at the ends, while clubbing will decrease that tendency. Feathering and texturising can produce extra lift and bounce.

Suitability and satisfaction

As you will by now understand, the main aim of every hairdressing service is that the client feels satisfied with the results when he or she leaves the salon. In men's cutting and styling, the central aim is to fashion shapes that are suitable to the individual client: that is, that he will find them acceptable and pleasing.

The client will be helped to feel safe, comfortable and satisfied if you are thoughtful and considerate in every aspect of client care. Indeed, that must be built into your activities in the salon (see also page 84).

Wet and dry cutting

If the hair is dirty, then for hygienic reasons it must be washed before you cut it. Wet hair may be preferred for blow-shaping and finishing, but on wet hair some scissor tapering movements have to be restricted. Clean, dry hair should not be cut with a razor because of the discomfort to your client and the tearing and dragging of the hair.

If you wish to dry-cut, then wash and dry the hair first. Explain this to your client so that he can express his wishes and needs.

Remember, wet hair stretches by anything from a third to half its length. Allow for this if you cut stretched hair, so that when it reverts back to the original length it is not too short.

CUTTING TECHNIQUES

TIP

Competent handling of tools achieves the most precise results.

As well as the techniques featured on pages 94–8, you may find the following particularly helpful when you are dealing with short layered styles.

Club-cutting or **clubbing** is more often required for shorter styles. Clubbing can be done 'over the comb'; continuous clubbing over the comb with scissors is often used for short graduations, such as that at the nape or the lower sides, or shingling. With an 'over the fingers' technique the hair is combed out, transferred to the fingers, and then cut straight across. Angles are determined by the amount of graduation required and the size of the section taken.

Clubbing over fingers

In another technique that may be helpful and effective, you lift a small section of hair with the scissors, transfer it to the comb, and then cut across.

Thinning techniques, using special thinning scissors with serrated blades, may be required but you must take great care with short hair. The hair could become spiky, particularly when it begins to grow again.

Razoring, on wet hair, may be easier than scissor tapering. Take short, gentle strokes with the razor, to ensure evenness.

Clippering over comb or fingers is ideal for clubbing level lengths on short styles. It can also be used on its own; it is an invaluable technique for graduation. Clippers are made in a range of sizes for different purposes, and are numbered accordingly (see table).

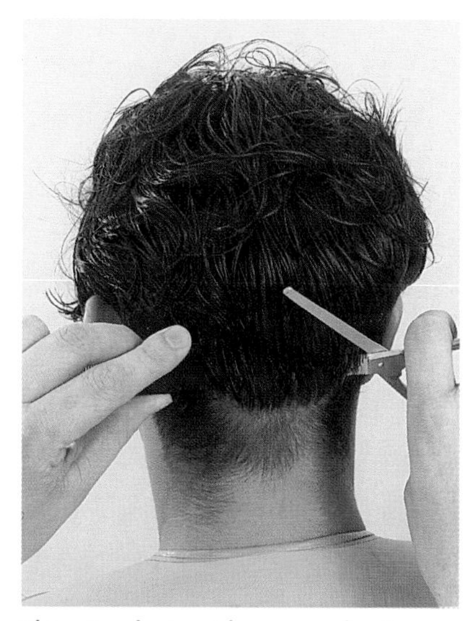

Thinning hair with serrated scissors

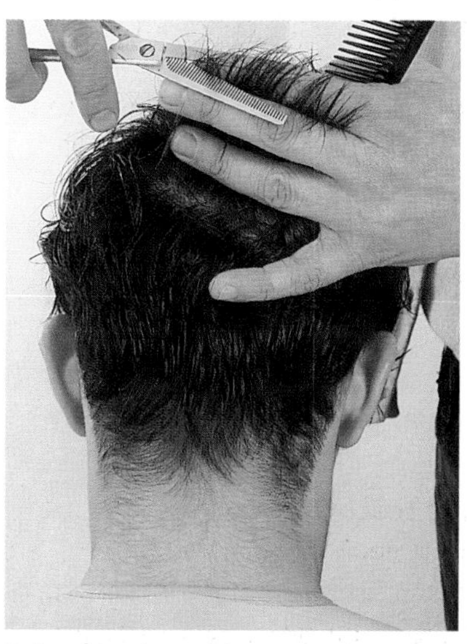

Point thinning with serrated scissors

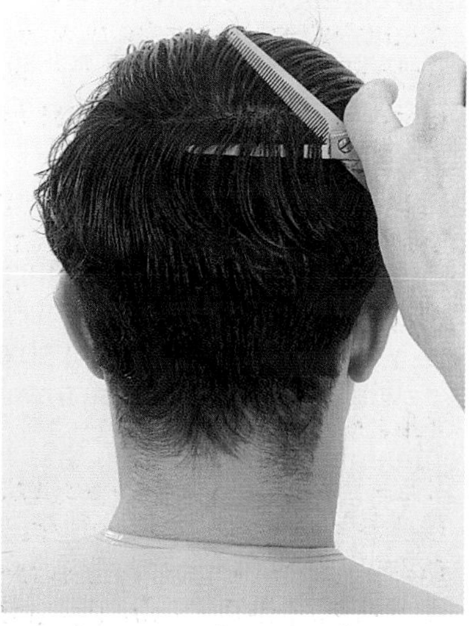

Root thinning with serrated scissors

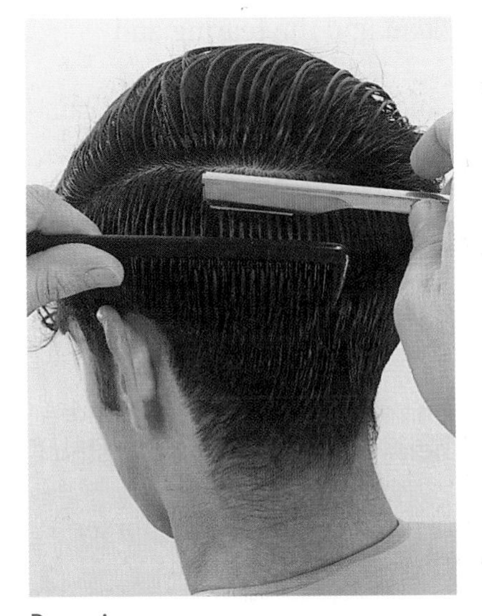

Razoring

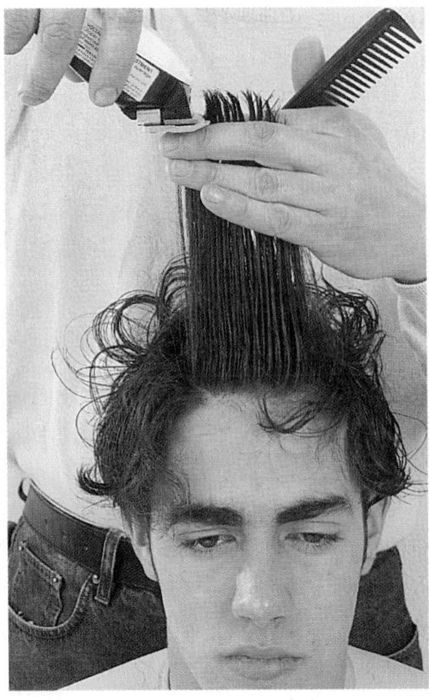

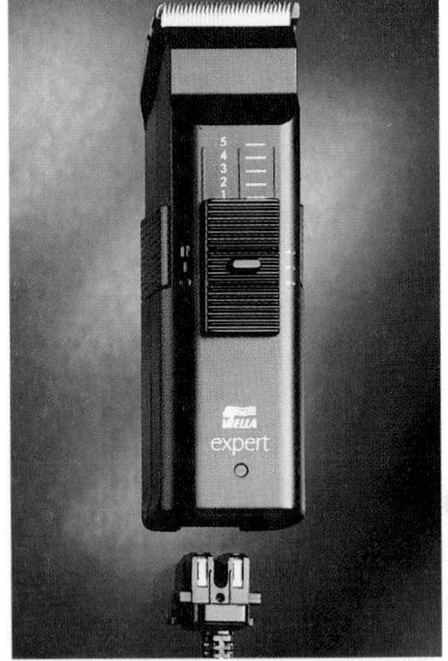

WELLA

Clippers (*above*)
Clipper clubbing (*left*)

Size	*Length of cut hair*
0000*	Very close to skin, like shaving
000*	0.3 mm (close cutting)
00	0.4 mm
0*	0.8 mm
0A	1.2 mm
1*	3.3 mm
1A	4.0 mm
1½	4.8 mm
2†	6.4 mm
3†	7.9 mm

*Most commonly used
†Mainly for beards and short crops

ACTIVITY
Each manufacturer may have its own sizing system for clippers, so make sure that you are aware of the maker's system before you buy. Make notes, and keep them in your folder.

Cutting techniques: a summary

Club-cutting or clubbing:

- over the fingers with scissors or clippers
- over the comb with scissors or clippers
- with razor between fingers and head.

Tapering:

- with scissors, backcombing first or slithering along section
- with razor, lightly under sections
- with clippers, with light stroking movements
- with thinning scissors towards hair points.

Thinning:

- with scissors
- with clippers
- with razor
- with thinning scissors.

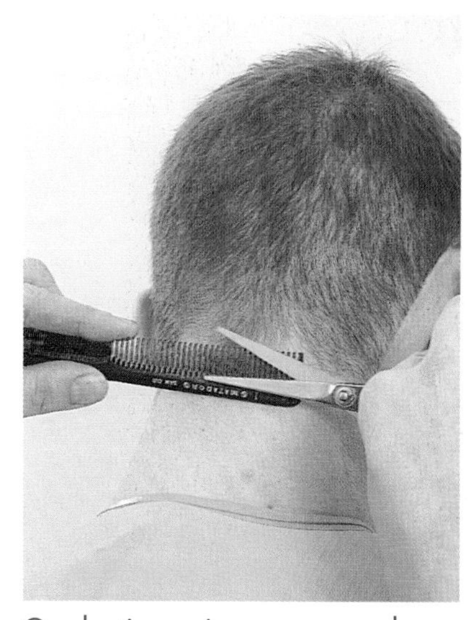

Graduation: scissors over comb

Graduation:

- with clippers, varying the blade sizes to produce the slope (see page 99) between short and long hair
- with scissors over comb, lifting sections
- with scissors over fingers
- with scissors, lifting sections, transferring to comb and clubbing.

ACTIVITY
Check with the salon's wholesaler and equipment manufacturer to see what cutting tools are available. Try to get illustrations of the current models. There are frequent changes in types and models and this enables you to keep up to date. Make notes on the various tools and the differences between them.

LAYERING

In **layer cutting** or **layering**, sections of hair are cut at varying angles from the head. The aim is to achieve an unbroken series of tiny, imperceptible lines or layers. The higher the sections are taken and cut, the greater is the amount of layering produced. Conversely, the lower the sections are held and cut, the less is the layering produced.

Layering is a method of shaping and controlling a head of hair. If you cut the layers that follow the underlying contours of the head and face, you can achieve attractive and satisfying results: of course, as usual, you have to take into consideration the limitations of the hair, growth patterns, head and face shape, wearing of spectacles or hearing aids and so on. Make allowance too for any varying face shapes, such as bumps and hollows, that need to be 'disguised' or hidden by the overlying hairstyle.

REGIS

VIDAL SASSOON

Procedure

- Prepare your client for cutting and styling.
- Fully discuss your client's requirements with him.
- Examine his hair and note its length, quantity and texture, his face and head shape, and any abnormal or unusual features.
- Determine what needs to be done, with the agreement of your client.
- Decide which cutting techniques are likely to achieve the desired results.
- Make sure you have all tools and equipment to hand.
- Position your client's head carefully so that you can carry out your chosen techniques efficiently.
- Where to start the cut is an individual choice. The best position is one at which you can make the following cuts continuously, without hindrance.

Cutting method

- Accurate graduation achieves fine layering. This is partly determined by how much hair there is to cut. Longer lengths can be sectioned with the comb and taken between the fingers. Shorter lengths are best tackled by club-cutting with clippers, lifting sections with the comb and scissor-cutting, lifting with scissors and cutting over the comb, and so on.
- With short layered styles, clippers must be used to tidy the neckline, graduating from the natural line out from the head. How far up the head and how short this cut needs to be is determined by the style and shape agreed with your client. If longer lengths are required higher in the back hair, then the clippers need to graduate away from the head sharply.
- If you are just removing a few hairs clipper size 0000 may be used.
- If you are cutting deeply into the hair bulk, clipper size 1 may be more suitable.

TIP

The sequence is: comb the section, transfer to the fingers of the other hand, cut the hair, re-section; move across the back of the head, cutting as you go.

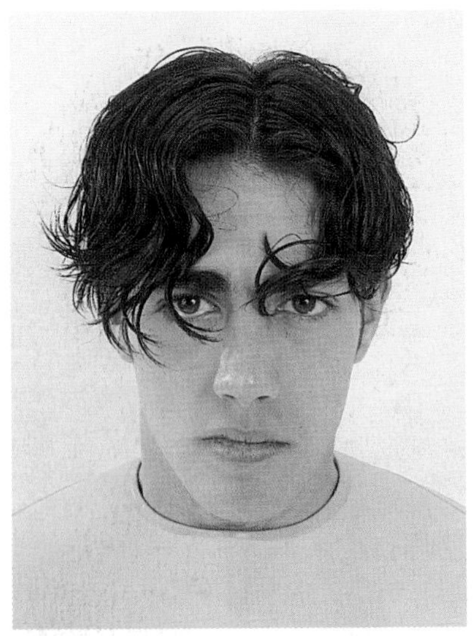

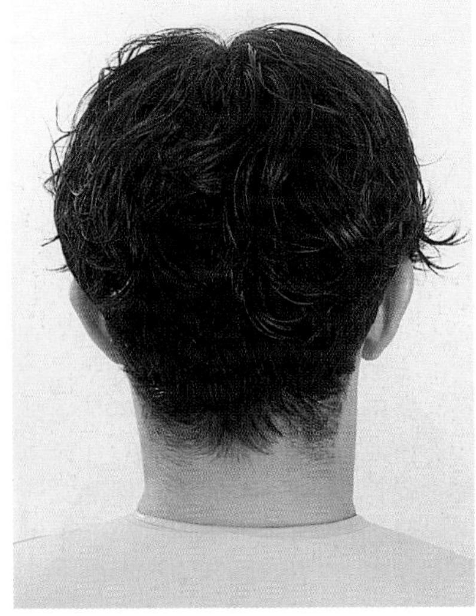

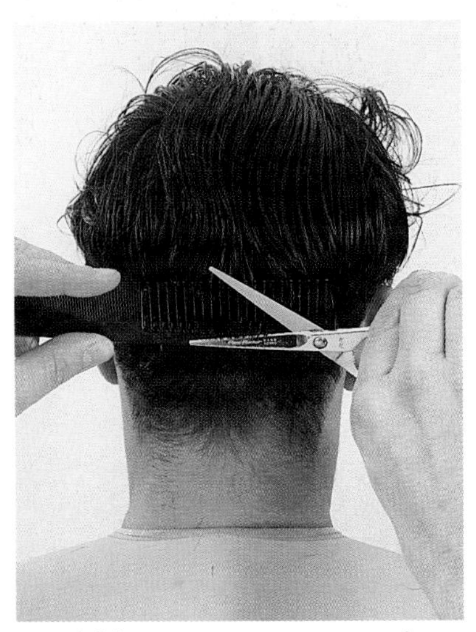

Cutting method: (a) Before – front (b) Before – back (c) Clubbing: scissors over comb

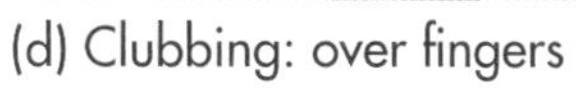

(d) Clubbing: over fingers

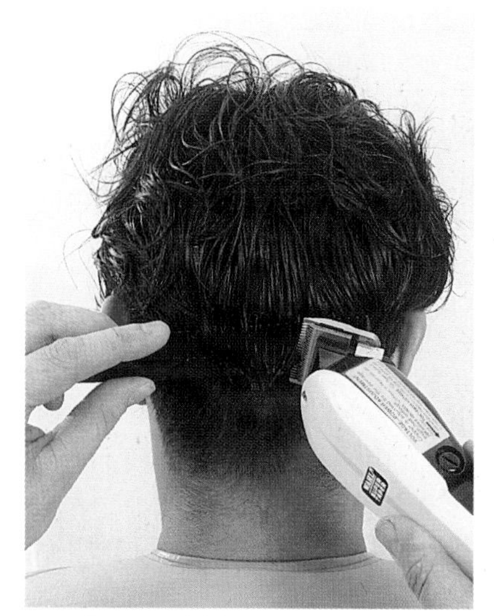

(e) Clipper clubbing

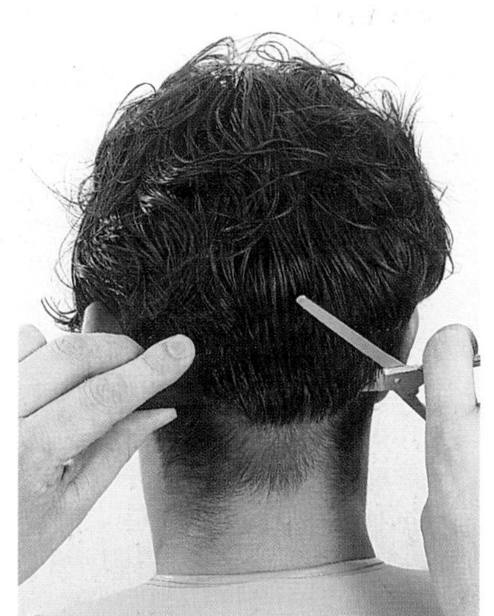

(f) Thinning

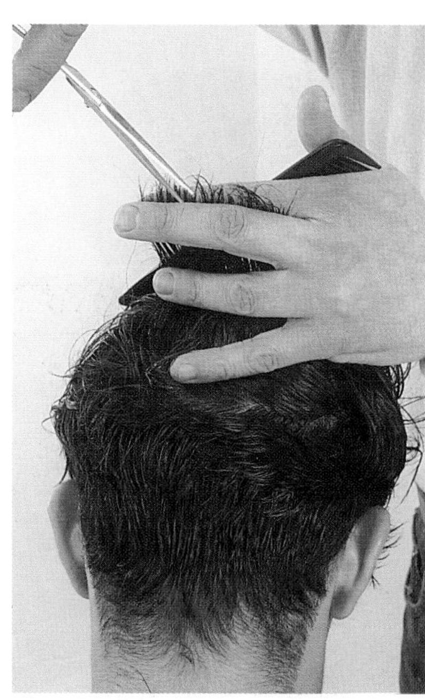

(g) Texturising

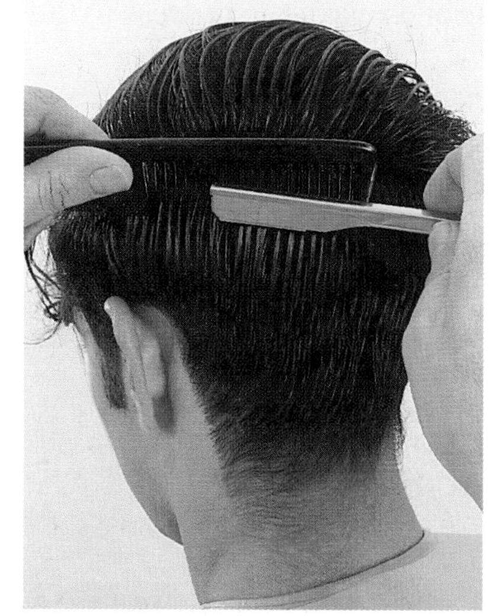

(h) Razoring

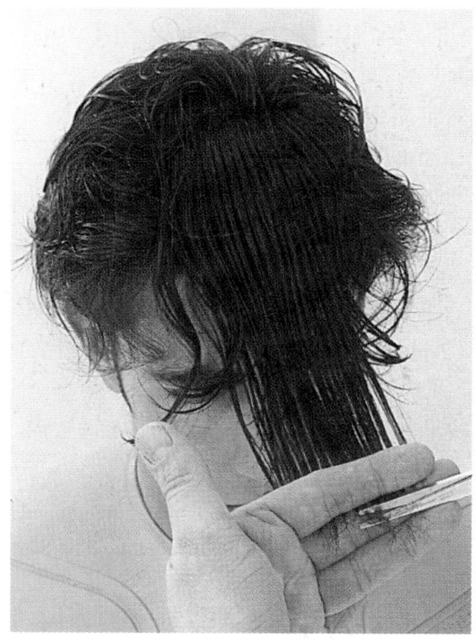

(i) Fringe shaping

(j) Outlining

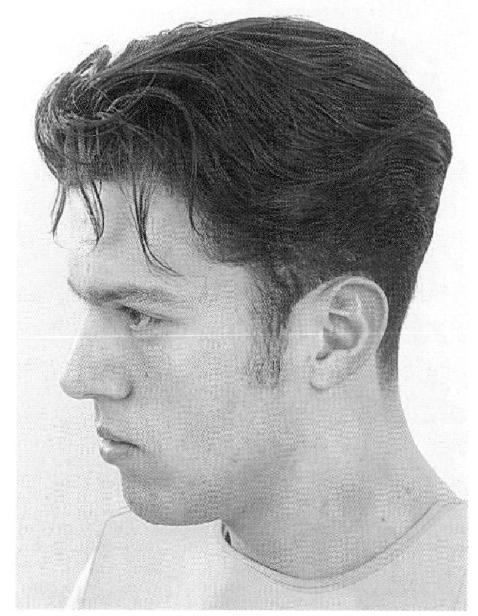

(k) Completed cut: front/side

- Graduate with scissors over comb into the napeline.
- This is the point at which to shape a man's sideburns, if required (and the lower side hair for a woman).
- If the hair is long enough comb a small section out from the head with the right hand, and transfer it to the fingers of the left. Cut the hair protruding beyond the finger straight across. If the hair is too short to section in this way, lift sections with the scissors and cut over the comb.
- Repeat this movement from the starting point. Continue taking small sections of hair out from the head, gradually moving over the side towards the lower back hair.
- Slightly overlap the sections so that the previously cut hair acts as a guide for cutting the next section.
- Continue to the centre back; then start at the other side and work towards the centre back again.
- When both sides and lower back hair have been cut, move up the head following the contours and begin to cut the upper sides and upper back towards the centre.
- Again move to the opposite side and repeat the process to the centre back.
- Repeat these movements as necessary until all the hair has been shaped.

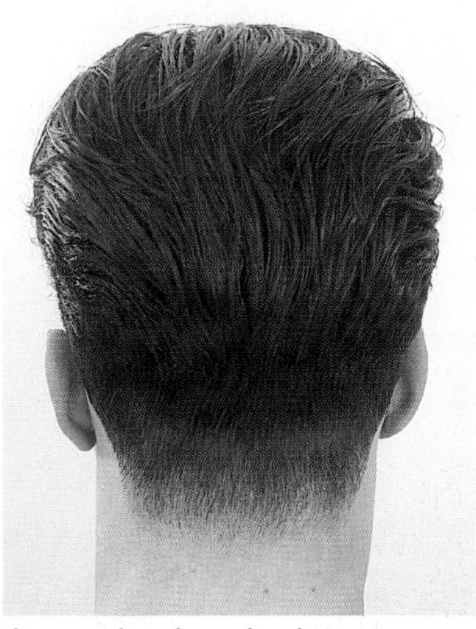

(l) Completed cut: back

ACTIVITY

There are many different methods of cutting short layered hairstyles. Make notes of all the procedures that you meet in the salon, training centres, shows and demonstrations. Include notes on the techniques applied, the sequence of methods, and the style produced. Use sketches or photographs where possible of layered hair styles.

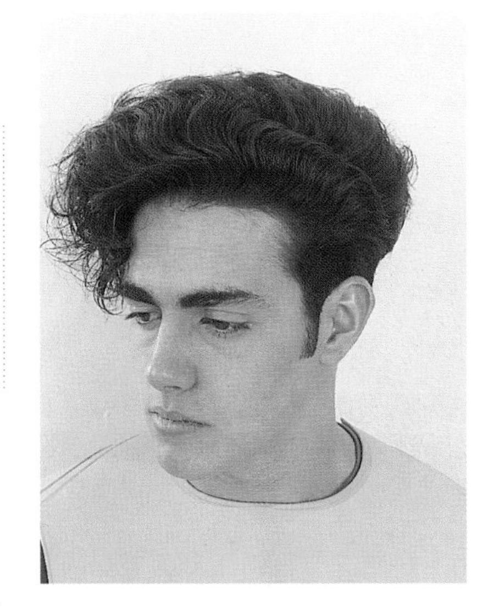

REGIS

Fringes

The front hair can be included in this procedure or it can be first combed into a fringe shape, either left to right or right to left, straight forward, blunted, feathered, pointed, rounded, tapered or layered.

A fringe shape should not be left looking too heavy and 'wiggy'. It should not be reduced so much that it looks so fine that the hairline can be seen through it. You have to strike a balance that looks just right. Make sure that you do not make areas of strong growth too short, or the hair will lift at the front and cause problems. Shape the fringe going with, rather than against, the natural movement flow. Don't overtaper or overthin, don't club-cut too short, and don't forget to refer constantly to the features of the head and face.

Method variations

Methods of cutting vary. You can start at any part of the head. You can use any of the cutting techniques you find most comfortable. You can work in whichever way you feel will achieve

CHEYNES TRAINING FOR PAUL MITCHELL LUXURY HAIRCARE

the results required. All good methods of cutting have the following in common: continuous sections are taken throughout the process, smaller rather than larger sections of hair are taken, and movements must (of course) ensure a single technique or a combination of techniques can be used.

If after clubbing the hair is still too bulky, it can be given its final shape by razoring. When razoring, make sure that you do not cut the top sections too heavily. This would produce too many short ends which might spike out.

ASSIGNMENTS: CUTTING MEN'S HAIRSTYLES

A practical activity

Cutting hairstyles for men or women requires careful planning and precision. This requires practice. Cutting slip-ons can be helpful in the beginning, but practising on models is the main means of gaining proficiency. Competitors and hair displays, magazines, photographs and sketches are useful sources of ideas. Collect together and record as much guidance and information as you can, and retain it in your folder. Here are some suggestions.

1. Create a men's hairstyle book. Include styles that you think are fashionable and attractive.
2. List the requirements of ladies' and men's styling.
3. Which styles look masculine or feminine? Why is this?
4. List the various barbering techniques and the effects they produce.
5. When do you need to use creative interpretation? Outline some ways in which you would do this.
6. Try to sketch layering and the effects it produces.
7. What differences do partings make to a style?
8. List the points to consider with respect to ears, spectacles and hearing aids.
9. List the different forms of fringe and their effects.

For you to find out

Investigate sources of information regarding men's styling. You can find a variety of novel sources if you look hard enough.

- Apart from hairdressing competitions, displays and demonstrations, there are clothes shows, fashion and design exhibitions, art college departments, private studios and other design centres to investigate. All have something to offer, and can give you new ideas that may stimulate your creative thinking.
- Theatrical, television and photographic studios are further sources of artistic design and display. Both traditional and modern hairstyles for men and women are often featured.
- Consider the design aspects of men's hairstyles. What are the patterns of men's hair shapes that form our styles? (See pages 84–91.)

- How does colour feature in your men's hairstyling? What are the likely advantages and effects?
- Explain with reasons, how clothes fashions, hair accessories, earrings and jewellery influence hairstyling.

Discuss these topics with your colleagues and note any new ideas or information that come out of the discussion.

A case study

Your client's hair is below shoulder length. It is medium-textured and in poor condition. He is thinking of growing a beard or moustache. How might you deal with this suggestion?

1. List the questions that you need to put to your client.
2. List the questions that your client might ask you. Note the answers and record them.
3. What hairstyle would you recommend? State your reasons.
4. What considerations would you give to the growing of a beard and or moustache? What questions would you ask?
5. Outline the techniques you would use and state why you would use them.
6. What are the important influencing factors in designing men's hairstyles?
7. Which hair cosmetics can you recommend to your male clients? How do you justify their use?
8. What advice on hair care and maintenance can you give?
9. What are the current hairstyles for men? Do you have photographs, sketches, magazines, journals, videos, advertisements and so on to show to your client?

PREPARING FOR ASSESSMENT

In preparing for assessment on cutting men's hairstyles the following checklist may be helpful. Check that you have covered and now fully understand these items:

- discussing and agreeing with clients' requests
- consulting and advising clients
- determining a suitable hairstyle to cut
- assessing the hair quality, quantity, density, texture, condition and growth patterns
- selecting the right tools, techniques and combination of techniques
- competently cutting current fashion styles
- competently cutting basic layered styles
- finishing with appropriate dressings if required
- advising on the after-care and maintenance required
- recommending suitable hair care products or cosmetics
- making a 'before-and-after', perhaps pictorial, record of work carried out
- achieving client satisfaction
- dealing with the problems that may arise.

When you feel that you are ready for assessment, talk to your trainer and arrange a suitable time.

Shaving and face massage

REGIS

INTRODUCTION

For as long as barbers' shops have existed, shaving has been one of their most popular services. Indeed, at times they were visited routinely by many men for their daily shave. Face massage, too, has been enjoyed by both men and women.

Shaving techniques and tools have altered comparatively little in the last few years, but a broader range of cosmetic products is used today than in the past. Nowadays many men shave themselves at home, but face massage in conjunction with shaving is easier to carry out in a salon. This specialist skill is still sought after by many.

For those wishing to qualify in these barbering techniques, we will be looking in this chapter at the following topics:

- shaving – wet and dry
- shaving preparation
- shaving methods
- materials, products, tools and equipment
- razor sharpening and stropping
- shaving techniques: lathering, hot towels
- shaving procedure and completion
- shaving problems that may arise
- face massage: preparation and materials
- clients' skin and massage techniques
- facial massage: a routine
- the vibratory facial
- vibro massage: a routine.

SHAVING

Shaving is the removal of hair, by means of a razor or some other close-cutting implement. It is widely applied to both men and women, but here we will consider mainly its use in the salon on men.

Shaving is used to remove facial hair and to outline moustaches, beards, sideburns and necklines. From time to time there are, it is true, fashions that feature the 'unshaven look'; 'designer stubble' comes to mind. But shaving is a necessity for most men, for whom it is part of the personal daily routine for social, business and hygienic reasons.

Shaving can be either dry or wet. **Dry shaving** is achieved by means of electric shavers, of which a wide variety exists, and is usually done at home. In **wet shaving** the face is wetted or lathered with soap, foam or gel, and the hairs are removed while wet. This is the service traditionally offered in men's salons.

Wet shaving can be achieved with different types of razor. The open ('cut-throat') razor consists of a finely ground, very sharp blade protected by a hinged cover. A safety razor contains a detachable blade inside a guard framework. Safety razors are sold in different forms – some have a hinged cover, others have a fixed blade – and are used in different ways.

ACTIVITY
Find out from your wholesaler details of the variety of razors available. Note the differences between them, and how they affect shaving. Your list should include open razors, safety razors and electric razors, both battery- and mains-powered.

METHODS OF SHAVING

Shaving methods are largely chosen on the basis of the type of razor used, the client's requirements and the condition of the facial skin and beard.

Open razors have over the years been very popular for wet shaving: with an open razor, fewer and longer shaving strokes need to be made. They must never be used dry, as this will tear the skin and drag the hair. The two main types are the **French razor**, with a solid blade, and the **German razor**, with a hollow-ground blade. The main differences between the two lie in the ways in which the blades are made and sharpened, and the way they are applied to the skin. Several British varieties are available.

Safety razors have advantages over open razors: the blades are removable, need no sharpening and are more hygienic. For salon use they are more efficient and time-saving. With safety razors more, shorter, strokes are required.

Both types of razor require their cutting edges to be slightly angled so that the shaving stroke becomes a slicing action. If this is not done the blade will lose its edge and drag at the hairs; the skin may even tear. The shave will be a painful experience for the client.

TIP
Shaving once round the face, called **once over**, is gentler to the skin than shaving twice round the face (**twice over**).

HEALTH AND SAFETY
Both open and safety razors have very sharp blades and must at all times be used with care. Make sure that the edges are covered when they are not in use. Never place a razor in your overall pocket, or within reach of children.

Preparation for shaving

- Always take time to discuss the client's requirements with him.
- Ask questions such as: does the client require a very close shave? are there any problems that need special consideration? which shaving method would the client prefer?
- Ensure all protective materials, such as towels, are in place.
- Position your client so that all angles of shaving can be comfortably applied.

CLINIQUE

Materials needed

Assemble all the products, tools and equipment you will require before you begin work.

- **Products** include types of skin lubricant for lathering (aerosol foam, gel, cream and so on), talcum powder for finishing, first aid materials in case of accidents and styptic in case it is needed to stem blood from small nicks or cuts. Styptic must be in a form that can be individually applied, such as a liquid or a powder. A styptic stick is not hygienically acceptable (unless it is used only once, which is uneconomical).
- **Tools** required include the razor chosen for the client. The hygienic safety razor, with a new blade for each client, is usually to be preferred. An open razor, kept for one client's personal use and no one else's, is acceptable, however. The traditional shaving brush, soap and bowl are hard to clean, and unless special sets are reserved for individuals they should not be used. Modern lathering lubricants are far easier and cleaner to use.
- **Equipment** required includes a suitable adjustable chair which can be positioned so that the client can recline comfortably while he is shaved.

HEALTH AND SAFETY
Never contaminate materials by dipping fingers into pots and jars. Always use a spatula.

Open razor sharpening

The edges of open razors must be keen and sharp. To achieve this they must be set or **honed** and **stropped**. Various types of stone are used to set razors. The stones are lubricated, depending on the type, with water, spirit or oil.

Open razor setting

1. Lubricate the stone.
2. Place the blade of the razor flat on the stone, with its edge towards the centre.
3. Slide the razor across and along the stone, moving it from heel to point.
4. Turn the blade on its back. Hold it flat at the far end of the

HEALTH AND SAFETY
When testing a razor edge for sharpness do not apply more than the lightest pressure, or the nail will be cut through.

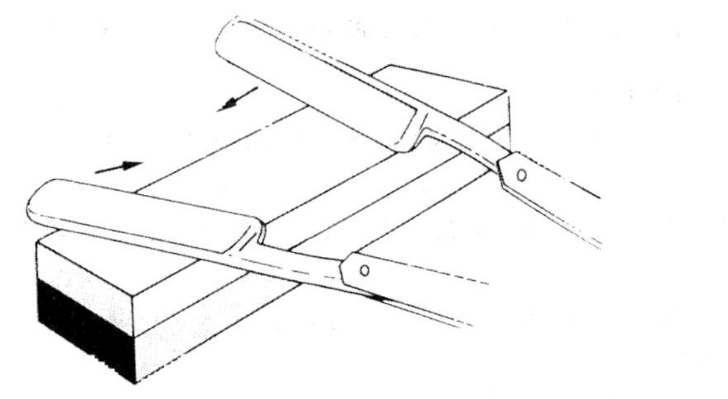

Razor setting (*left*) and razor testing (*right*)

stone from your body, and then slide it back along the stone. Again, move the blade from heel to point.

5. Repeat these movements, using only light pressure, and moving the blade backwards and forwards over the stone.
6. Test the cutting edge by gently (and carefully!) placing it on your fingernail. Move the blade along, just a little; if it grips or tugs the nail the edge will be keen.

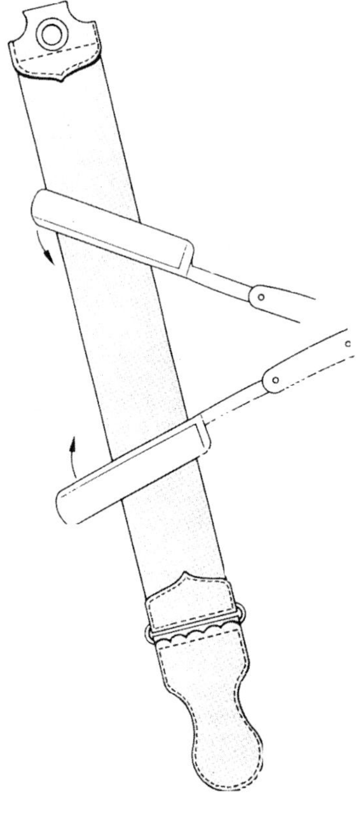

Razor stropping

Stropping the razor

1. Strop (smooth) the razor's edge by gently stroking it up and down a leather strop. The stropping action is reverse to the setting action.
2. Place the blade flat on the leather, with the edge away from the centre. Draw the razor *down* the leather. Take care not to knock the edge.
3. Turn the razor on its back, and gently push it *up* the leather.
4. Repeat these strokes several times. The edge will then, if set correctly, easily cut a single strand of hair.

HEALTH AND SAFETY

It is difficult to maintain good hygiene with leather strops. After stropping your razor, remove any oil or dressing from the leather surface with the back of a knife and thoroughly wash with soap and water. Always sterilise razors after stropping.

Using hot towels

Hot towels may be applied to the face before shaving and face massage. They are soothing and relaxing for the client. Steam from the hot towels softens the hair and helps to lubricate the beard. Dirt and grease are removed, which makes the shaving process easier and more comfortable.

Prepare hot towels either in a special steamer or by soaking them in hot water. Wring them out thoroughly and apply them as dry as possible. Wrap the hot towel firmly around the client's face and leave it to cool. You may apply two or three hot towels in succession. The quicker you can prepare the towels, the more effective they are likely to be.

Always test the hot towels gently on the client's skin before wrapping, to make sure they are not uncomfortably hot.

Here are some points to bear in mind when using hot towels.

- All towels must be clean.
- Towels must never be used on another client without washing.
- Always ensure that towels are firmly in position, to protect the client.
- Make sure the client can breathe comfortably – avoid covering his nose.
- Towels must never be dripping wet.
- Check for signs or symptoms of disease that might indicate that, to prevent the spread of infection, shaving should not be carried out.

CHOICE OF SHAVING METHODS AND TECHNIQUES

When you are choosing which shaving method or technique to use, you must consider the following:

- the client's preferences, to be assessed and agreed between you and him
- the results of your consultation with the client
- the texture of the client's beard – whether it is coarse, medium or fine
- the density of beard – its thickness and length
- the presence of any distinctive features such as cleft chin, or scars or dimples
- whether outlining is required for sideburns or moustache
- the state of the facial skin
- the hair growth patterns.

SHAVING PROCEDURE

Lathering

It is said that a good shave is determined by the **lathering** process: without competent lathering, the shave cannot be satisfactory. The purposes of lather are:

- to clean the facial skin by removing dirt and grease
- to soften the facial hairs
- to lift the hairs from the skin surface so that they remain erect and can be easily cut
- to lubricate the skin surface.

Traditionally, lathering was achieved by thoroughly massaging soap into the beard with a shaving brush and briskly rubbing the skin with the fingertips using a circular motion. The coarser and denser the beard, the more prolonged the process became. Modern preparations now allow an instant lather to be applied with the minimum of movement, preparing the beard for easier shaving. These may be in the form of brushless foams, gels or creams and require little massaging. They are also more hygienic, since you no longer need the old shaving brushes and mugs.

Soap-based products are still available for those who prefer them, but they do require a certain amount of 'working up'.

The shave

1. Prepare the client. Make sure that his clothes are fully protected.
2. Position the chair and your client so that your movements will not be restricted while you are giving the shave.
3. If you plan to use hot towels, apply one or two at this stage before the lather.
4. Check that the razor is ready for use – keen and sharp and clean.
5. Your choice of razor is partly determined by the beard density and growth pattern. Use a solid blade for a heavy, dense growth, where you will need to make a larger number of strokes, and a hollow-ground blade for lighter growths.
6. Apply the lather to the areas to be shaved. Don't let it run and drip messily.
7. Remove some lather from the sideburn on the client's right side so that you can position the razor for its first stroke.

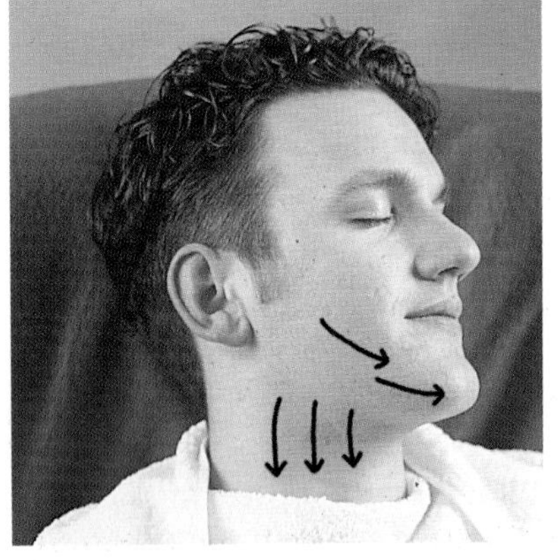

Shaving:
(a) First position for strokes 1–5

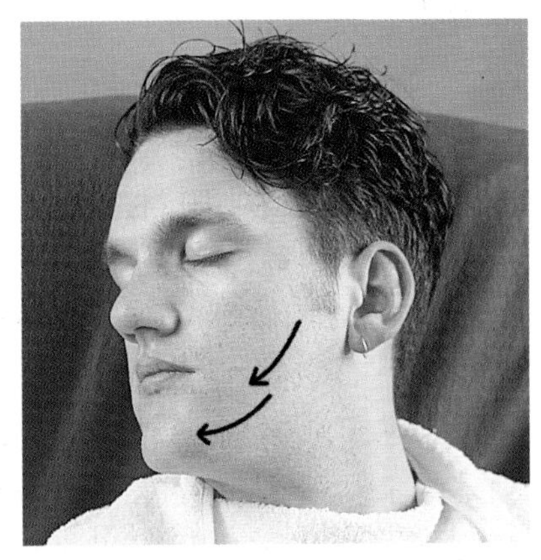

(b) Turn head for strokes 6 and 7

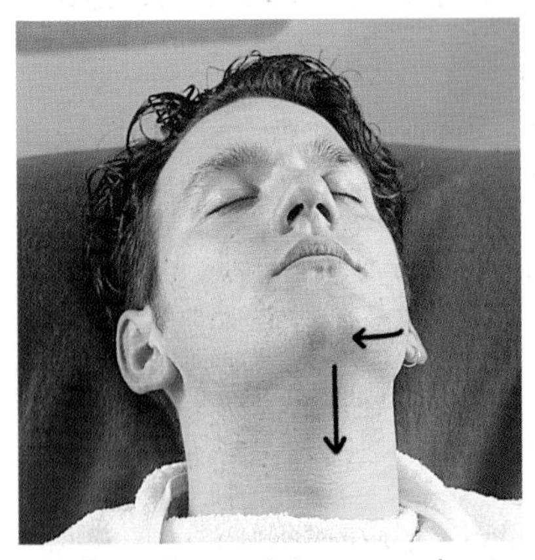

(c) Clear chin and down to adam's apple for strokes 8 and 9

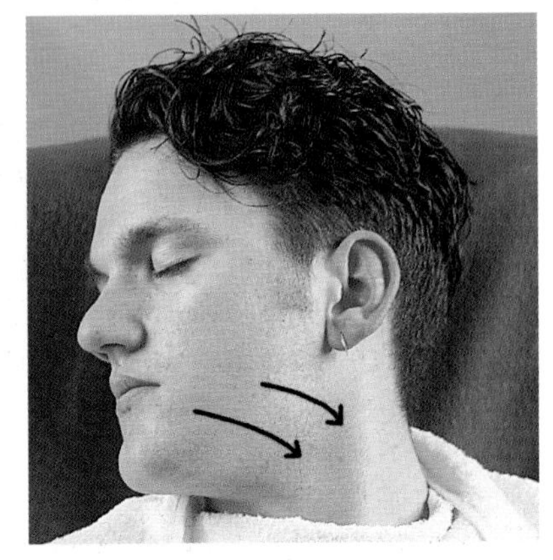

(d) Strokes 10 and 11

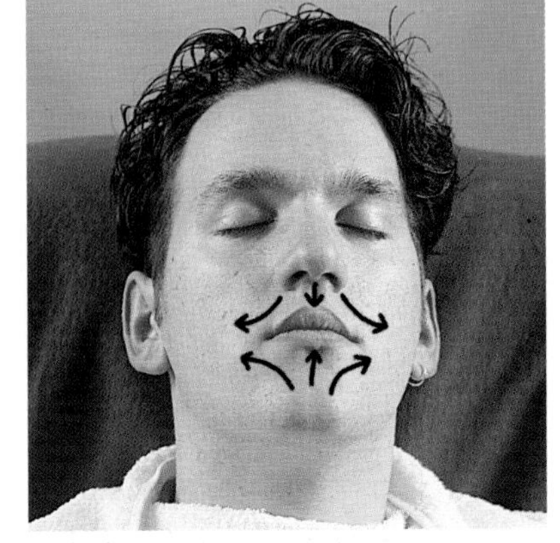

(e) Clear above and below lips with three short strokes

(f) Shaving strokes – summary

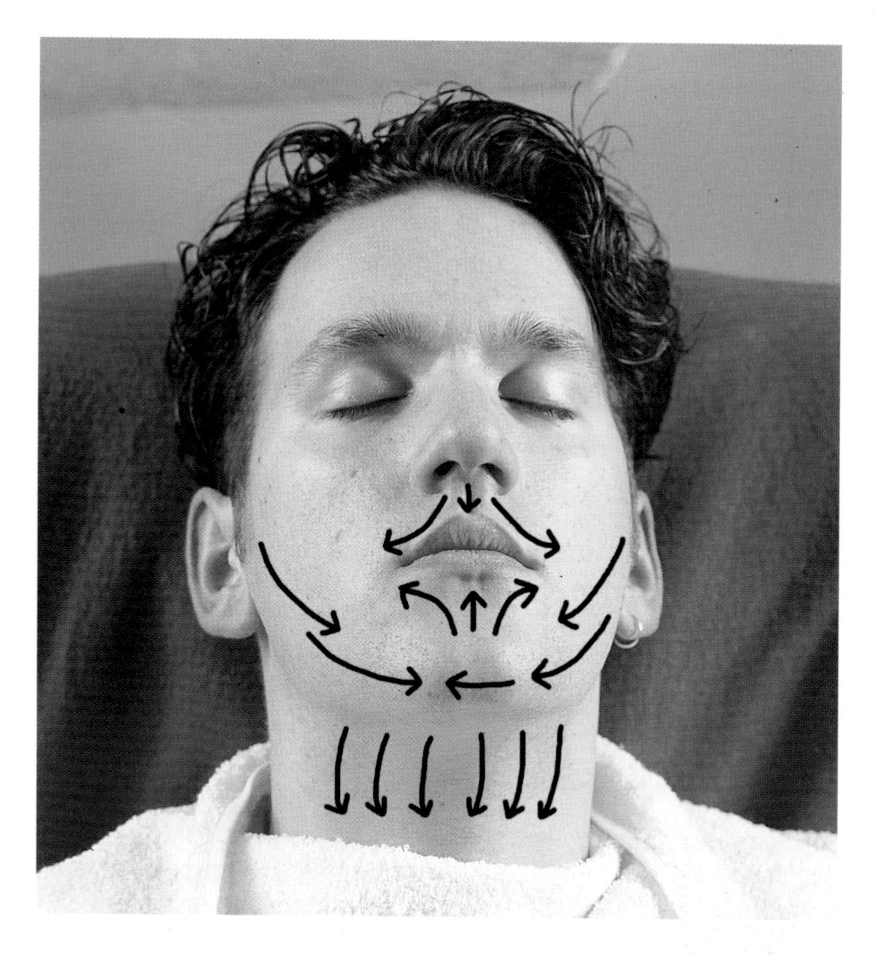

8 At the same time, stretch the skin with your fingers so that it is taut and even. You need to do this before each shaving stroke to prevent skin damage and leaving areas of uncut hairs.
9 With the razor slightly angled, slide it down towards the chin, moving it from point to heel as you remove the lathered beard. This makes the first stroke.
10 Turn your hand right over and make the second razor stroke from above the jawline to the point of the chin.
11 For the third razor stroke, resume the forward hand position and remove the beard from the chin point to the lower neck.
12 With the fourth and fifth strokes, remove the rest of the beard of the right side of the neck.
13 For the sixth stroke turn your hand completely over again and, after removing the lather from the left sideburn, slide the razor down the left side to the jawline.
14 Resuming the forward hand position, make the seventh stroke downwards towards the chin point.
15 With the eighth stroke, clear the point of the chin.
16 Still with your hand in the forward position, make the ninth stroke immediately under the chin, down towards the 'adam's apple'.
17 Using the back hand position again, make the tenth and eleventh strokes so as to remove the rest of the beard on the left side of the client's neck.

TIP

After each shaving stroke the razor needs to be cleared. Rinse the razor in water or wipe it on a tissue placed conveniently near. Fold the tissue each time it is used.

18 Clear the top lip with three short strokes, and under the bottom lip with up to three further strokes. The upper and lower lips should be manipulated into a suitable position for the razor to glide easily across the skin.

19 If required, the shaving sequence and movements can be repeated for a second round. Re-moisten the face with water first. If the skin permits these movements can be taken against the natural growth pattern.

ACTIVITY
You will need to practise the different hand and razor positions before trying to shave a 'live' client. This can be done by applying lather to a balloon, which must be safely tied down or else firmly held. Go through the shaving sequence and get the feel of the strokes. If the balloon bursts you will know that you were holding the razor too sharply, too heavily or at too great an angle. When you can clear the balloon without difficulty, you can move on to shave your first model.

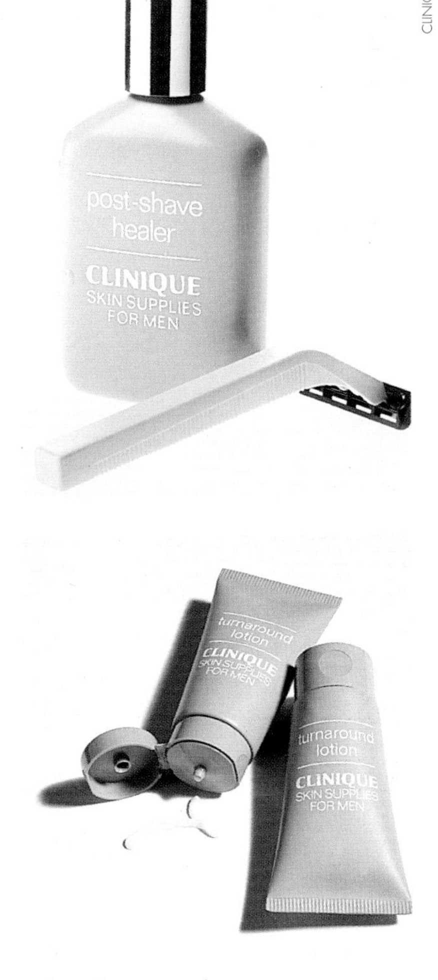

After-shave products

Completing the shave

You may apply hot towels when the shave has been completed. Face massage, if required, may now be applied. If massage is not required, clear the skin of any lather remaining and dry it thoroughly. At this stage use aftershave materials such as astringent lotions, moisturisers or talcum powder. These soothe and smooth the skin. Some clients may enjoy the application of pleasant-smelling perfumed products; others may prefer little or no perfume.

HEALTH AND SAFETY
All practice must be under the supervision of your teachers. Avoid working too close to another student – you might impede each other's progress and even endanger each other. Never play about with unguarded razors – accidents can easily happen.

TIP
It is important that each shaving stroke is in line with the natural growth pattern. If it is made to go against the grain then the result could be a very tender, possibly bleeding, skin.

ACTIVITY
Several ranges of preshaving and aftershaving products will be available from your wholesalers and manufacturers. Collect information about them, and find out exactly what these products do.

TIP
Sponges are often used to moisten and lubricate the skin for very close shaving. These must be clean and ideally kept for a client's sole use. You can use disposable tissues instead.

HEALTH AND SAFETY
Refer to page 270 for information regarding the cleaning of shaving tools and the disposal of blades, often called 'sharps'.

Shaving: problems, faults and corrections

Problems	*Possible causes*	*Corrections*
Uneven shave	Blunt razor Incorrect skin tension Incorrect razor angle Poor lathering	Ensure edge is sharp Stretch smoothly Correct angle so as to slice hair Lather evenly
Painful razoring	Blunt blade Shaving dry Razoring squarely	Test edge, hone if necessary Lubricate skin well Angle razor correctly
Facial cuts	Incorrect razor angle Not enough skin tension Heavy razoring Blunt razor	Adjust razor angle Keep skin taut Use razor more lightly Check blade, sharpen
Skin rash	Shaving dry Razor drag Razoring against grain Blunt razor Lather drying out Towels too hot Shaving too close	Lather well Correct razor angle Go with growth Hone/strop Keep moist Check and cool Rest skin
Follicles inflamed	Ingrowing hair	Refer to doctor
Blackheads	Blocked follicles	Gently remove

ASSIGNMENTS: SHAVING

A practical activity

You need to practise shaving carefully and thoroughly before attempting to apply it on clients. Practising with balloons is of limited help. It is essential to have models on which to practise. Become as proficient as possible, and collect together as much information as you can. Include the following:

1. List the details required for shaving preparation.
2. List the questions that you need to put to your clients.
3. List the questions your client might ask you.
4. Outline the different shaving techniques and say when you would use them.
5. Which shaving products can you recommend? Include those for both salon and home use.
6. Make sure you know how to hone and strop a razor – how and why.
7. What are the important factors of shaving?
8. What are the problems that may arise? How would you deal with them, and what you do if you can't?

For you to find out

Collect together information on shaving. Visit and investigate your local barber shop. Wholesalers and manufacturers can be helpful. Compile notes, with your source references, and retain them for your folder. Include the following in your collection.

1. Collect sketches and photographs of shaving techniques.
2. Examine old and recent trade journals for information.
3. Outline how you deal with moustaches and sideburns.
4. State why lubricating the skin is necessary.
5. State why tensioning the skin is necessary.
6. What is the growth rate of the beard?
7. Outline the different forms of shaving.
8. What are 'once over' and 'twice over'? When does this apply?
9. How do you test the razor sharpness?
10. What are 'hot towels' and when are they used?
11. What abnormalities are there? How do you deal with them?

A case study

Your client has a tender skin and requests a 'twice over' shave. He has been using an electric razor for several months. How do you deal with this? Simulate the consultation, record it and retain for your folder. It should include the following:

1. Examine and discuss skin problems.
2. Explain the differences between electric razors and open razors.
3. Advise on the need for a 'once over' shave – give reasons.
4. Describe how you would prepare the skin.
5. Outline the wet shave procedure.
6. List possible client's questions and your answers.
7. Outline any home care of skin required.
8. Advise on facial cosmetics to be used.
9. Which products do you recommend? How do you do this?
10. How do you handle the possible hazards that could arise?

PREPARING FOR ASSESSMENT

In preparing for assessment on shaving the following checklist may be helpful. Check that you have covered and now fully understand these items:

- communicating effectively
- choosing the range of preshave, aftershave and other cosmetic products available, with your reasons
- lathering, moistening, lubricating the skin
- shaving: different methods, wet and dry
- shaving tools available
- stropping and honing razors
- applying shaving: full face, partial face, nape and sideburns, moustache outlining
- applying hot towels
- dealing with hazards as they might arise
- listing the precautions to take
- completing the shave to the client's satisfaction.

When you feel that you are ready for assessment, talk to your trainer and arrange a suitable time.

INTRODUCTION

Massage of the face – a **facial** – is a popular salon service with many men, and women too. When professionally and competently applied, facials can be pleasant and relaxing and at the same time stimulating and enjoyable. Usually a facial follows shaving or makeup removal. Its purposes include:

- cleansing and softening the skin
- nourishing the skin and the underlying tissues
- stimulating the facial muscles
- soothing, stimulating, and toning the nerves
- increasing the blood supply to the face (producing **hyperaemia**)
- increasing glandular secretions
- relaxing the client, both physically and mentally.

CLIENT PREPARATION

The first essential is good communication with your client. You need to understand your client's reasons for deciding to have a face massage, and what he or she expects to be the results. Other things to remember include the following.

- Check the client's exact requirements.
- Especially if the client has not had a face massage before, explain what is involved.
- Make sure that the client and his or her clothes are fully protected.
- Examine the skin and note any feature that might contra-indicate massage.
- Make sure that the client is in a position that will be comfortable throughout the massage application.

> **HEALTH AND SAFETY**
> If you notice signs of inflammation, swelling or disease, do not go ahead with the massage. Consider whether you should advise your client to see a doctor. If in doubt, check with a senior member of your salon staff.

PRODUCTS, TOOLS AND EQUIPMENT

ELLISONS

Facial products

In addition to general salon services, when you are giving a facial you will need the following to be ready to hand:

- **Cleansing creams** Different types are available for dry, normal and oily skins.
- **Massage creams** These lubricate the skin and ensure that the hands slide easily over the skin surface during the

massage. Emollients, moisturisers and other creams specially made for dry, normal or oily skins are available.

- **Finishing lotions** These are astringents for closing the pores after massage; again different products are available for dry, normal and oily skins. Talcum powders of various types are used to ensure thorough drying after treatments.
- **Equipment required** The most useful pieces of equipment are **your hands**. These must be pliant and clean. The hands are held and positioned differently for each massage movement, which must be well practised. Make sure your nails are well manicured and therefore cannot snag your client's skin.
- A **vibro machine**, with its different applicators, is required for mechanical massage (see page 240).
- **Towels** for steaming are required. Paper tissues or towels may be used for drying and covering. A **face steamer** can be used instead of hot towels.
- A **reclining chair** is most important to allow the angles required for massaging to be achieved. A suitable neck rest should be correctly positioned and must be hygienically covered with towels or tissues.

All the equipment and materials needed before, during and after massaging should be close at hand, preferably on a suitable trolley, to ensure you can work efficiently.

ACTIVITY

A huge range of cosmetics and skin care produces is available. You should be aware of what is on the market, so go to your wholesalers or manufacturers and ask them about the products they sell. Keep this information in your notebook or folder.

EXAMINATION OF THE CLIENT'S SKIN

Examine the client's skin, and note whether it is dry, normal or excessively greasy. Discuss this with your client, since this information determines which skin care products to use.

Prepare the skin by removing all dirt and grease. This can be done by applying hot towels to clear, open the pores and relax the underlying muscles. For men the skin should be shaved and for women all traces of makeup removed.

Lubrication of the skin is essential during massage. If movements do not glide then too much pressure will be applied. This would be uncomfortable for the client, and possibly even rupture small blood vessels and cause bruising. Small amounts of lubrication are required throughout the massage, but never so much as to become messy.

TIP

Determine your client's skin type – thick, thin, fine or coarse – before starting the facial. Different skins need different treatment: the finer the skin, the gentler and more careful the massage must be.

MUSCLES OF THE FACE AND NECK

If you are giving a face massage, you need to understand the muscular structure of the face, and how the muscles act. The table overleaf lists the principal muscles of the region, and indicates their approximate points of attachment. To help you in your massage work, the list of facial muscles given in Chapter 2 (page 20) has been extended here.

Muscles form an integrated, interlinked structure. One end of every muscle (the **origin**) is attached to a fixed bone, another muscle or underlying tissue. The opposite end (the **insertion**) is attached to a bone or muscle that is more easily moved. Massage movements should generally be towards the origin.

MASSAGE TECHNIQUES

Each of the massage techniques – effleurage, pétrissage, tapotement, pinching, friction, tapping – may be used (see page 64). This is in part determined by the client's facial structure. If the face is well formed, full and muscular, then you may apply the deeper and more vigorous movements. If the structure is lean and gaunt, then deep massage movements are neither acceptable nor practical.

Massage techniques applied to the face must be light, slow, gentle and rhythmic. Both client and operator should find them pleasantly relaxing, but they must always be controlled. Apply most massage movements upwards and outwards. The many underlying arteries, veins, capillaries, lymph vessels and nerves all require gentle stimulation. Use your fingertips for most facial massage techniques. Use the two fingers between the index and little fingers for light movements, and the index fingers, occasionally the thumbs, when deeper movements are required.

There are numerous combinations of movements that you can use, and you must choose which sequence or massage routine you should use for any individual client. The differences between clients will help you to determine this.

HEALTH AND SAFETY

Check that your client is not allergic or otherwise sensitive to the products you intend to use.

TIP

A face massage should take about 20–30 minutes to complete.

A FACIAL MASSAGE APPLICATION

1 Apply cleansing cream to the whole face and neck. Stroke cream into skin in circular motions.
2 Remove cleansing cream. Use hot towels, moisten cottonwool with astringent and wipe off with soft tissues. Work from the chin, clear cheeks and jaw, around lips, down the nose, carefully around the eyes, down the neck, finally the forehead. Use upward and outward movements generally.
3 Apply massage cream. Follow the same pattern as for cleansing cream. Do not overload the skin.
4 Gently lift the chin and position the client's head.
5 Slide your hands up the sides of the face to the temples. Place the tips of your middle fingers (next to the index fingers) on the sides of the forehead and gently move them up and down

Name of muscle	*Origin*	*Insertion*
Scalp		
Frontalis	Aponeurosis	Lower forehead
Occipitalis	Occipital bone	Aponeurosis
Eyelids		
Orbicularis oculi	Nasal bone	Outer orbit
Corrugator	Frontal bone	Inner orbit
Ears		
Auricularis anterior	Frontal bone/ aponeurosis	Ear front
Auricularis posterior	Temporal mastoid	Behind ear
Auricularis superior	Aponeurosis	Upper ear
Nose		
Nasalis	Maxillae/ nose wings	Lower nose bridge
Procerus	Nose bridge	Frontalis muscle
Depressor septi nasi	Maxillae	Nose wing/septum
Dilator naris anterior	Nose cartilage/ nose wing	Nose tip
Dilator naris posterior	Maxillae	Edge of nostrils
Mouth		
Orbicularis oris	Nasal septum/ mouth muscles	Other mouth muscles
Quadratus labii superioris	Maxilla/eye orbit/ zygomaticus	Nose cartilage/ orbicularis oris/ upper lip
Quadratus labii inferioris	Mandible	Lower lip
Zygomaticus	Malor bone	Mouth angle
Caninus	Maxillae	Mouth angle
Mentalis	Mandible	Chin skin
Triangularis	Mandible	Lower lip/mouth angle
Buccinator	Jaws	Orbicularis oris/ mouth angle
Risorius	Masseter muscle	Mouth angle
Masseter	Malor bone	Mandible
Temporalis	Temporal bone	Mandible
Neck		
Platysma	Clavicle	Mandible
Trapezius	Occipital bone/ cervical vertebrae	Clavicle/scapula
Sternomastoid	Clavicle/sternum	Occipital bone/ temporal bone

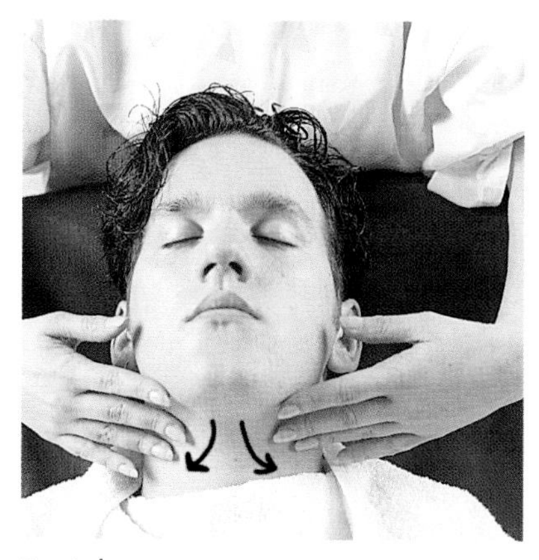

Facial massage:
(a) Applying cleansing cream

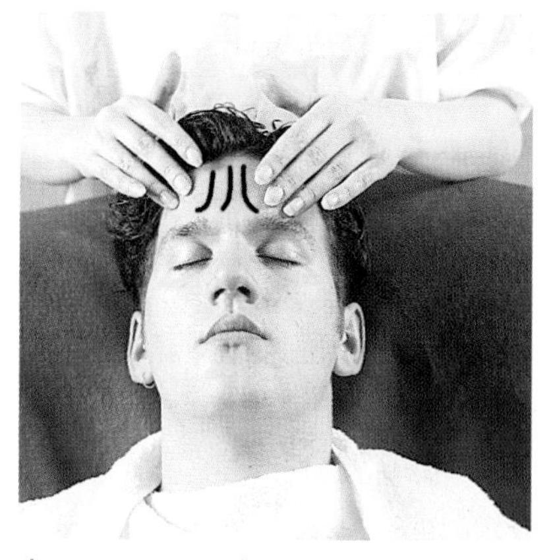

(b) Movements between the hairline and brows

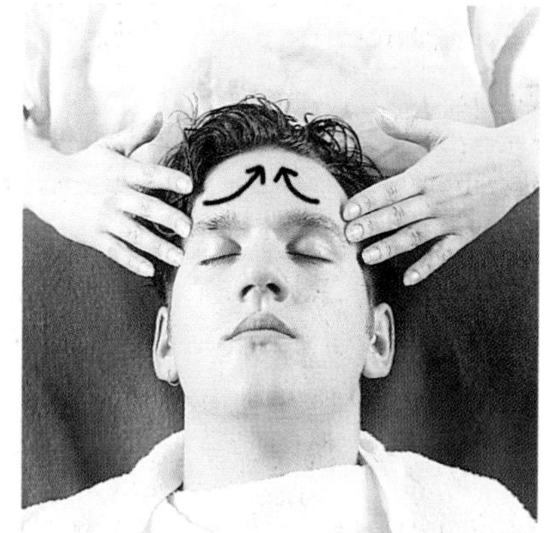

(c) Temples to hairline

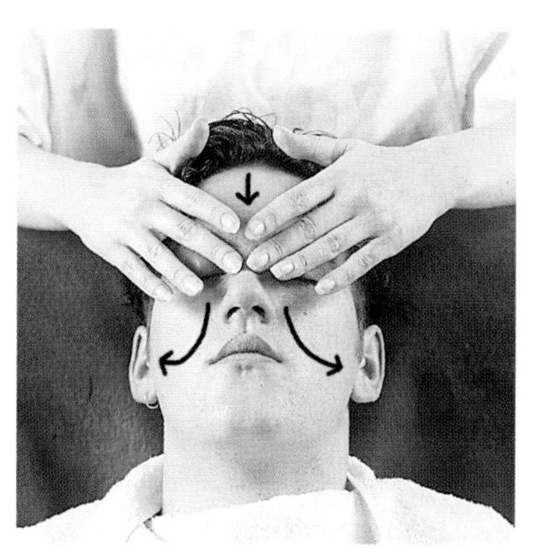

(d) Sliding fingers down nose to upper cheeks

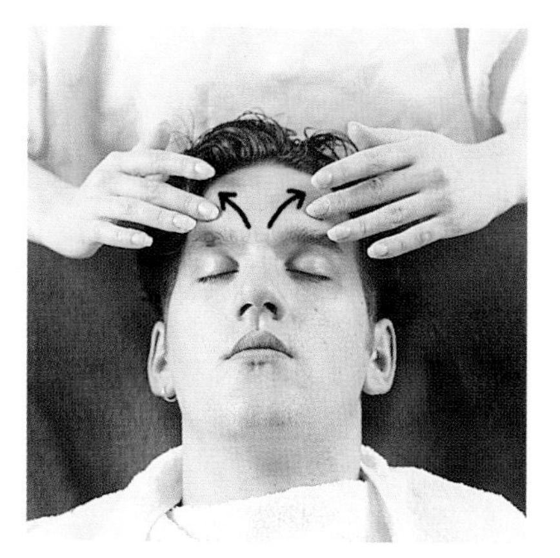

(e) Stroking around eyes

between the hairline and the brows (effleurage). Alternate your hand directions – as one moves forwards, the other moves backwards. Work towards the centre.

Main muscles affected: frontalis
orbicularis oculi
corrugator.

6 Move fingers in upward strokes from eyes to hairline (effleurage). Finish with your hands at the temples.

Main muscle affected: frontalis.

7 From the temples and with your hands working together, rotate your fingertips towards the centre forehead covering the whole area and eyebrows. Then place one hand back at the temple followed by the other and repeat the moves (pétrissage). Finish at the centre forehead above nose bridge.

Main muscles affected: frontalis
dilator naris anterior
dilater naris posterior.

8 Slide your fingers down the sides of the nose. Rotate across upper cheeks. Move to the temple. Slide your fingers under the eyes to the nose bridge. Use effleurage along the nose sides and light pétrissage across the cheeks.

Main muscles affected: orbicularis oculi
nasalis
procerus
corrugator
nares
depressor septi nasi
quadratus labii superior.

9 At the nose bridge place your middle finger at the inner corner of the eye. Place your index finger over the brows. Stroke to the outer corners of the eyes (effleurage only).

Return under the eyes lightly with your middle finger to the nose bridge.

Main muscles affected: orbicularis oculi
corrugator
frontalis (edge).

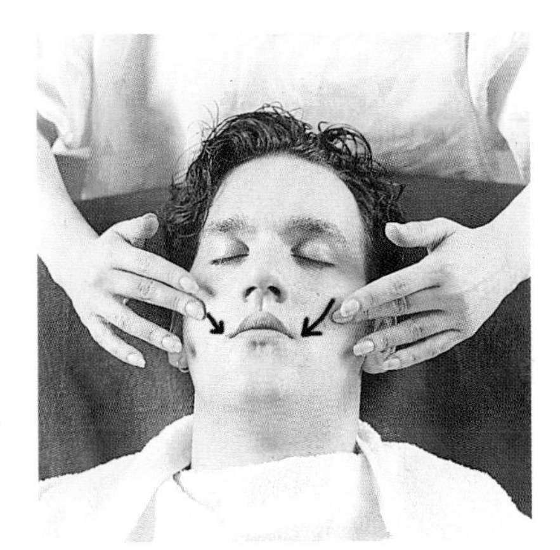

(f) Cheeks to mouth

10 Stroke over the brows. Slide down the sides of the cheeks to the mouth corners. Rotate upwards along the sides of the nose to the bridge (effleurage and pétrissage).

Main muscles affected: orbicularis oculi
zygomaticus
risorius
buccinator
triangularis
quadratus labii inferior
masseter.

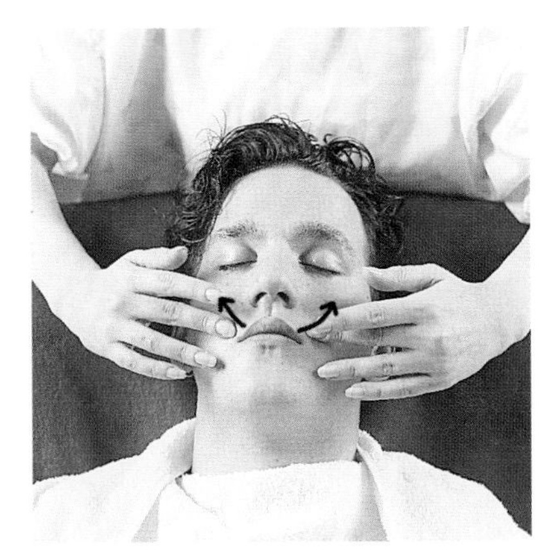

(g) Mouth corners to mid-ear

11 Slide down the nose sides. Stroke from the centre upper lips around the mouth corners (slightly firmer effleurage). Move into the centre bottom lip and around the chin.

Main muscles affected: masseter
orbicularis oris
risorius
upper platysma
muscles of the upper lip.

You do not necessarily need to use all three movements **12a**, **12b** and **12c** – any two of these may be sufficient.

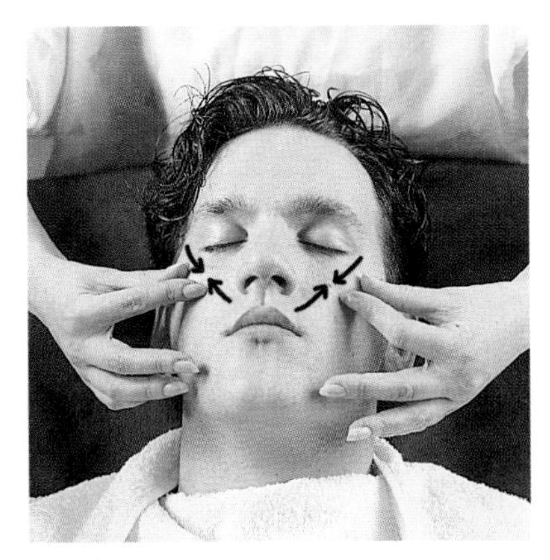

(h) Light pinching movements

12a From the chin, using very light pinching movements, work outwards and up the jaw line to the ear lobes, then from the mouth corners to the mid-ear area, and finally from the lower corners of the nose to the lower temples. Cover all the cheek areas. This can be preceded or followed by the movement **12b**.

Main muscles affected: all the muscles of the chin, cheeks, mouth and upper lips.

12b From the chin towards the ear lobes use a deeper, rotating, pétrissage move. Follow this by moving from the mouth corners to mid-ear. Finally move from the outer nostrils to the upper ear/lower temples. Cover all the lower facial areas above the neck. Use a light to slightly firm pétrissage moving outward and upward.

Main muscles affected: all the muscles of the lower face.

12c Following the same lines of movement as **12a** and **12b**, apply a very light, rhythmic tapotement (tapping) movement. Remove your fingertips from the skin surface as soon as they touch it, so as to avoid applying to much pressure.

Main muscles affected: all the muscles of the lower face and cheekbones.

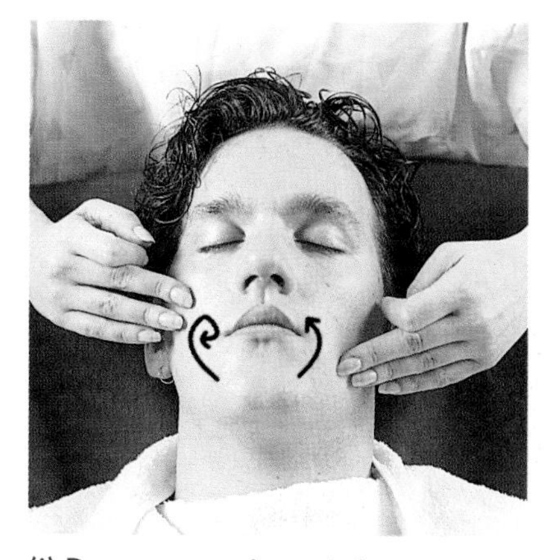
(i) Deeper, rotating pétrissage movements

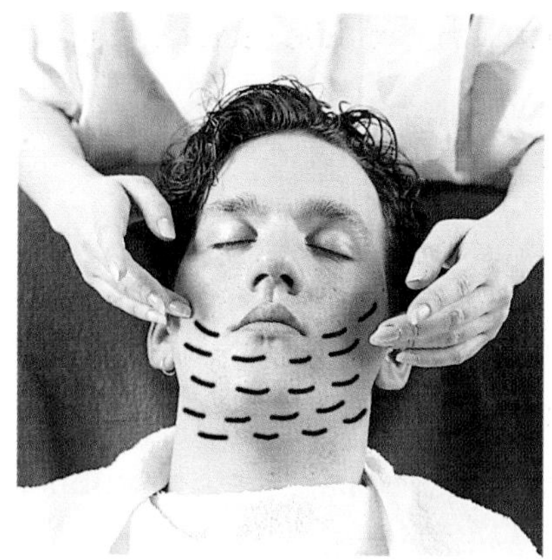
(j) lLght tapotement movement

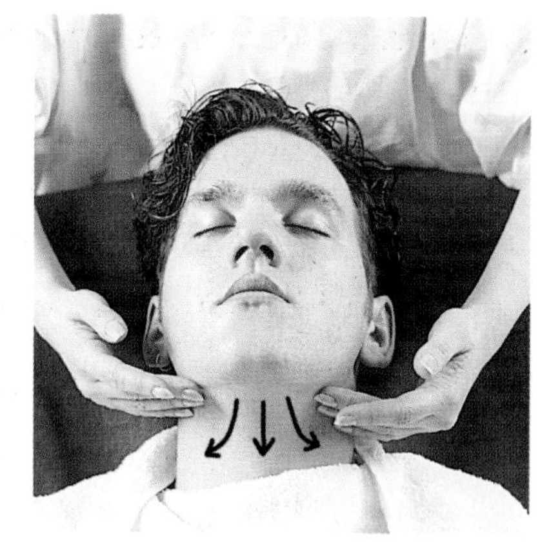
(k) Stroking the neck area

13 Slide your fingers down along the jawline to the chin. Under the chin begin to apply light gentle, rotating movements (very light pétrissage) down the neck and outwards. Cover all the neck area.

Main muscles affected: platysma
corrugator
quadratus labii inferior
triangularis
part of sternomastoid and trapezius.

14 Finally, place your hands under the chin and gently stroke the whole of the neck area. Use smooth, soothing moves. Finish the sequence of movements with effleurage.

Main muscles affected: all the muscles of the neck area.

15 Finish the massage routine by applying hot towels and removing all traces of massage cream. Apply astringent if required. Apply talcum and dry thoroughly.

Bear in mind the following:

- The above sequence of massage movements is intended to cover all the areas of the face.
- Each movement can be repeated two or three times before progressing to the next one.
- The movements must flow continuously without interruption. Avoid all jerky actions.
- Keep one of your hands in contact with the skin surface all the time.
- Never rush the routine.
- All movements should be lightly applied, especially around the eyes. Never massage deeply under the eyes, as this could stretch the skin.
- Successful massage is pleasant and enjoyable for both you and your client.

THE VIBRATORY FACIAL

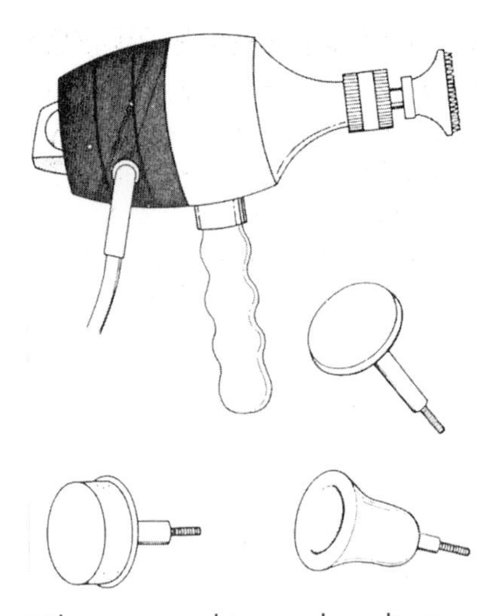

Vibratory machine and applicators

The **vibratory facial** is a mechanical massage, in which the vibratory machine imitates the hand movements of shaking, friction and tapping. It can be used in conjunction with hand massage or on its own. The vibro is best used on the fuller formed tissues rather than the leaner ones. The more pressure that is applied to the machine, the deeper the effects are felt.

The vibro is controlled by both hands: one holds the machine firmly while the other controls its direction. Several applicators are supplied. The spiky one is used for scalp massage. The rubber bell-shaped (or cup-shaped) one and the rubber sponge applicators are all intended for use on the face. Others that may be included are intended for work on larger areas of the body.

Vibro massage routine

Stand to one side of your client. Follow each of the preparatory stages as for the hand face massage and the general routine, except that at stage 5 you will apply the vibro instead of hand movements. Proceed as follows:

1. Apply cleansing cream.
2. Remove cleansing cream.
3. Apply massage cream.
4. Gently lift and position the client's head.
5. Instead of using your hands, apply the cup applicator to the lower central forehead. Starting from either left or right, use small, rotating movements. Proceed towards the temple. Move down the side and under the cheek. Move towards the upper lip, then back round the mouth and towards the chin.
6. Then move along the jawline towards the ear, and back under the jawline to the chin. Proceed down the neck – very gently – around the 'adam's apple' – up the side of the neck and under the chin again, and continue covering the neck. Move to the front of the ear lobe and back up to the temple to the upper centre forehead.
7. Move down to the bridge of the nose and over the eyebrow and around the eye, and along the side of the nose to the bridge. When moving around the eyes and nose, place one hand over the brows, lower orbit rim and nostrils and apply the machine to the hand rather than the skin. This will protect the delicate tissues of the eyes and nose.
8. Apply this movement pattern to the opposite side of the face.
9. Repeat the whole routine two or three times, ensuring that all the facial areas are covered in a continuous, steady sequence.
10. Clear the face with warm towels, followed by cooler ones. Apply astringents where required to close skin pores.
11. Dry the face thoroughly and apply talcum powder.
12. At this stage you can use the sponge applicator, either directly on the skin or over a small towel or tissue. Take small circular movements following the previous pattern used with the cup applicator.

TIP

Remember that very little pressure should be applied generally to avoid tissue damage.

TIP

Lean the machine towards the rim on one side of the cup applicator, so that it glides along the skin smoothly: jerking moves can damage the skin. There should be no sucking sounds, which could indicate that too much tissue is being drawn up into the cup.

TIP

Clean rubber applicators by first applying shampoo and leaving for a few minutes, then rinsing. This emulsifies the grease. If water is applied to the grease first it will be difficult to clear.

After completing the massage allow your client to remain seated for two or three minutes, to fully appreciate and enjoy the massage effects. Rushing your client at this stage could undo your good work.

ACTIVITY

Various vibro and hand massage routines are available, and are equally acceptable. Try them for yourself and make notes as to which you, and your clients, prefer.

ASSIGNMENTS: FACE MASSAGE

A practical activity

Your practice for massage can only be done on models. Closely watching others helps. A visit to your local beauty salon allows you to make comparisons between various applications of face massage for men and women. Gather as much information, and practice, as you can, and when you are assessed to be competent apply your skills to clients. Record the information derived from the questions set below and retain it for your folder.

1. List the advantages and disadvantages of facial massage.
2. Explain how you would present these to your client.
3. List the points and questions you would put.
4. List the answers you might receive from your client.
5. Outline the various hand massage movements and state when and where you would use them.
6. Outline the sequence of facial massage movements.
7. How do you justify the products that you use?
8. What are the contra-indications to massage?
9. State which massage movements should not be used on the face, and give your reasons.
10. In which directions should massage be generally be directed? State why.
11. State the precautions that you would take and why.
12. List the problems that might arise and how you would deal with them.

For you to find out

Investigate the different places where professional face massage is carried out. Include your local beauty salons, health clubs, college salons, product demonstrations and exhibitions etc. Record and retain information for your folder. Include the following:

1. Give your reasons for wanting to have good communication with your client.
2. Why is it necessary to examine your client's skin and face?
3. Why must information be recorded in confidence?
4. How do you record this information?

5 What action do you take if disease is evident?
6 What are the differences between hand massage and vibro massage of the face?
7 Which method would you recommend to your client, and why?
8 Outline a sequence of movements of vibro massage.
9 When is vibro massage contra-indicated?
10 What are the precautions that need to be taken with vibro massage?
11 What problems might arise during a face massage? How do you deal with them?

A case study

A male client asks you for a shave and face massage. He has alternated between electric and open razors for his daily shaves. His skin is sometimes tender and sore.

Explain how you would deal with this client and record the action you might take. Include the following:

1. List the points of your discussion with the client.
2. Which shaving method do you finally agree is most suitable?
3. When examining a client's skin, what should you look for?
4. What are your recommendations for a tender skin?
5. Which shaving and massage cosmetics do you recommend and why?
6. How do you present these and justify their use?
7. Outline a suitable shaving method.
8. List the precautions to be taken.
9. Outline the problems that might arise and how you might deal with them.
10. How do you keep records of all that you have done?

PREPARING FOR ASSESSMENT

In preparing for assessment on face massage the following checklist may be helpful. Check that you have covered and now fully understand those items:

- dealing with problems
- communicating with the client
- discussing and agreeing the client's requirements
- outlining the advantages and disadvantages of massage
- selecting suitable methods and movements of massage
- explaining the difference between massage movements
- recognising and naming facial muscles
- listing the effects of vibro massage.

When you feel that you are ready for assessment, talk to your trainer and arrange a suitable time.

Working together

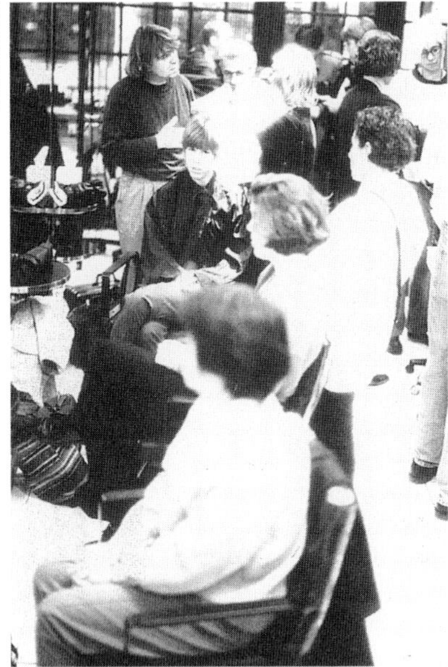

INTRODUCTION

This chapter is about working together productively as a team and covers the following topics:

- getting yourself organised
- how to work as part of a team
- personal development.

GETTING ORGANISED

All salons use the same tabular system for organising work, although different salons use this system in differing ways. The appointment system provides them with the following:

- a daily detailed action plan
- a schedule of individual work allocations
- a clear overview of business activities
- a general indication of expected time scales
- a general indication of expected sales.

The appointment system also has direct links with:

- resource requirements (such as stock and equipment)
- client records
- till transactions (such as daily sheets and till rolls).

As you can see, this system is the hub of an efficiently run business. The information it contains must therefore be clear, accurate and up to date.

But maintaining the appointment system correctly will not ensure the smooth running of the salon. You will always need to be prepared for the unexpected!

Your salon may have specific contingency procedures for coping with the following unplanned situations and circumstances, but generally these simple rules apply.

Late arrivals of clients

Suppose that a client arrives 15 minutes late for her appointment and apologetically explains that she was unavoidably held up (in circumstances beyond her control).What should you do?

First and foremost, be sympathetic and understanding. Find out if her stylist has still sufficient time to provide the service. If not, find out if anyone else can attend to her needs. Find out how long she may have to wait (if at all). Will there be any extra costs to the client? Will the appointment have to be re-booked?

Arrivals of unscheduled clients

A client who arrives unexpectedly without a booked appointment should always be accommodated, provided that there is an operator available and sufficient time to carry out the service or treatment.

Over/double booking

This does occur but, it is to be hoped, not too often. Normally this situation arises accidentally when a client or a staff member has made a mistake, or through poor communications. Deliberate overbooking is only done by the over-optimistic staff member. The result is that other people will need to be drawn in to help; otherwise delays will be unavoidable.

Don't try to beat the appointment system; you may upset clients, colleagues or both. Providing a high-quality service includes making sure people know the expected time scales and duration of services and treatments, and if there will be any waiting.

Changes to booked requirements

It often happens that a client who has booked for one service will, following consultation, change her mind and require something different. Don't worry! This could be good business – a client may come in expecting a restyle cut and finish, and go out with a change of hair colour as well. In fact many salons set incentives around this type of situation; for example, staff performances and/or commissions may be based on numbers of 'customer conversions'.

Staff absences

Staff absence will always stretch the salon to its limits but your salon should have contingency plans to cover this situation. Generally this will involve:

- checking customer records to see if other staff members have provided the service previously
- checking availability of appointments with other staff at the same time
- rescheduling in the appropriate spaces
- if all else fails, contacting the client to rebook the appointment at a later date.

EFFECTIVE COMMUNICATIONS

Good communication is always important – not just between clients and staff (see page 14), but also between staff and management.

Most hairdressers are good communicators. The relationship between stylist and client is built on quality of service, professional advice, trust, support and a listening ear.

Good communication ensures productive and effective action and promotes the on-going success of the business. On the other hand poor communication, arising from misunderstanding or misinterpretation, can lead to mistrust, arguments and embarrassment.

Oral communication

When providing information to others, whether face to face or on the telephone, remember to speak clearly; don't waffle, and try not to speak too fast. Be polite and listen carefully to the other's responses. To check that the information has been received correctly, ask if you have been understood and heard clearly. If not, repeat a summary of the main content of the information.

Written communication

A **memorandum** (or **memo**) is an ideal means of providing a written communication to team members. An effective memo clearly indicates:

- to whom it is addressed
- who wrote it
- the date
- the purpose of the memo
- its content (including, if relevant, clear and concise instructions).

Memorandum

TO: John

FROM: Linda

DATE: 1/10

SUBJECT: Staff absence

Jayne will not be in for the rest of the week as she has a virus. Please Could you reschedule her appointments, and advise all clients accordingly

Thanks.

Written communication: a memorandum

WORKING AS A TEAM

Always remember that your work colleagues need your assistance to help them do their job. Sharing the work load *is* working as a team. This can be achieved by:

- providing support
- anticipating the needs of others
- maintaining harmony
- maintaining good communication.

In some salons, you might see some staff busy attending to their clients, but others hanging about around reception, flicking through magazines or disappearing off to the staff room for a coffee. Teamwork is about making an active contribution, seeking to assist others even if it is only passing up rollers. It is good for staff morale and it shows a good image to the clients. In short make yourself useful, and contribute to the team effort by assisting your fellow workers.

Anticipating the needs of others follows on from providing support. Clean and prepare the work areas ready for use, locate and prepare products as and when they are required. (This will help the smooth operation of the salon.) Cooperate with your colleagues, make a positive contribution to your team by assisting them to provide a well-managed and coordinated quality service. Be self-motivated, keep yourself busy. Don't wait to be asked to do things.

Maintain harmony and try to minimise possible conflicts. Most good working relationships develop easily; others, however, need to be worked at.

Whatever your personal feelings are about your fellow work associates, clients must never sense a bad atmosphere within the salon caused by a friction between staff. You will spend a lot of time in the company of people you work with, but you will not always like everyone you meet. People are different: at work, in order to work as a team, a mutual respect for others is more important than close friendships. So remember:

- treat others with respect
- be sensitive and responsive to others' feelings
- show concern and care for others.

As for maintaining good communication – apart from the methods of effective communication outlined earlier in this chapter, there are other methods that we need to be aware of.

Body language

As well as using words, we express our interest and attitudes by non-verbal communication – our eye contact, posture and general body positioning. So it is very important that we convey the right *message*, particularly when dealing with clients and potential customers.

- **Eye contact** Maintain eye contact with the client when

talking to her. Where possible, maintain the same eye level as the client; for example, when you carry out a consultation with a client and she is seated, sit beside or opposite her. Standing over or above her and looking down will convey a feeling of authority, or as if you are trying to assert control. This is intimidating and definitely the wrong signal to send to a customer.

- **Distances** People have a 'comfort zone', a space around the body within which they feel at ease. Within a close, intimate relationship shared proximity may be welcome, but *uninvited* invasion of this space is at least uncomfortable, at its worst menacing or threatening.
- **Posture/body positioning/gestures** Volumes have been written on this subject alone and the psychology of body language is far too complex to address in a few paragraphs. But following certain obvious 'rules' can help us convey the right message and impression.
  - Slouching in the salon looks really unprofessional.
  - Folded arms – crossing the arms on the chest is a protective gesture and suggests a closed mind or a show of defensiveness.
  - Open palms – as a gesture supporting explanation or information, with hands at waist height, palms upwards, this indicates that the person has 'nothing to hide'. This is interpreted as openness or honesty.
  - Scratching behind the ear or rubbing the back of the neck while listening indicates that the listener is uncertain or doesn't understand.
  - Talking with your hand in front of your mouth may lead the listener to believe that you are not being honest. You are hiding yourself by your gestures.

ACTIVITY
Use role-play with a colleague to experiment with non-verbal communication. See if you can interpret what *is* or *isn't* being said!

These forms of communication are only indications of feelings and emotions. In isolation, they may not mean anything at all. Taken together, however, they can convey a very clear message. Make sure that you show the appropriate signals; be – and look – interested, keen, ready to help and positive. Above all, show that you can listen.

PERSONAL DEVELOPMENT

Managers of people use performance appraisal or progress reviews to evaluate the effectiveness of the work team. An **appraisal** is a system whereby you and your manager, in an interview situation, review and evaluate your personal contribution and/or progress over a predetermined period of time, as measured against expected targets or standards.

A similar process would take place at suitable points within a personal programme of training in order to review progress and training effectiveness, measured against specific training objectives.

Performance Appraisal	
Name:	Jane Manners
Job Title:	Trainee stylist
Date of Appraisal:	30/10/95
Objectives:	To obtain competence within:- Cutting hair - layering techniques across the range. Blow drying hair - on a variety of hair types and lengths
Notes on Achievement:	- competence has been achieved across the range for all the cutting requirements. - competence has been achieved for most blow drying range requirements.
Training Requirements:	Further training and practice is needed within the area of blow drying longer length effects.
Any other comments on performance by Appraiser:	Jane has achieved most of the objectives set out during the last appraisal.
Any comments on the Appraisal by the staff Appraised:	I feel that this has been a fair appraisal of my progress although I did not achieve all of my performance targets. J Manners.
Action Plan:	- To achieve occupational competence across the range for blow drying (i.e. longer length hair). - To undergo training and practice in perming methods and techniques. - To take assessment for perming.
Date of Next Appraisal:	28 April 1996

An appraisal form

Measuring effectiveness

To measure progress towards training targets as well as overall work contributions, there need to be clear stated expectations of the performance required. For both training and work activities, this is the standard in which competence will need to be demonstrated.

In training situations trainees undergo a programme of training which states:

- what training activities will take place
- what tasks need to be performed
- what standards are expected to be reached
- when assessment should be expected
- when a review of progress towards the agreed targets is to take place.

In normal, on-going work situations, **performance appraisal** will be based on the following factors:

- results achieved against objectives and job requirements
- any additional accomplishments and contributions
- contributions made by the individual as compared with those of other staff members.

The job requirements would be outlined in the employee's **job description**. A job description is a written specification of the

	Job description – Stylist
Location:	Based at salon as advised
Main purpose of job:	To ensure customer care is provided at all times To maintain a good standard of technical and client care, ensuring that up-to-date methods and techniques are used following the salon training practices and procedures
Responsible to:	Salon manager
Requirements:	To maintain the company's standards in respect of hairdressing/ beauty services To ensure that all clients receive service of the best possible quality To advise clients on services and treatments To advise clients on products and after-care To achieve designated performance targets To participate in self-development or to assist with the development of others To maintain company policy in respect of: • personal standards of health/hygiene • personal standards of appearance/ conduct • operating safety whilst at work • public promotion • corporate image as laid out in employee handbook To carry out client consultation in accordance with company policy To maintain company security practices and procedures To assist your manager in the provision of salon resources To undertake additional tasks and duties required by your manager from time to time.

main purposes and functions expected within a given job. Good job descriptions will include details of the following:

- the job title
- the work location(s)
- responsibility (to whom, and for what)
- the job purpose
- main functions (listed)
- standards expected
- any special conditions.

Standards expected from the job holder will often include standards of behaviour and appearance. If these have been stated from the outset, the job holder will know what is expected of her.

The appraisal process

At the beginning of the appraisal period, the manager and the employee discuss jointly, develop and mutually agree the objectives and performance measures for that period. An **action plan** will then be drafted outlining the expected outcomes.

During the appraisal period, should there be any significant changes in factors such as objectives or performance measures, these will be discussed between the manager and employee and any amendments will be appended to the action plan.

At the end of the appraisal period, the results are discussed by the employee and the manager, and both manager and employee sign the appraisal. A copy is prepared for the employee, and the original is kept on file.

An appraisal of performance will contain the following information:

- employee's name
- appraisal period
- appraiser's name and title
- performance objectives
- job title
- work location
- results achieved
- identified areas of strength and of weakness
- on-going action plan
- overall performance grading (optional).

Self-appraisal

In order for you to manage yourself within the job role, you need to identify the areas where you meet the expectations of your job and also the areas where there is room for improvement. Measuring your own strengths and weaknesses against laid-down performance criteria (as found in the NVQ Level 2 Standards of Competence) is one way of monitoring your own progress. Simply use the performance criteria set out within the standards as a checklist; this will help you to:

- identify areas where further training is required
- identify areas where further practice is required
- identify area where competence can be achieved.

HAIRDRESSING TRAINING BOARD

Unit 8:	Contribute to the overall effectiveness of the work team
Element 8.3:	**Improve personal effectiveness within the job role**
Performance Criteria:	(a) **own strengths and weaknesses within the job role are identified with the relevant person, taking into account salon and national occupational standards, and relevant legislation**
	(b) **potential for improving effectiveness is identified with the relevant person, and realistic targets agreed**
	(c) **opportunities available for improving self-motivation and effectiveness are actively sought and are used to best effect**
	(d) **progress towards achievement of agreed targets is reviewed regularly with the relevant person**
	(e) **results of reviews are used constructively to assist personal development**
	(f) **awareness of current and emerging fashion trends and developments in technology within the industry is maintained**
Range Statements:	(i) Developments in technology: * products and their usage * tools * equipment
Essential Knowledge and Understanding Requirements:	* How to identify own strengths and weaknesses
	* How to react positively to reviews and feedback, and why this is important
	* How to maintain awareness of current and emerging trends and developments within the industry, and why this is important

NVQ element

ASSIGNMENTS: WORKING TOGETHER

A practical activity

This assignment offers you the opportunity to study and assess your professional strengths and weaknesses. The table consists of three columns. The first column contains headings covering personal skills, while the second and third columns are left blank, ready for you to complete.

After completing the table ask your training supervisor to check your answers. If she agrees with your answers, keep the completed document for use in your folder or personal portfolio.

Personal skills	*My strengths are*	*My weaknesses are*
Organising myself at work		
Communicating with other staff		
Communicating with the clients		
Helping and supporting others in their work		
Solving problems on my own		

For you to find out

In relation to your salon, find out the following information and record the details along with any drawings, illustrations or photographs in your folder or personal portfolio.

1 What contingency action is taken in respect of the following circumstances?

- late arrival of clients
- arrival of unscheduled clients
- over/double booking
- services/treatments running later than planned
- clients changing their previously booked services/ treatments
- staff absences.

2 What things can you find to do when the salon isn't busy?

3 Passing information to clients and staff is all part of maintaining good communication. By what methods do you pass on information to management? Make particular reference to:

- handling personal matters
- maintaining the provision of services/treatments
- health and safety issues.

A case study

For this assignment you are required to carry out a self-assessment of your own skills. You will find this activity is easier to do if it is carried out after completing the first assignment in this chapter.

The checklist shown below has been devised from the current national standards (Hairdressing NVQ Level 2). This checklist relates to Unit 8 element 8.3: 'Improve personal effectiveness within the job role'.

Have a go at completing the checklist. If you do not understand the words used, or if you cannot yet tick all the boxes, ask your training supervisor to help you. Keep the completed document for use in your folder or personal portfolio.

When I'm at work . . .	*Yes, I do this* ✔	*No, I don't do this* ✘	*My training supervisor's comments*
I discuss my different job strengths and weaknesses with my training supervisor			
I discuss ways of improving my work effectiveness with my training supervisor			
Where possible, I always do jobs without having to be asked first			
I discuss my progress during regular reviews with my training supervisor			
I like to keep abreast of hair fashion and new products and equipment			

PREPARING FOR ASSESSMENT

Whilst making preparations for assessment on working as a team, the following checklist may be helpful. Check that you have covered and now fully understand these items:

- getting yourself organised
- the tasks and activities you perform in your work
- handling appointments and coping with scheduling problems
- providing information to management
- supporting and helping others in their work
- self-appraisal.

When you feel that you are ready, talk to your trainer to arrange a suitable time for your assessment.

CHAPTER 12

Salon resources

INTRODUCTION

VIDAL SASSOON

This chapter looks specifically at the usage, maintenance and control of:

- stock
- tools
- equipment
- utilities.

These terms are collectively known as the salon's **material resources**. Salons cannot function without them and it is your job to ensure that they are handled, operated, used and/or maintained in the proper manner.

STOCK MAINTENANCE

In general, stock is purchased by the salon. It will then be either used within the salon, or resold to clients in order to extend the hairdressing service as an after-care (home use) option. Products used in this way are referred to as **consumables**, and fall into a variety of types and categories. These will include:

- hairdressing products for use in the salon
- hairdressing products for resale to clients
- cleaning products for salon maintenance
- protective items kept for health and safety reasons
- food and drink products.

In order for salons to maintain adequate levels of stock, managers need up-to-date information on all stock, whether it is currently held in the salon, or on order.

This will relate directly to what has been used and sold.

STOCK MANAGEMENT PROCESS

Salon stock in hand

The designated salon stock-holding levels represent the basic amounts required for the salon to function effectively over a set period of time. The length of time varies from salon to salon, depending on the individual needs of each.

The stock will be made up of many types of goods, which have different 'lifespans' – short, medium or long.

For example, products purchased solely for resale or client application will have a limited life. Some will need to be used before a certain date (their **shelf life** is limited). Sundry items such as towels, brushes and combs will, with use, need to be replaced regularly. Small pieces of electrical equipment, such as hand dryers, tongs and clippers, will be expected to last considerably longer. The large items of salon equipment, such as chairs, styling units or hood dryers, are not included within the salon stock. These items are **capital equipment** and are accounted for in a different way.

Most products used for client application are chemical-based, and there are strict laws controlling the handling and usage of such items. Products that have been assessed as potential **hazards** need to be kept in a safe and secure location (see page 280).

The rest of the supplies awaiting use will also need to be kept securely. Many products – for example, shampoos, conditioners, setting and styling aids – are kept out in the salon for current use. Other items may be strategically displayed for promotional purposes – at styling positions, perhaps, or in the reception area. These products can then be touched and handled, smelt and seen.

The placement of such items will generate interest, and offer opportunities for conversation between staff and clients. This will help to create product awareness, and may well increase additional sales of products, services and treatments.

Stock taking and stock control

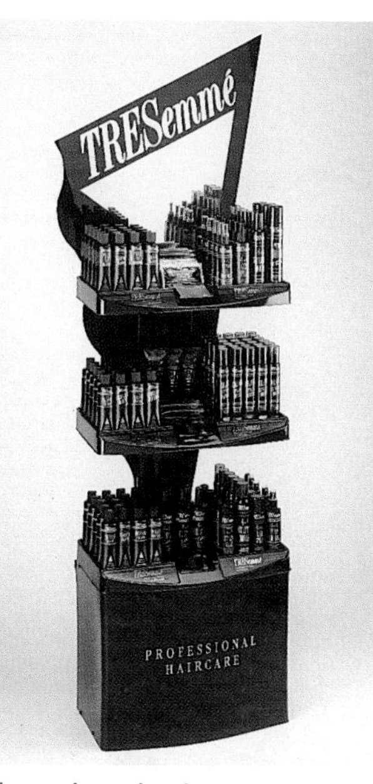

TRESemmé

Retail product display

A **stock take** is a procedure whereby all the salon's supplies are checked and accounted for. This will include checking the goods for quantity, quality and condition.

Regular monitoring of the goods in this way will provide the salon's managers with up-to-date, accurate information. This they can use when planning and making decisions regarding their current financial commitments, their cash flow forecasts, stock movements and possible future promotions.

Checking the quantity

This is carried out by physically counting both the products in store and any others within the salon.

In a perfect world, if a new salon on January 1st takes delivery of one dozen retail conditioners, then sells eight of them within the month, a stock take on February 1st will show that four remain.

Unfortunately the accounting task is more complicated than that. Some (though not all) of the supplies purchased by the salon will be used during normal salon services; this would be fairly straightforward if they were used in their entirety, but some part-empty packs may remain to be used up later. Products purchased

on can vary in their volumes; for example,
ystems are packaged for individual applications
in packs of six. And shampoo, conditioner and
s for salon use are normally bought as multiple
How many individual shampoos do you think
it of a five-litre container?
andardise' the services and treatments to clients,
eed accurate information from the stock take so
lentify any discrepancies.
ke must involve three key factors.

1. Count the current stock in hand.
2. Check for product damage or deterioration.
3. Complete the necessary documentation.

Depending on the salon's policy and requirements, you may be asked to record the stock take by writing details on a piece of paper, or by completing a pre-printed **(pro-forma)** form. In any event you will have to understand:

- how the items are counted
- who the manufacturers are
- what the product categories are
- what the product types are.

The method of **counting the items** will depend on the purchasing arrangements of the individual salon or company. They may, for instance, be counted as designated units, sets, multiples or packs.

STOCK RECORD

Description ________________

How packed ________________ Type/Grade ______ Colour ______ Size ______

Stock code ☐☐☐☐☐☐

Stock levels: Maximum ______ Minimum ______ Re-order ______

Record of receipts and issues					Record of orders			
Date	Ref	In	Out	Remarks	Date	Supplier	Qty	Received

A stock record card

The **manufacturers** are the companies that produce different product ranges. Their names and logos are familiar, and appear on product labelling; examples include Wella, L'Oréal, Goldwell, TRESemmé and many more.

The **product categories** are the general product groups that manufacturers make, such as shampoos, conditioners, perms, colours, gels and hairsprays.

Each product group will encompass a variety of different **product types**. For example, different shampoo types are formulated for dry, greasy and normal hair, for treating dandruff, and so on.

Checking the quality (and stock rotation)

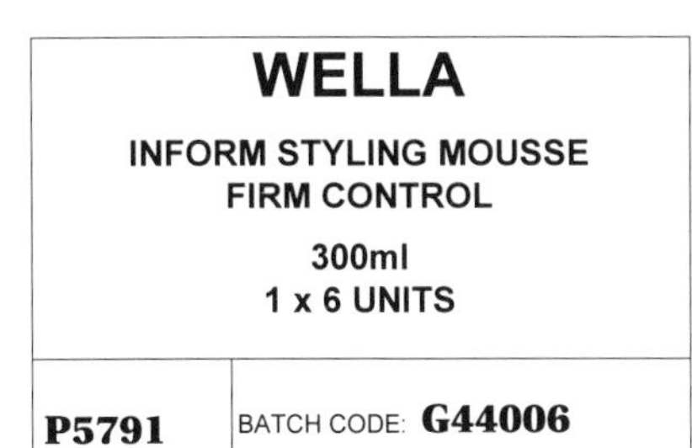

A batch code on packaging

This can be carried out at the same time as the stock count. But in any event, products that are purchased (and sold) by the salon come under the provisions of the **Sale of Goods Act** and relevant sections of the **Consumer Protection Act**. Products sold must be of **merchantable quality** – an expected standard that refers to product condition.

In order for goods to remain of merchantable quality, stock needs to be monitored and, if required, rotated. This means that when a stock order arrives, you should bring older stock to the front of the shelves and store the new stock behind. (Remember that products can deteriorate if their expected shelf life is exceeded.) At the time of writing hairdressing products with limited shelf lives do not carry 'use by' dates. Manufacturers often print **batch codes** on their products, however. These are encrypted codes which, for quality assurance purposes, contain all the necessary data relating to product manufacture. If you note these batch codes when taking delivery, it will help you to recognise older and newer stock.

Checking the condition

Damage to supplies can occur in several ways. It may arise

- during manufacturing or in transit, or
- through incorrect handling or storage.

Goods that have been damaged during manufacture or in transit should be identified when checking the products during delivery. This damage is not the responsibility of the salon, and therefore the goods cannot be accepted.

Damage often arises from incorrect handling or storage of goods. This could be potentially hazardous. Consider the following possibilities:

- caustic or corrosive chemicals – can be dangerous if spilt
- pressurised canisters and aerosols
- inflammable/combustible materials
- electrical faults or defective equipment.

Hazardous materials are usually identified on packaging by standard warning symbols ('icons').

Hazard icons

Checking for damage and/or deterioration should be a routine part of stock taking. If products are discoloured, split, spilt or dented, notify someone in authority immediately. Take care too that products are stored/stacked away safely.

Taking deliveries

When stock arrives at the salon it should be moved from the reception to a secure location away from the working area. The movement of stock is subject to stringent health and safety requirements and you must have adequate training before attempting to handle it.

Most products used in salons arrive pre-packed and many contain chemicals. Look at the packaging for any specific handling requirements. These may be indicated by labels such as 'fragile', 'this way up', 'handle with care', 'do not bend' or 'contains corrosive materials'.

When goods arrive at the salon, check to see if the packaging corresponds to the contents. Orders made at the wholesalers may involve smaller, individual items and could therefore be packed into any container of a suitable size.

All deliveries should arrive with either a delivery note or an invoice.

A **delivery note** should contain information relating to the goods received. Details of the items, volumes, date, sender and

HAIRDRESSING SUPPLIES
BLYTHE AVENUE, LONDON, W1 Tel No. 0171 123 456

DELIVERY NOTE

GOODS DELIVERED TO:

HEADQUARTERS
40 THORPE AVENUE
KENTON
MIDDLESEX

INTERNAL REF NO: TGA122
DELIVERY NOTE NO: 1234-5
DATE: 30/09/95

A/c No: DW71143X
Customer Order No: BC/JJ/12

LINE NO	PRODUCT CODE	PRODUCT DESCRIPTION	UNIT	LOCATION	QUANTITY SENT	QUANTITY TO FOLLOW
1	A114-9	DISPOSABLE GLOVES X 100	1		1	0
2	A324-0	HAIRDRESSING TOWELS	1		6	0
3	T078-2	SCULPTING MOUSSE	1		12	0
4	C160-0	PROFESSIONAL CLIPPER	1		1	0
5	T412-0	SHAMPOO	1		12	0

DATE OF DESPATCH	METHOD	NO OF BOXES	WEIGHT	CUSTOMER SIGNATURE

A delivery note

delivery address should be clearly visible. When a delivery is received the goods *must* be checked against:

- the relevant stock order
- the delivery note.

Before the goods are signed for, check that there are no indications of damage or deterioration, or discrepancies between the goods supplied and the documentation. If there are any problems, tell the appropriate staff member, and record exactly what the difficulty is.

An **invoice** may arrive with the stock, but more usually reaches the salon some time after delivery. The invoice also contains information relating to the goods received, such as the items, volumes, date, sender and delivery address. The invoice will in addition indicate the unit cost for each item and the total remittance due. It is a request for payment and should be processed accordingly.

HAIRDRESSING SUPPLIES

BLYTHE AVENUE, LONDON, W1 Tel No. 0171 123 456

SALES INVOICE

INVOICE ADDRESS:

HEADQUARTERS
40 THORPE AVENUE
KENTON
MIDDLESEX

INVOICE NO:	501367
CUSTOMER A/C NO:	DW71143X
OUR REF:	TGA122
CUSTOMER REF:	BC/JJ/12
DATE:	30/09/95

QUANTITY	DESCRIPTION	CODE	UNIT PRICE £	TOTAL PRICE £
1 box	DISPOSABLE GLOVES	A114-9	5.95	5.95
6	HAIRDRESSING TOWELS	A342-0	2.50	15.00
12	SCULPTING MOUSSE	T078-2	2.95	35.40
1	PROFESSIONAL CLIPPER	C160-0	27.50	27.50
12	SHAMPOO	T412-0	3.25	39.00
PAYMENT SHOULD REACH US BY:		30/10/95		
		TOTAL GOODS		122.85
		VAT @ 17.5%		21.50
		TOTAL AMOUNT DUE		144.35

VAT Reg No. 012 345 67 TERMS & CONDITIONS OF SALE OVERLEAF

A sales invoice

Handling stock

Once the goods have been received, they will need prompt moving into suitable storage.

Lifting presents a potential hazard, as the incorrect handling of supplies can cause injuries. If a package or box seems heavy, **do not** try to lift it. Inform the appropriate person and they will take a suitable alternative course of action.

Lifting safely (guidance on manual handling from the Health and Safety Executive)

The correct method of lifting involves a co-ordinated process of events.

- **Stop and think about the task in hand.**
  Plan the lift. Where is the load going to be placed? Use appropriate aids if possible. Do you need help with the load? Remove obstructions such as discarded wrapping materials. For a long lift, such as from the floor to shoulder height, consider resting the load half-way, perhaps on a table in order to change your grip.
- **Place your feet properly.**
  Put your feet apart, giving a balanced and stable base for lifting (tight skirts and unsuitable footwear make this difficult), with your leading leg as far forward as is comfortable.
- **Adopt a good posture.**
  Bend your knees so that your hands when grasping the load are as nearly level with your waist as possible (but don't kneel, or overflex your knees). Keep your back straight. Lean forward over the load if necessary to get a good grip. Keep your shoulders level and facing in the same direction as your hips.
- **Get a firm grip.**
  Try to keep your arms within the boundary formed by your legs. The optimum position and nature of the grip depends on circumstances and individual preference, but it must be secure.
- **Don't jerk.**
  Carry out the lifting movement smoothly, keeping control of the load.
- **Move your feet.**
  Don't twist your trunk when turning to the side.
- **Keep close to the load.**
  Keep the load close to the trunk for as long as possible. Keep the heaviest side of the load close to your body. If a close approach to the load is not possible, try sliding it towards you before attempting to lift it.
- **Put down, then adjust.**
  If precise positioning of the load is necessary, put it down first, then slide it into position.

The main piece of health and safety legislation affecting the handling of stock is the Health and Safety at Work Act. The provisions of this Act include the following sets of regulations:

- COSHH (The Control Of Substances Hazardous to Health Regulations 1988)
- Workplace (Health, Safety and Welfare) Regulations 1992
- Manual Handling Operations Regulations 1992
- Personal Protective Equipment at Work Regulations 1992.

Further information on these regulations can be found on pages 279–82.

TIP

Remember that retail products displayed on shelves may:
- become dusty or dirty
- be easily damaged if handled
- get stolen.

Correct storage

Most of the stock in hand (and all potentially hazardous substances) should be stored in a lockable store-room or large cupboard. The shelving should be adjustable so that varying sizes of boxes and containers can be accommodated. All goods should be stored upright, and not stacked on top of each other unless the packaging specifies otherwise.

The storage surfaces need to be:

- easily accessible
- washable and hygienic
- clearly labelled
- safe
- secure.

TRESemmé

Retail products

The most frequently used products should be placed at eye or shoulder level, so that staff do not have to bend and stretch unnecessarily. Large or heavy items should be placed on the floor or on the lower shelves.

Retail product lines should be displayed in suitable cabinets or merchandisers where they can be seen by the clients. Where product security could present a problem, it may be possible to display dummies (packaging with promotional information, without product content.)

Security of stock

As far as possible, stock should be available for use as and when required. if any shortages are noted, the reason may be the presence of a thief.

Theft during business hours by salon visitors (such as clients, friends and business contacts) can be minimised if staff are trained to establish the identity of all salon callers. Most people will be able to give a valid reason for their visit.

If you approach someone who is acting suspiciously and they cannot give you a satisfactory reason for their visit, alert a senior member of staff immediately. Do **not** put yourself at any risk. If the individual runs away, report the incident at once. It is likely that the police will need to be called and therefore you should document the facts. You will need to tell them clearly and accurately

- the date and time of the incident
- where the incident happened
- what actually took place
- what the intruder looked like.

The police will also require statements from any other witnesses.

If most stock is kept in a locked, secure area such as a store-room, a cupboard or a retail cabinet, the opportunity for theft is minimised. Some salons designate specific individuals as key holders with the authority to dispense products. This reduces the chance of theft even further.

Stock is a valuable asset belonging to the salon. If the salon has an accurate stock control system, it will be easier to spot discrepancies and shortages.

Unfortunately, theft by salon visitors is not the only way in which stealing occurs. Theft by staff (now often referred to as **shrinkage**) is something else of which salon managers must be aware. Theft of money or goods or equipment is an act of gross misconduct, and if discovered will be followed by disciplinary action, which would mean instant dismissal (see also pages 278–9).

Avoiding waste and damage

Regular checks on goods and equipment, through careful stock control and health and safety checks, will assist in minimising shortages. But shortages can still occur if items are misused or neglectfully wasted. Using tools for purposes other than their intended use could be negligent, if not dangerous: think of the risks in changing a plug using a pair of scissors instead of a screwdriver, or preparing a colour using a whole tube of tint where half would have been enough.

Other salon resources can be misused too:

- **The telephone** Making personal calls in business hours will, at least, block incoming calls from clients; at worst, it can even be classed as theft if the calls are not paid for.
- **Water** Leaving the taps on between shampoos or conditioning treatments, or excessive rinsing during neutralising (beyond the manufacturer's instructions), wastes energy and money.
- **Electricity** Heaters left on in the staff room during normal working hours, or lights left on in unoccupied areas of the salon, or hood dryers running after the client has finished, are also extravagantly wasteful.

ACTIVITY

We have listed a few examples of misuse and/or wastage. Make a list of other possible situations where
- water
- power
- tools and equipment

could be misused, wasted or damaged.

ASSIGNMENTS: SALON RESOURCES

A practical activity

You are asked to create a stock master file in the form of a card index. With permission from your supervisor, create an alphabetically indexed, product master file for the products that are used within your salon. Use the example format suggested below. (If you prefer not to use A5 card, you can use paper instead.)

When you have completed the assignment ask your training supervisor to check your indexing system. If the system is correct, write notes to

- describe exactly what you did
- explain how you obtained the necessary information.

Product name	Product category	Product type	Manufacturer
....	....	....	....
Supplier: Direct (manufacturer) .... Wholesaler	Supplier address	....	Tel. no. .... Fax no. ....
COSHH (handling details)		Stock holding Size/volume Qty .... Location	Levels ....

For you to find out

In relation to your salon, find out the following information and record the details along with any drawings, photographs or other illustrations in your folder or personal portfolio.

1. Give a full explanation of the stock control procedures that take place within your salon, make particular reference to the following stock processes:
   - monitoring, i.e. checks made on amounts, condition, discrepancies and damages
   - rotation
   - records and documentation.
2. Products which are purchased for retailing to customers need to be displayed within the salon. Explain
   - how your salon promotes products for resale
   - how your salon displays products for resale.
3. What are the COSHH implications in relation to storing and displaying stock?

A case study

Each salon has different ways of making sure that wastage and damages are kept to a minimum. These will involve specific handling procedures, regular checks and particular methods of using resources.

With particular reference to your own salon's procedures, find out the following information. Keep the resulting documentation along with any illustrations for use in your portfolio your folder or portfolio.

1 For each of the following, how can wastage (a) occur, (b) be avoided in respect to the handling or application of:

- shampoo
- conditioner
- tints
- perms
- hairspray
- mousse
- setting lotions.

2 When stock is received into the salon from the supplier, describe what you would do to ensure that there are not any (a) shortages of stock, (b) damages to stock.

3 Say what you think constitutes misuse of each of the following resources:

- salon telephone
- salon fax (if applicable)
- salon tools and equipment.

PREPARING FOR ASSESSMENT

Whilst making preparations for assessment on handling resources, the following checklist may be helpful. Check that you have covered and now fully understand these items:

- stock monitoring procedures
- stock rotation procedures
- handling stock
- storage and display procedures for stock and equipment
- stock security
- reasons for minimising wastage.

When you feel that you are ready, talk to your salon assessor to arrange a suitable time for your assessment.

Health, safety and security in the salon

INTRODUCTION

This chapter looks at health, safety and security with specific relevance to:

- personal health, hygiene and appearance
- working safely in the salon
- maintaining salon security in the salon
- health and safety legislation.

Legislation provided within the Health and Safety at Work Act 1974 (see page 279) requires all employees to:

'*take reasonable care for the health and safety of himself and any others who may be affected by his actions or omissions . . . and to cooperate with their employer, so that their employer can fulfil his obligation by complying with the current (UK and EC) health and safety requirements.*'

It is therefore just as important to maintain personal standards of health and hygiene as to work safely in the salon.

PERSONAL HEALTH AND HYGIENE

TIP

You don't get a second chance to create a good first impression.

Hairdressing is a personal service industry. It relies solely on the profits generated from the sales of services and treatments to clients. Every member of staff has a role within the task of **establishing** and then **maintaining** a satisfied clientele.

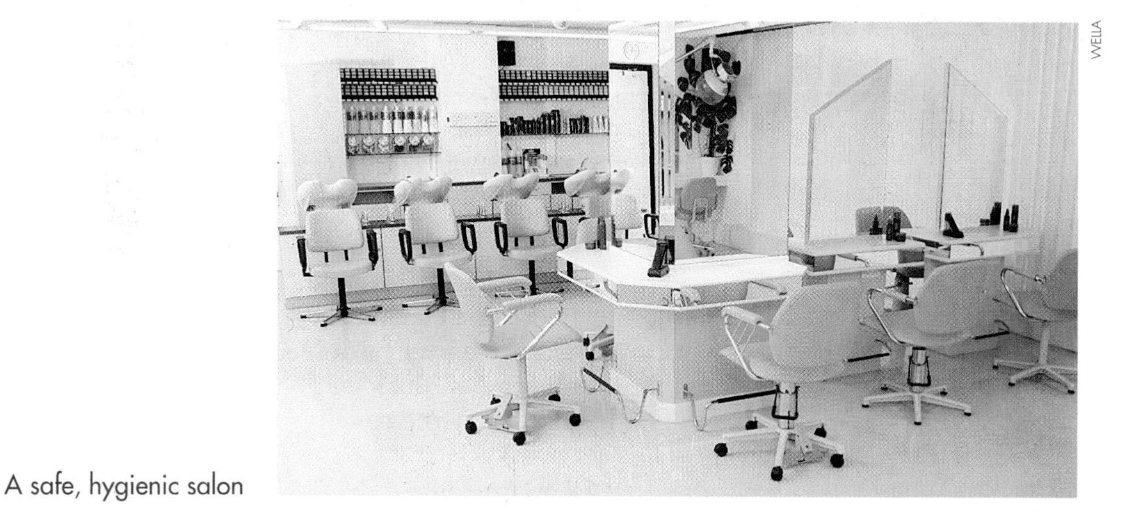

WELLA

A safe, hygienic salon

Initially, your clients will judge your personal and professional standards by the way in which you present yourself. Remember, hairdressing is an image-conscious industry. We strive to provide a high-quality service that gives clients well-cut, well-styled and well-groomed hair, so that they feel pleased and confident, and have a greater self-esteem. What confidence could you provide them with if you turned up for their appointments with stained overalls, unkempt hair and dirty hands and nails?

Hands and nails

Your hands should always be perfectly clean. Dirt on your hands and under your nails will harbour bacteria. By spreading germs you could infect other people. Your hands need washing not only before work, but several times throughout the day. Where hands regularly come into contact with water or detergents, the skin may lose its moisture, become dry and crack. Cracked, broken skin allows germs to enter and infection may follow. To prevent this from happening you should regularly moisturise your skin after washing. If your hands are often in water (for example, in shampooing or conditioning), you may find it helpful to use a **barrier cream**. Barrier creams cover the skin with an invisible barrier which greatly reduces the penetration of hairdressing cleansing and conditioning agents. (Many trainees have given up hairdressing after developing the skin condition called **dermatitis**, in which the hands become sore, cracked, itchy and red. At this stage work becomes painful and medical advice should be sought.)

Long nails not only trap dirt underneath, but also can cause discomfort to clients. In certain hairdressing procedures it is quite possible that longer nails could even scratch or damage the skin. This risk of spreading infection and disease can be prevented by keeping nails short and neat. Clean, well-manicured nails without splits or tears are hygienic and safe.

HEALTH AND SAFETY

All salons carry out a risk assessment of the substances they use. Any substances that have been identified as potentially hazardous to health will have special handling instructions. These instructions, along with any necessary personal protective equipment (PPE), must be available within the salon.

Body

Taking a daily bath is necessary to remove the build-up of sweat, dead skin cells and surface bacteria. Skin in areas such as armpits, feet and genitals has more sweat glands than elsewhere, and the warm, moist conditions in these areas provide an ideal breeding ground for bacteria. Regular washing is therefore essential if 'BO' (body odour) is to be prevented.

> **ACTIVITY**
> Certain jobs require personal protective equipment. Find out from your supervisor what jobs in your salon require special equipment. List the jobs, and any relevant equipment that must be used.

Antiperspirants will reduce under-arm sweating. These products contain astringents, which narrow the pores that emit the sweat and cool down the skin. Alternatively, **deodorants** may be used. These products will not reduce the amount of sweating but can 'mask' any odour by killing the surface bacteria with antiseptic ingredients.

Mouth

Unpleasant breath is offensive to clients. Bad breath **(halitosis)** is the result of leaving particles to decay with in the spaces between the teeth. You need to brush your teeth after every meal. Bad breath can also result from digestive troubles, stomach upsets, smoking and strong foods such as onions, garlic and some cheeses.

Personal appearance

Personal appearance

In addition to personal cleanliness, your personal appearance is an important factor too. The effort you put into getting ready for work reflects your pride in the job. It is all right for you to have your own individual look, provided that you appreciate and accept that there are professional standards of dress and appearance that must be followed – a sort of personal code of practice.

Clothes

Clothes or overalls should be clean and well-ironed. It is sensible to wear clothes made from fabrics that are suitable not only for your intended work but also for the time of year. Clothes that are restrictive or tight will not allow air to circulate around your body and will prevent you from keeping cool and fresh; they could lead to uncomfortable perspiration or possibly BO. Apart from the clothes that other people see, remember that a daily change of underwear is essential.

Shoes

Wear shoes that have low heels. They should be smart, comfortable and be made of materials suitable for wearing over long periods of time. Remember that hairdressing involves a lot of standing and your feet can therefore get tired, hot, sweaty and even sore. It is worth wearing shoes that allow your feet to 'breathe', as ventilated feet remain cool and comfortable throughout the working day.

Hair

Your hair reflects the image and expected standards of the salon in which you work. It should be clean, healthy and manageable. Don't let long hair fall over your face, as this will obstruct good communication with the clients and your poor body language may give them the wrong message.

Jewellery

Only the minimum of jewellery should be worn in the salon. Rings, bracelets and dangling necklaces will get in the way of normal day-to-day duties and will make the client uncomfortable. In many hairdressing operations, such as shampooing and conditioning, jewellery can catch and pull at the client's hair as well as provide unhygienic crevices for dirt and germs to lurk in.

Posture

Bad posture will lead to fatigue or even longer-term injury. Adopting the correct posture is essential for trainee and competent hairdresser alike. An incorrect standing position will put undue strains on both muscles and ligaments, as well as giving your clients an impression of an uncaring, unprofessional attitude towards work.

Posture fatigue will occur when a part of the body is out of line with another part immediately below. Hairdressers have to be on their feet a great deal, therefore adopting a good posture is a requirement of the job. You will achieve correct posture when your head, shoulders, upper torso, abdomen, thighs and legs distribute your body's weight in a balanced, equally proportioned way, over feet that are positioned forward and slightly apart. Dropping a shoulder will shift your body's weight over one foot. This will cause curvature of the spine, applying strains on muscles and ligaments, as well as exerting pressures on the intervetebral discs in your spine. This will at least be uncomfortable and at worst dangerous, possibly starting a longer-term back problem or injury.

Your posture whilst sitting should be restful. Your back should be supported all the way down. This does not mean that chairs must have a continuous back or have contoured, moulded panels, but that your sitting position should provide your body with support so that the pelvis and not the base of the spine takes the body's weight.

Avoid sitting with crossed legs, as this will restrict blood circulation. It will result in numbness and a sensation of 'pins and needles'.

Infection and disease

We all carry large numbers of micro-organisms inside us, on our skin and in our hair. These organisms, such as **bacteria**, **fungi** and **viruses**, are too small to be seen with the naked eye. Bacteria and fungi can be seen through a microscope, but viruses are too small even for that.

Many micro-organisms are quite harmless, but some can cause disease. Those that are harmful to people are called **pathogens**. Flu, for example, is caused by a virus, thrush by a fungus and bronchitis often by bacteria. Conditions like these, which can be transmitted from one person to another, are said to be **infectious**.

The body is naturally resistant to infection; it can fight most pathogens using its inbuilt immunity system. So it is possible to be infected with pathogenic organisms without contracting the disease.

When you have a disease, the **symptoms** are the visible signs that something is wrong. They are the the results of the infection and of the reactions of the body to that infection. Symptoms help you to recognise the disease.

Infectious diseases should always be treated by a general practitioner. Non-infectious conditions and defects can often be treated in the salon or with products available from the chemist.

WORKING SAFELY IN THE SALON

You have a duty to your employer and your colleagues to keep the working environment safe. You need to be alert, spotting potential hazards and preventing accidents, thus helping to avoid emergency situations arising. Suppose, for example, that someone had carelessly blocked a fire door with a recently delivered stock order. You could take the initiative and remove a possible hazard by moving the box to a safe and secure location. If you notice a potential hazard that you cannot easily rectify yourself, tell your supervisor immediately. Imagine, for instance, that someone accidentally tripped over a trailing lead from a hand dryer while it was plugged in, wrenching the lead from the dryer handle on to a wet floor. Under no circumstances should you enter the wet area and try to retrieve the trailing lead; but you should tell a senior member of the staff at once, so that they can shut off the power at the mains supply.

Avoiding potential hazards

Obstructions

It is dangerous to obstruct areas used as thoroughfares, such as doorways, corridors, stairs and fire exists. In an emergency, people might have to leave the salon, or part of it, in a hurry – perhaps even in the dark. It could be disastrous if someone injured themselves, or fell, in these circumstances.

So always be on the lookout for any obstruction in these areas. If you see something that could present a risk, move it away as quickly as you can.

ACTIVITY

List the things that staff use in the salon that could be unsafe if they are not used in the right way.

Find out what things could be a danger in areas where staff work.

Spillage and breakages

Take care when you have to clear up spilt chemicals or damaged equipment. First of all find out what has been spilt or dropped. Is this something that needs special care and attention when handling? (See page 282.) Does personal protective equipment need to be worn? (See page 281.)

Disposal of waste

General salon waste

Everyday items of salon waste should be placed in an enclosed waste bin fitted with a suitably resistant polyethylene bin liner. When the bin is full the liner can be sealed using a wire tie, and placed ready for refuse collection. If for any reason the bin liner punctures, put the damaged liner and waste inside a second bin liner. Wash out the inside of the bin itself with hot water and detergent.

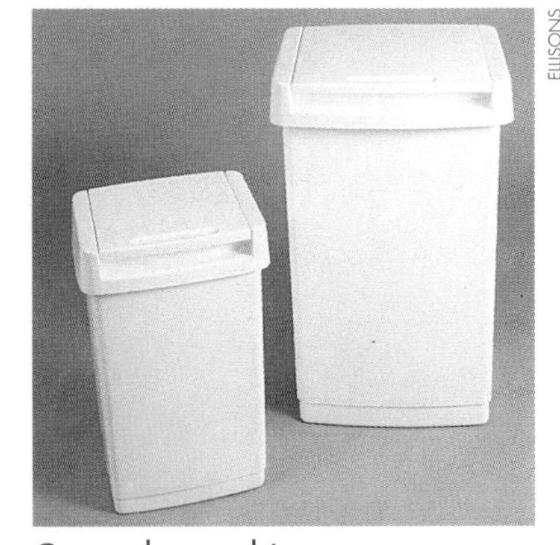

ELLISONS

Covered waste bins

Disposable sharps

Used razor blades and similar items should be placed into a safe screw-topped container. When the container is full it can be discarded. This type of salon waste should be kept away from general salon waste as special disposal arrangements are provided by your local authority. Contact your local council offices for more information.

ACTIVITY
Design a checklist to cover the safety requirements for your salon that concern fire doors, corridors, exits etc.

ACTIVITY
Find out what types of waste are generated within your salon, and how each type is disposed of.

GENERAL SALON HYGIENE

The salon

A warm, humid salon can offer a perfect home for disease-carrying bacteria. If they can find food in the form of dust and dirt, they may reproduce rapidly. Good ventilation, however, provides a circulating air current that will help to prevent their growth. This is why it is important to keep the salon clean, dry and well aired at all times – and this includes clothing, work areas, tools and all equipment.

A tidy salon is easier to clean. So get into the habit of clearing up your work as you go.

Floors and seating

Floors should be kept clean at all times. That means that they will need regular mopping, sweeping or vacuuming. When working areas are damp-mopped during normal working hours, make sure that adequate warning signs are provided close to the wet areas. (You will notice that this is a standard procedure in fast food chains.)

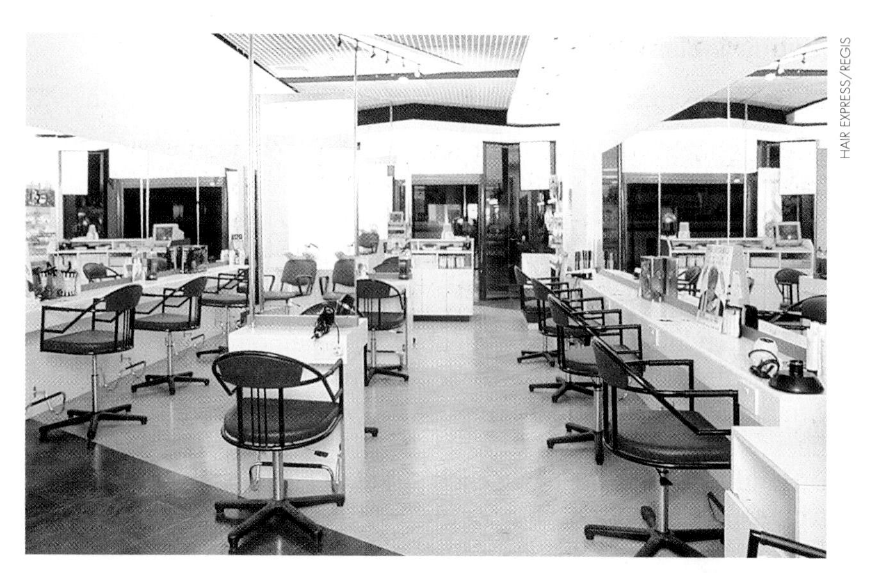

A salon

The salon's seating will be made of material that is easily cleaned. It should be washed regularly with hot water and detergent. After drying the seats can be wiped over with disinfectant or an antiseptic lotion.

Working surfaces

All surfaces within the salon, including the reception, staff and stock preparation areas, should be washed down at least once each day. Most salons now use easily maintained wipe-clean surfaces, usually some form of plastic laminate. They can be cleaned with hot water and detergent, and after the surfaces are dry they can be wiped over with a spirit-based antiseptic which will not smear. Don't use scourers or abrasives as these will scratch plastic surfaces. Scratched surfaces look dull and unattractive as well as containing minute crevices in which bacteria will develop.

Mirrors

Glass mirrors should be cleaned every morning before clients arrive. Never try to style a client's hair whilst she sits in front of a murky, dusty or smeary mirror. Glass surfaces should be cleaned and polished using either hot water and detergent, or a spirit-based lotion that evaporates quickly without smearing.

HEALTH AND SAFETY
You have a duty to your colleagues and clients to minimise the possible spread of infection or disease. Hairdressers by the nature of their work are in constant close contact with their customers and need to pay particular attention to healthy, hygienic and safe working practices.

Salon equipment

Towels and gowns

Each client must have a fresh, clean towel and gown. These should be washed in hot soapy water to remove any soiling or staining, and to prevent the spread of infection by killing any bacteria. Fabric conditioners may be used to provide a luxurious softness and freshness.

Styling tools

Most pieces of salon equipment, such as combs, brushes, curlers and so forth, are made from plastics. These materials are relatively easy to keep hygienically safe, if they are used and cleaned properly.

Combs should be washed daily. When not in use they should be immersed into a antibacterial solution. When needed they can be rinsed and dried and are then ready for use.

If any styling tools are accidentally dropped on to the floor, do not use them until they have been adequately cleaned. Don't put contaminated items on to work surfaces as they could spread infection and disease.

Handle non-plastic items, such as scissors and clipper blades, with care. Clean them with surgical spirit by carefully wiping over the flat edges of the blades. Although most of these items are made of special steels, don't immerse them in sterilising fluids. Many of these contain chemicals that will corrode their precision-made surfaces.

PREVENTING INFECTION

Some salons use sterilising devices as a means of providing hygienically safe work implements. **Sterilisation** means the complete eradication of living organisms. Different devices use different sterilisation methods, which may be based on the use of heat, radiation or chemicals.

Autoclaves

These provide the most effective method of sterilisation. They work on the principles of the pressure cooker. The items to be sterilised are heated with a small amount of water inside a pressurised container to a temperature of 125°C for 10 minutes. The high-temperature steam produced destroys all micro-organisms.

DEPILEX

An autoclave

Ultra-violet radiation

Ultra-violet (UV) radiation provides an alternative sterilising option. The items for sterilisation are placed in wall- or worktop-mounted cabinets fitted with UV-emitting light bulbs, and exposed to the radiation for at least 15 minutes. Penetration of UV radiation is low, however, so sterilisation by this method is not guaranteed.

Chemical sterilisation

Chemical sterilisers should be handled only with suitable personal protective equipment (see page 281), as many of the solutions used are hazardous to health and should not come into contact with the skin. The most effective form of sterilisation is achieved by the total immersion of the contaminated implements into a bath of fluid. This principle is widely used in the sterilisation of babies' feeding utensils.

Disinfectants reduce the probability of infection and are widely used in general day-to-day hygienic salon maintenance. **Antiseptics** are used specifically for treating wounds. Many pre-packaged first aid dressings are impregnated with antiseptic fluids.

DEALING WITH ACCIDENTS

If you are going to have to deal with minor accidents within the salon, you must have a basic understanding of the use of first aid. More serious injuries *must* be treated by a qualified first aider or a professional medical practitioner. The present law suggests that the ideal ratio for workplace-trained staff in low-risk occupations like hairdressing should be one trained first aider for every fifty employed (or self-employed) staff.

First aid kit

A basic first aid kit should consist of the following items (obviously details will depend on the number of staff employed):

- a first aid general guidance card
- 20 assorted adhesive plasters (preferably waterproof)
- 6 medium sterile dressings
- 2 large sterile dressings (for more serious wounds)
- 6 individually wrapped triangular bandages
- 2 sterile eye pads
- a pair of scissors
- 6 safety pins
- a pair of tweezers.

ACTIVITY
Find out how tools and equipment are made hygienically safe in your salon What special precautions are taken?

ACTIVITY
Find out where the first aid kit is within your salon.

List the contents of the first aid kit.

SMITH & NEPHEW

First aid kits

In addition, the following items could prove very useful:

- antiseptic cleanser
- eye bath and eye cleansing lotion
- cottonwool
- burn ointment
- disposable bags
- disposable gloves.

Remember that any first aid materials used from the kit must be replaced as soon as possible.

All accidents and emergency aid given within the salon must be documented in the accident book (see page 276).

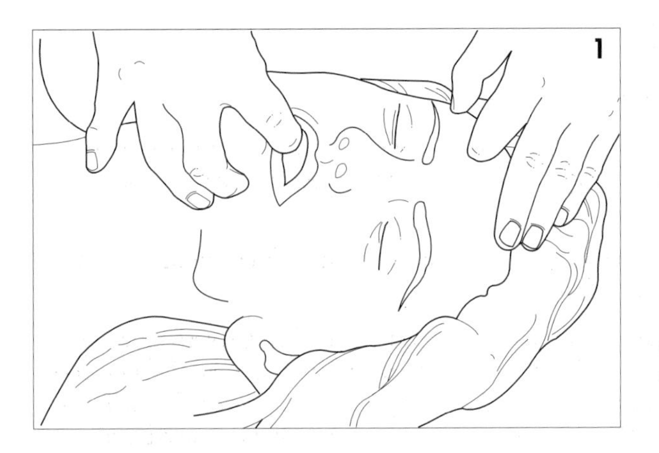

Mouth-to-mouth resuscitation procedure (see table opposite)

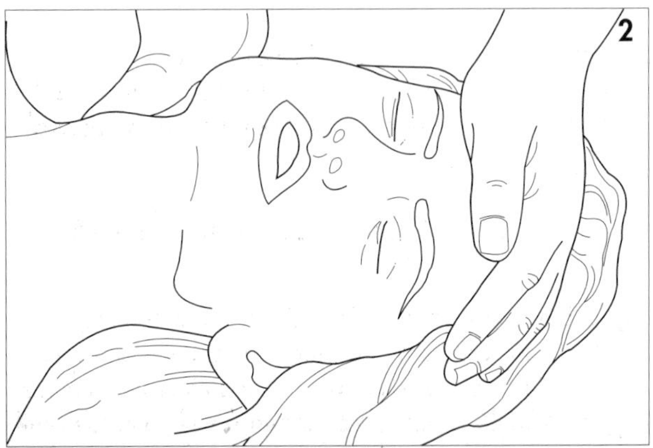

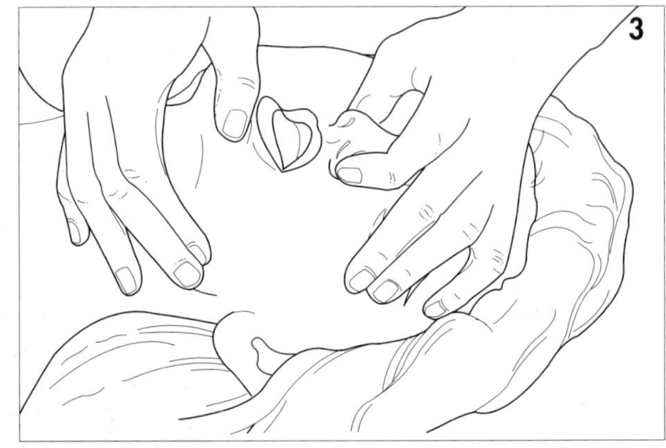

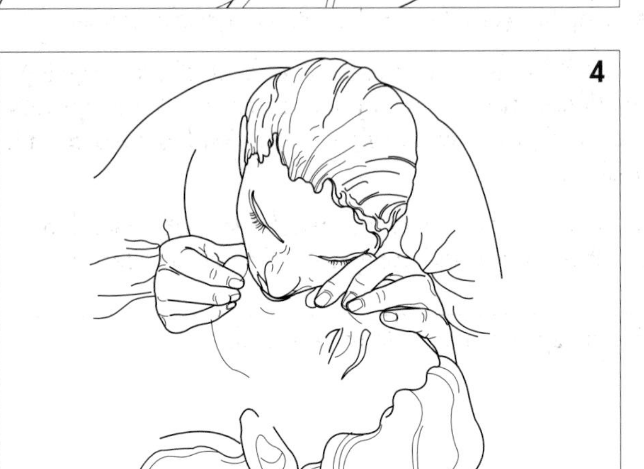

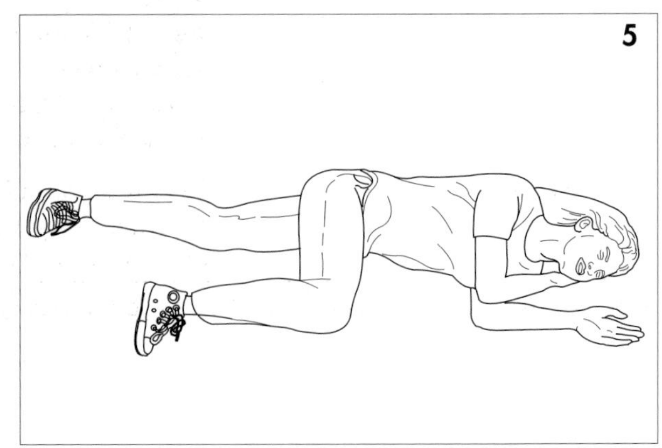

General guidance on first aid

Normally a casualty should be seated, or lying down, when being treated by a first aider.

Problem	*Action to be taken*
Casualty is not breathing	**1** Place the casualty on her back. Open and clear her mouth. **2** Tilt head backwards to open airway (maintain this position throughout). Support the jaw. **3** Kneel beside casualty, while keeping head backwards. Open her mouth and pinch her nose. **4** Open your mouth and take a deep breath. Seal her mouth with yours and breathe firmly into it. Casualty's chest should rise. Remove your mouth and let her chest fall. If her chest does not rise, check her head is tilted sufficiently. Repeat at a rate of 12 times a minute until the casualty is breathing herself. **5** Place her into the recovery position.
Unconscious	Place into recovery position.
Severe bleeding	Control by direct pressure using fingers and thumb on the bleeding point. Apply a dressing. Raising the bleeding limb (unless it is broken) will reduce the flow of blood.
Suspected broken bones	Do not move the casualty unless he is in a position which exposes him to immediate danger.
Burns and scalds (due to heat)	Do not remove clothing sticking to the burns or scalds. Do not burst any blisters. If burns and scalds are small, flush them with plenty of clean, cool water before applying a sterilised dressing. If burns and scalds are large or deep, wash your hands, apply a dry sterile dressing and send the casualty to hospital.
Burns (chemicals)	Avoid contaminating yourself with the chemical. Remove any contaminated clothing which is not stuck to skin. Flush with plenty of cool water for 10–15 minutes. Apply a sterilised dressing and send to hospital.
Foreign body in eye	Wash out eye with clean cool water.*
Chemicals in eyes	Wash out the open eye continuously with clean, cool water for 10–15 minutes.*
Electric shock	Don't touch the casualty until the current is switched off. If the current cannot be switched off, stand on some dry insulating material and use a wooden or plastic implement to free the casualty from the electrical source. If breathing has stopped start mouth-to-mouth breathing and continue until the casualty starts to breathe himself or until professional help arrives.
Gassing	Use suitable protective equipment. Move casualty to fresh air. If breathing has stopped start mouth-to-mouth breathing and continue until the casualty is breathing himself or until professional help arrives. Send to hospital with a note of the gas involved.
Minor injuries	Casualties with minor injuries of a nature they would normally attend to themselves may wash their hands and apply a small sterilised dressing from the first aid box.

*A person with an eye injury should be sent to hospital with the eye covered with an eye pad.

If you are fortunate, you may never need to use your first aid skills. But you should nevertheless be prepared for the following types of incident:

- cuts
- burns
- eye injury
- sprains
- bruising
- fainting
- electric shock
- epileptic fit
- heart attack

In a serious emergency, you could save someone's life if you knew how to give mouth-to-mouth resuscitation (see pages 274–5).

RECORDING ACCIDENTS

All accidents must be recorded in the **accident book**. The recording system should always be kept readily available for use and inspection.

When you are recording accident details you will need to document the following information:

- the full name and address of the casualty
- the occupation of the casualty
- the date of entry in the accident book
- the date and time of the accident
- accident details: location, circumstances, the work process involved
- injury details
- signature of the person making the entry.

FIRE

Your salon will have set fire safety procedures, which must always be followed.

Raising the alarm

Most salon fires arise from either smoking, an electrical fault or a gas escape. **Smoking** can cause fires when lit cigarettes are dropped, discarded or left unattended to smoulder in ash trays. Faulty or badly maintained **electrical equipment**, such as hand dryers or hood dryers, may malfunction and overheat, and even ignite occasionally. **Gas appliances,** such as ovens or hobs, present a possible risk if they are left unattended. Staff cooking facilities need to be closely monitored to prevent gas being left on, whether lit or not.

In the event of fire breaking out your main priorities are to:

- **Raise the alarm.** Staff and customers must be warned, and the premises must be evacuated.

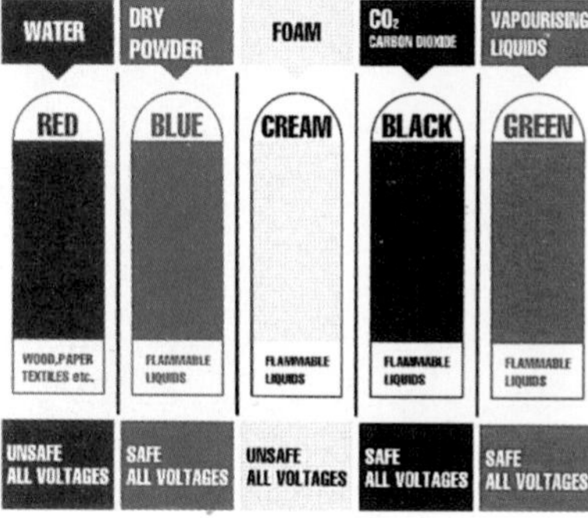

Fire extinguisher colour codes

- **Call the fire brigade,** even if you believe that someone else has already phoned. Dial 999, ask the operator for the fire service, and give the telephone number from where you are calling. Wait for the transfer to the fire service, then tell them your name and the address of the premises that are on fire.

Fire fighting

If the fire is small, you may tackle it with an extinguisher or fire blanket.

Under the Fire Precautions Act 1971, all premises are required to have firefighting equipment, which must be suitably maintained in good working order.

Different types of fire require different types of fire extinguisher. For example, *never* try to use water to put out a fire caused by an electrical fault.

ACTIVITY

Find out the answers to the following questions.

1. Where is the fire fighting equipment in your salon?
2. What does it consist of?
3. What is involved in the checking of fire extinguishers?
4. What is your salon's fire drill?

Fire escape

All premises must have a designated means of escape from fire. This route must be kept clear of obstructions at all times and during working hours the fire doors must remain unlocked. The escape route must be easily identifiable, with clearly visible signs. In buildings with fire certificates, emergency lighting must be installed. These lighting systems automatically illuminate the escape route in the event of a power failure and are operated by an independent battery backup.

Fire safety training

It is essential for staff to know the following fire procedures:

- fire prevention
- raising the alarm
- evacuation during a fire
- assembly points following evacuation.

Training is given to new members of staff during their induction period. This training must be regularly updated for all staff, and fire drills must be held at regular intervals.

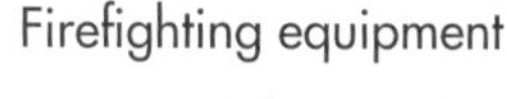

Firefighting equipment

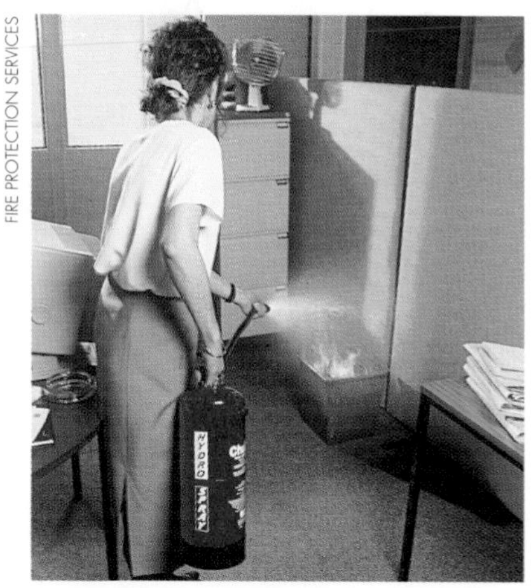

MAINTAINING SALON SECURITY

Effective salon security is essential and your employer is required by law to provide secure business premises. Moreover, insurance companies either would refuse to insure a salon where adequate precautions were not taken, or demand premiums that were so high no salon could afford them. In order for your employer to establish and maintain the security of people and their belongings, money, equipment and premises, set procedures will have been laid down and put into action.

The potential threats to salon security come from either external or internal sources, both in and out of business hours.

External provisions

No salon can make its premises totally burglarproof, but steps may be taken to deter entry by unauthorised people and to minimise any damage they might do. As long as reasonable measures have been taken, insurance will not be withheld. These could include the security devices such as the following:

- five-lever mortice locks ('deadlocks') to all external doors: these are locks that are rebated into (cut out of) both the door and the frame (not surface-mounted like latch locks) and which require keys to both lock and unlock them
- locking catches or bolts on all external opening windows
- security bars or grilles on potentially vulnerable points of entry
- burglar alarms that sound in the event of forced intrusion or damage.

In addition to the advised security features, particular attention should be paid to:

- never leaving money or valuables on the premises overnight
- strict control of the number and location of keys and designated key holders
- switching off all electrical or gas appliances, especially at the end of the day.

During normal hours of business be very alert to the following risks:

- people in areas without the relevant authority
- unauthorised people asking for private or business information
- security of details relating to customers and staff.

Internal provisions

Unfortunately outside intruders are not the only threat to the salon's security. Pilfering by staff and clients is also a possibility.

Don't let yourself think that taking the occasional product home is a 'perk' of the job. Unless it has been paid for, or you have permission, *it is theft!*

Your salon may have its own policy in respect to staff purchases. Always ask.

Theft at work is defined as an act of **gross misconduct**. A thief faces instant dismissal if your employer exercises his disciplinary rights.

Your employer will have taken preventative steps to minimise the risk of theft. Procedures will be set in place to monitor till transactions, stock movements and personal items and valuables.

Money missing from the till will show up during the daily cashing up and book-keeping exercises. Shortfalls will be noticed when the number of clients attended, services and treatments provided and retail items sold do not tally with the available money and cash equivalents, the till rolls and the expected cumulative totals and the daily reports and transaction breakdowns.

Missing items of stock will be noticed during normal stock control procedures, in routine situations where stock is not available as expected, and during spot checks and searches.

The **personal possessions** of both clients and staff also need protecting from theft. Make sure that these are kept safely away from risk situations. Clients' handbags, jewellery and any other valuables should remain with them at all times. Valuable items or money belonging to staff should be securely stored during working hours, or kept with the individual, perhaps in an overall pocket.

Here is a **security checklist**:

- Don't leave valuables in the salon overnight.
- Don't leave money in the till.
- Leave the till drawer open overnight.
- Lock all doors, windows and cupboards.
- Secure all data/information relating to staff and clients.

The Health and Safety at Work Act

HEALTH AND SAFETY LEGISLATION

This section will provide you with an outline of the main health and safety regulations that affect hairdressers and their work.

The **Health and Safety at Work Act 1974** is the legislation that covers a variety of healthy, safe working practices and associated regulations. You do not need to know the contents of this Act, but you should at least be aware of the existence of relevant regulations made under its provisions. Those that are applicable at the time of writing are as follows:

- Control of Substances Hazardous to Health (COSHH) Regulations 1988
- Personal Protective Equipment (PPE) at Work Regulations 1992
- Workplace (Health, Safety and Welfare) Regulations 1992
- Health and Safety (Display Screen Equipment) Regulations 1992
- Manual Handling Operations Regulations 1992
- Provision and Use of Work Equipment Regulations (PUWER) 1992

- Electricity at Work Regulations 1989
- RIDDOR (Reporting Injuries, Diseases and Dangerous Occurrences) Regulations 1985

Managers and employers have additional requirements that they must be able to address and/or demonstrate. But their main duty is to **identify the potential hazard** within the workplace, and then **eliminate the identified potential hazard** to public and staff health, or **minimise the risk** to public and staff health by taking precautionary action.

Potential hazards are identified during **risk assessment**. This process includes:

- evaluating the processes and activities that occur at work
- recording the resulting information
- defining precautionary action to be taken.

COSHH Regulations 1988

The Control of Substances Hazardous to Health Regulations 1988 set out the requirements that must be observed in respect of the handling and usage of substances that are or could potentially be, hazardous. In hairdressing terms this relates to shampoos, setting agents, perming lotions, colouring agents – all the products that we work with.

Your salon will have made a risk assessment of the products held by or used within it, and this will give you specific information on their handling and precautionary requirements.

COSHH Regulations

ACTIVITY
Make a copy of the COSHH risk assessment carried out for the products used within your salon. Keep this for your portfolio of work.

Personal Protective Equipment (PPE) at Work Regulations 1992

The PPE Regulations 1992 require managers to make an assessment of the processes and activities carried out at work and to identify where and when special items of clothing should be worn. In hairdressing environments the potential hazards and dangers revolve around the task of providing hairdressing services – that is, in general, the application of hairdressing treatments and associated products.

Potentially hazardous substances used by hairdressers include:

- acidic solutions of varying strengths
- caustic alkaline solutions of varying strengths
- flammable liquids, which are often in pressurised containers
- vapours and dyeing compounds.

There are also potentially hazardous items of equipment and their individual applications, such as:

- electrical appliances
- heated/heating instruments
- sharp cutting tools.

All these items require correct handling and safe usage procedures, and for several of them this includes the wearing of suitable items of protective equipment.

ACTIVITY

Make a list of the items of protective clothing that should be worn when

- handling a range of hairdressing products
- handling a range of hairdressing equipment.

Workplace (Health, Safety and Welfare) Regulations 1992

These provide the employer with an approved code of practice for maintaining a safe, secure working environment. The regulations cover the legal requirements in respect of the following aspects of the working environment:

- maintenance of workplace and equipment
- ventilation
- indoor temperatures
- lighting
- cleanliness and the handling of waste materials
- room dimensions
- workstations and seating
- conditions of floor and traffic routes
- falls or falling objects
- windows, doors, gates and walls
- ability to clean windows
- organisation of traffic routes

- escalators and moving walkways
- sanitary conveniences
- washing facilities
- drinking water
- accommodation for clothing
- facilities for changing clothing
- facilities for staff to rest and to eat meals.

Health and Safety (Display Screen Equipment) Regulations 1992

Specific regulations apply to visual display units, terminals and computer monitors. These regulations cover the safety aspects of computer operation, the accepted radiation emissions from display screens, the user's posture and seating position, along with permitted working heights.

Manual Handling Operations Regulations 1992

These regulations apply in all occupations where manual lifting occurs. They require the employer to carry out a risk assessment of the work processes and activities that involve manual lifting. The risk assessment should address detailed aspects of the following:

- any risk of injury
- the manual movement that is involved in the task
- the physical constraints the loads incur
- the (work) environmental constraints that are incurred
- the worker's individual capabilities
- steps/remedial action to take in order to minimise risk.

Provision and Use of Work Equipment Regulations 1992

These regulations lay down important health and safety controls on the provision and use of work equipment. They state the duties for employers, the persons in control (the users) and the self-employed. In general they affect both new and old equipment alike. In addition to this they cover the selection of suitable equipment, maintenance, manufacturer information, instruction and training). Specific regulations address the dangers that could arise from operation of the equipment and the potential risk of injury.

The Electricity at Work Regulations 1989

These regulations state that electrical equipment must be adequately maintained and checked by a suitably qualified person. A written record of the equipment tests should be kept and made available for inspection.

ASSIGNMENTS: HEALTH AND SAFETY IN THE SALON

A practical activity

Copy the table shown below. Then find out the information required to complete it. Keep the finished document for use in your portfolio.

To find the necessary information, re-read the section headed 'General salon hygiene' in this chapter (page 270). Also ask your fellow work colleagues for help.

Work areas	*Potential hazards*	*Reasons for keeping clean*	*Methods of keeping clean*
Reception			
Styling units			
Drying areas			
Dispensary			
Stock room/ cupboard			
Staff room			
Toilets			

For you to find out

With reference to your salon, find out the following information. Record the details along with any drawings, photographs and other illustrations that you wish to use. Keep them in your folder or personal portfolio.

1. What are your salon's expected standards of personal hygiene?
2. With reference to both yourself and the clients, what would happen if you disregarded these expected standards?
3. What are your salon's expected standards relating to personal appearance/conduct?
4. What would constitute unacceptable appearance or conduct?

5. Why are posture and deportment so important? In what ways can poor posture cause harm?
6. The Personal Protective Equipment at Work Regulations 1992 (PPE) have legislative expectations of both employers and their employees. How can you fulfil your obligations whilst carrying out your day-to-day duties?

A case study

It was Tuesday morning at 'Jenny's Hair Salon'. Jenny had allocated Karen, one of the juniors, to remain on reception whilst she attended to paperwork in the office. Steve, one of the stylists, has clients booked in. Sharon, the other stylist, had most of the morning free.

A well-dressed woman with short greying hair came in and asked Karen if she would be able to have her hair tinted before travelling to London that afternoon. Karen said that Sharon could help her.

Sharon greeted the lady, putting her at her ease and carried out a consultation and colour selection. She asked Claire, another junior, to prepare the client for the service. Claire seated her in the salon, hung up her coat and looked for a tinting gown. There weren't any.

'Use one of the cutting capes, then,' said Sharon, 'the others are still at the launderette. I'll mix up the tint and you can apply it while I collect them.'

Claire had applied colours before but tended to be a little careless. Today her application was sloppy, and she did not bother to wear gloves. Ten minutes later Sharon returned. Horrified, she beckoned Claire into reception. 'You've not only tinted her hair, you've got tint on her neck and even on her jacket,' she exclaimed.

'I know,' said Claire, 'I'll change the gowns over now and ask her to take off her jacket so that it won't get creased. Then I'll clean it without her knowing.' 'OK, but keep it to yourself,' said Sharon.

When the hair do was finished, the client paid her bill and left.

Two days later, Claire told Jenny that she had visited the doctor because of sore, itching and burning hands. He had diagnosed dermatitis and told her it was an occupational disease and should be reported. He'd signed her off for a week.

On Saturday morning, Jenny received a letter from a firm of solicitors. This is what it said.

Re Ms Cane in pursuance of Compensation

Dear Madam

I regret to inform you that my client whilst attending your place of business on Tuesday 11th February did suffer due to the gross negligence of your staff an allergenic reaction following a colouring treatment. There are indications of burns and weeping pustules as well as damage sustained to her attire. We await a comprehensive medical report which we believe will provide the basis for our pursuance in court and recovery of damages. We will be contacting you in due course.

1. List in order the mistakes that were made.
2. What actions should, or could, have been taken to avoid the outcomes?
3. Who were to blame and why?
4. What are the possible short- and long-term effects for Jenny, her staff and her business?
5. How do COSHH and RIDDOR apply to this particular scenario?

PREPARING FOR ASSESSMENT

Whilst making preparations for assessment on health and safety in the salon, the following checklist may be helpful. Check that you have covered and now fully understand these items:

- methods and reasons for maintaining personal health and hygiene
- clothes and equipment required for work activities
- safe salon working practices
- how to look out for the potential hazards in the workplace
- how to look after tools and equipment
- how to dispose of salon waste items
- salon policy in respect of emergency procedures
- salon policy in respect of first aid procedures.

When you feel that you are ready, talk to your trainer to arrange a suitable time for your assessment.

APPENDIX 1 ASSESSMENT

This section of the book will provide you with the background information and explain the principles surrounding the assessment of competence.

Before NVQs became available, trainees who wanted to gain nationally recognised qualifications would have to practise the technical skills, study art, science and design and then, after a period of training, be expected take both practical and theory examinations. Depending how they performed on the day, they either passed or failed. This system is considered to be unfair for vocational qualifications. Some trainees who were expected to pass with flying colours have actually failed because of the pressures exerted by taking the exam. The examination system neither provides a realistic working situation, nor truly reflects the candidate's previous training achievement.

The solution is at hand, however. Continuous assessment of performance provides a suitable option. Monitoring and recording the trainee's progress towards achievement (occupational competence) is now providing the currently preferred route to certification.

Trainees are enrolled with an approved centre and then undergo a period of initial assessment to identify their training needs. Following this assessment, a personal training and assessment plan is devised. This plan will state **where**, **when** and **how** the training will be delivered, **who** will be responsible for monitoring, training and assessing, and **what** will be the expected time scale for training and reviewing of progress.

This detailed plan provides a tailor-made training programme which allows the trainee to:

- practise the required skills, and
- acquire the essential background knowledge.

Then, at the point where trainees can consistently perform the required tasks to standard and can demonstrate that they have the required knowledge, they are **deemed competent**.

WHAT IS THE REQUIRED STANDARD?

The standard could be described as 'the level of competence required in order to perform the task'. The currently nationally recognised standards have been devised by the Hairdressing

Training Board. This organisation is made up of representative bodies within the hairdressing industry. It is the **lead body** responsible for defining the standards of competence at each of the NVQ levels (Level 1, Level 2 and so on). After the standards have been agreed they are submitted to the National Council for Vocational Qualifications (NCVQ) for their approval and subsequent **accreditation** (accreditation is the giving of the Council's formal approval to a lead body's national standards, providing it with a **licence to operate**).

The standards are written specifications of how certain tasks or functions are to be performed. They are used in two ways to assess trainees:

- by observing their performance of practical ability within the specified conditions of the range
- by questioning candidates to find out their basic understanding and knowledge of the practical task.

Each standard is make up of the following components:

- element title
- performance criteria
- range statement
- essential knowledge.

The NVQ divides up the activities and tasks of hairdressing work into groups called **units**. For example, Unit 2 is 'Shampoo and condition hair and scalp'.

Level 2 in Hairdressing consists of ten core units, two optional units and three additional units. The **core units** are the basic essentials of the NVQ, and they must all be completed. The two **optional units** provide the trainee with a choice of women's or men's hairdressing, and at least one option must be undertaken. The three **additional units** provide further career options and, if chosen, give the trainee a chance of acquiring some specialised skills.

Each unit can be achieved and certificated separately. This means that candidates may accumulate units of competence:

- for specific work-related tasks
- for part-certification
- for full Level 2 certification
- in any order
- at their own pace of learning
- within the workplace or at a training centre.

Element title

Units consist of various numbers of individual standards called **elements**. The **element title** states the function or task that has to be performed competently. For example, Element 2.1 in the Hairdressing qualification is 'Shampoo and surface condition hair and scalp'.

Performance criteria

A standard specifies not only *what* has to be done, but also *how* it is to be done. It sets out a list of **performance criteria** for each task. These are concise statements of procedural functions, the specific steps that should be taken during the performance of the task if the standard is to be met. They are used as a checklist when the candidate is being observed during assessment.

For example, during assessment of Element 2.1, the trainee would demonstrate that the client had been prepared correctly, and that the products, tools and scalp massage techniques used were chosen as a result of consultation with the client.

Range statements

To enable the trainee to gain competence in a variety of situations the standard also states the **range** of circumstances for which competence must be demonstrated. For example, if a trainee were asked to perform a layered haircut on a model with straight hair, the finished cut would look different from the same cut carried out on a model with curly hair. Although the same methods and techniques are required in both situations, the result are by no means the same. The candidate needs to show competence in a broad range of contexts – hair types, lengths, conditions and so on – which imply a wide variety of conditions and complexity for the given task.

Essential knowledge and understanding

This refers to the candidate's awareness of *why* the task is done in a certain way. For example, in Element 2.1 the trainee will need to show a clear understanding of

- how hair varies in structure
- the range of available shampoos and surface conditioners and their suitability for use in conjunction with different hair structures, hair and scalp types, and other salon services
- manufacturer's instructions relating to the use of products.

THE ASSESSMENT ACTIVITY

Why do we assess?

Assessment isn't just a matter of finding out if a trainee can 'pass' a test. There are four main reasons for an assessment:

- to check whether a trainee can perform the job competently to the required national standard
- to identify where further improvement can be made
- to monitor and record progress towards competence
- to maintain accurate records of the trainee's achievement.

How do we assess?

Assessment is carried out by the collection and evaluation of evidence by a wide variety of techniques. But regardless of the technique used, only one of three possible assessment decisions can be made:

- the trainee is competent
- the trainee is not yet competent
- the trainee has provided insufficient evidence for the assessor to infer competence.

Observation of performance

A trainee's performance can be observed and assessed in two ways.

Formative assessment consists of watching normal, everyday performance within the workplace. It is the most reliable basis for the assessment of practical skills. Ideally the trainer/assessor can, and will, unobtrusively monitor a trainee's progress during day-to-day activities. The assessor can then recognise the point at which competence has been achieved and where occupational skills are retained.

In situations where further training, guidance, practice or support are needed the trainer/assessor is readily on hand to aid the trainee.

Summative assessment is normally based on observing the results of pre-planned training activities, possibly during model evenings or otherwise encountered in off-the-job training sessions (i.e. away from the normal workplace). When and if trainees are to be summatively assessed they should be made aware of the assessment conditions prior to the assessment taking place. They will need to know:

- what is required of them
- what task(s) they are to perform
- any additional preparations that are necessary.

Oral questions

Oral assessment should take place during or shortly after the practical performance. Oral questions will have been previously devised by the assessor, who will frame them around the element's 'essential knowledge', and will be relevant to the task(s) being carried out. Oral questioning can provide additional evidence to supplement the assessor's observation of the trainee as he or she carries out the specified task. It can also establish whether or not the trainee will be competent to carry out that task in a range of different situations and conditions.

Written or documented information

This will include answers to written questions, projects and assignments, records of case studies and descriptions of methods and techniques. The trainee will be encouraged to provide illustrations, whether drawings, photographs or diagrams. The variety, quality and quantity of recorded evidence will depend on the trainee. What is important is that it should show that the trainee has a clear understanding of the required knowledge. This type of assessment of **portfolio evidence** is currently the preferred route. Although portfolio evidence is less 'focused' than answers to written questions, it is valuable in that it provides evidence relating to the trainee's practical experience.

These three modes of assessment are the most reliable sources of evidence. Trainees are, however, expected to offer other evidences in support of their training. These may be of the following types, although others are possible.

Examination of products

The term **product** (or **products of experience**) relates to the result of a task such as a work activity or a set project/ assignment. A product could, for instance, be a set of completed client record cards, or of headpieces and wigs.

Witness testimony

This is evidence, either verbal or written, of an activity that the trainee has undertaken previously. This testimony could come from a manager, colleagues or clients.

Personal account

This is a description, again either verbal or written, of the actions that have been (or would be) undertaken in carrying out a given task.

Simulated activity

Simulated activities, or role play, are not normally encouraged for assessment purposes. But they are allowable under certain circumstances: during emergencies, for example, or when handling client complaints.

Historical evidence

This is evidence that results directly from activities undertaken in the past. Examples could include a video or photographs of a trainee's work or hairdressing demonstration or perhaps a newspaper cutting, provided that they can be reliably authenticated as the trainee's own work.

The organisations listed below should prove valuable sources of information and help to the professional hairdresser. Address any enquiries to 'The Secretary'.

Arbitration, Conciliation and Advisory Service (ACAS)
Clifton House, 83–117 Euston Road, London NW1 2RB
(Tel. 0171-396 5100)

Association of Hairdressing Teachers in Colleges of Further Education (AHT)
Department of Hairdressing, Kingston College of Further Education, Kingston Hall Road, Kingston-upon-Thames KT1 2AQ
(Tel. 0181-546 2151)

Black Beauty and Hair
Hawker Consumer Publications, 13 Park House, 140 Battersea Park Road, London SW11 4NB
(Tel. 0171-720 2108)

Caribbean and Afro Society of Hairdressers (CASH)
42 North Cross Road, East Dulwich, London SE22 8PY
(Tel. 0181-299 2859)

City and Guilds (C+G)
1 Giltspur Street, London EC1A 9DD
(Tel. 0171-294 2468)

Cosmetic, Toiletry and Perfumery Association (CTPA)
Jo Sharon House, 3–5 John Princes Street, London W1M 9HD
(Tel. 0171-491 8891)

The Cutting Edge/Estetica
Margarethe House, Eismann Way, Corby, Northamptonshire NN17 5ZB
(Tel: 01536 263669)

The Fellowship of Hair Artists of Great Britain
Waterloo House, High Street, Tisbury, Wiltshire SP3 6HD
(Tel. 01747 870310)

Freelance Hair and Beauty Federation
16 Chancelot Terrace, Edinburgh EH6 4SS
(Tel. 0131-552 0732)

Guild of Hairdressers (GUILD)
Syndicate House, 27–29 Westgate, Barnsley, South Yorkshire S70 2DJ
(Tel. 01226 291191)

Hair Magazine
IPC Magazines Ltd, King's Reach Tower, Stamford Street, London SE1 9LS
(Tel. 0171-261 5000)

Hair and Beauty
9 Lincoln's Inn Fields, London WC2A 3BP
(Tel. 0171-404 1499)

Hair Flair
4th Floor, 27 Maddox Street, London W1R 9LE
(Tel. 0171-493 3533)

Hairdressers Journal International
Quadrant House, The Quadrant, Sutton, Surrey SM2 5AS
(Tel. 0181-652 3500)

Hairdressing Council (HC)
12 David House, 45 High Street, South Norwood, London SE25 6HJ
(Tel. 0181-771 6205)

Hairdressing Employers Association (HEA)
10 Coldbath Square, London EC1R 5HL
(Tel. 0171-833 0633)

Hairdressing Manufacturers' and Wholesalers' Association (HMWA)
25 West Street, Hazelmere, Surrey GU27 2AP
(Tel. 01428 654336)

Hairdressing Training Board (HTB)
3 Chequer Road, Doncaster, South Yorkshire DN1 2AA
(Tel. 01302 342837)

Institute of Trichologists
228 Stockwell Road, Brixton, London SW9 9SU
(Tel. 0171-733 2056)

National Hairdressing Federation (NHF)
11 Goldington Road, Bedford MK40 3JY
(Tel. 01234 360332)

Union of Shop, Distributive and Allied Workers (USDAW)
188 Wilmslow Road, Fallowfield, Manchester M14 6LJ
(Tel. 0161-224 2084)

World Federation of Hairdressing and Beauty Schools
PO Box 367, Coulsdon, Surrey CR5 2TP
(Tel. 01727 551355)

APPENDIX 3
RECOMMENDED READING

Bennett, Ruth 1984. *The Science of Hairdressing.* Edward Arnold.

Boston, M. and N. Broomfield 1974. *How to Blow Style.* Permaids Products Ltd.

Coen, P., J. Maxwell and J. Wagenvoord 1988. *Beautiful Braids.* Century Hutchinson/Random House.

Cutting, P., R. Ross and R. Hill 1994. *Hairdressing – The Complete Guide.* Pitman.

Green, Martin, Lesley Howson and Leo Palladino 1994. *Professional Hairdressing – The Official Guide to Level 3.* Macmillan.

Hatton, Lesley and Phillip Hatton 1990. *Foundation Hairdressing.* Blackwell Scientific Publications.

Hatton, Phillip 1994. *Afro Hair.* Blackwell Scientific Publications.

Henderson, S. and M. Phillips 1988. *Hairdressing and Science.* Stanley Thornes.

Jackson, Barbara and Lydia Eagle 1984. *The Black Book of Beauty.* Macmillan.

Jarrett, Hyacinth 1988. *The Black Hairdressing and Beauty Training Manual.* Manpower Services Commission.

Lee, C. N. and J. K. Inglis 1983. *Science for Hairdressing Students.* Pergamon.

Mascola, Anthony 1988. *Hairstyling.* Toni and Guy.

Masters, T. W. 1984. *Hairdressing in Theory and Practice.* Technical Press.

Openshaw, F. 1986. *Hairdressing Science.* Longman.

Palladino, Leo 1989. *Principles and Practice of Hairdressing.* Macmillan.

Palladino, Leo and June Hunt 1992. *The Nail File.* Macmillan.

Sassoon, Vidal 1984. *Cutting Hair the Vidal Sassoon Way.* Heinemann.

Young, Marc 1979. *Creative Haircutting My Way.* Marc Young Artistes de Coiffeur Ltd.

GLOSSARY

accelerator a machine that produces radiant heat (infra-red radiation); can speed up chemical hair processes such as colouring or conditioning
acid a substance that gives hydrogen ions in water, and produces a solution with a pH below 7
acne a skin disorder, characterised by spots and pustules due to inflammation of the sebaceous glands
activator a chemical used in bleaches or some perm lotions to start or boost its action
Afro-Caribbean hair the very curly hair typical of African people
AIDS acquired immune-deficiency syndrome; a condition in which the immune system is damaged and the body becomes vulnerable to many infections
albino hair hair that contains little or no pigment; albino hair is nearly white or very pale yellow; the condition is usually present at birth
alkali a substance that gives hydroxide ions in water, and produces a solution with a pH above 7
alopecia baldness
anagen the stage of hair growth during which the hair is actively growing
anterior towards the front
antioxidant a substance that prevents or slows down deterioration due to oxidation
antiseptic a substance that kills disease-causing **micro-organisms** or stops them from growing
apocrine gland a gland whose secretions include a part of the secreting cells themselves (e.g. some sweat glands)
appointment a time and place arranged for a meeting
arrector pili the muscles that raise the hair (in humans they are very feeble)
arteriole a very small artery
artery a blood vessel that carries blood away from the heart
assessment judging the worth of something or of the results of a task; evaluation, appraisal
assignment a task or a practical activity
asymmetrical irregular, unevenly balanced
athlete's foot *see* **tinea pedis**

autoclave a device for sterilising items in high-temperature steam

backcombing/backbrushing pushing hair back to bind or lift the hair using a comb or brush
backdressing backcombing or backbrushing
bacteria a large group of **micro-organisms,** many of which live in or on the human body; a few cause diseases
bactericide a substance that kills bacteria
barbering the art of cutting and shaping men's hair
bleach a substance that removes natural colour; acts first on black pigments, then on brown, red and yellow
bleaching removal of natural colour
blepharitis inflammation of the eyelids
block colouring colouring areas of hair in a way that is intended to enhance the cut style
blow-drying drying and shaping hair using a hand-held dryer
blow-stretching (straightening) temporary straightening of the hair by smoothing the hair while blow-drying
blow-waving waving the hair while blow-drying
bob cut a hairstyle in which the hair is cut to a level length around the head
body language communication by means of body actions and/or posture rather than speech
braiding *see* **plaiting**
brighteners lightening (bleaching) shampoos or rinses

canities hair that is without pigment and is therefore grey or white
capillary strictly, a very fine tube; usually used to refer to a very small blood vessel
case study examination of a topic as exemplified by a particular event or occasion
castle serrations reducing areas of a hair section with special serrated scissors
catagen the stage of hair growth during which the hair stops growing, but the hair papilla is still active
Caucasian hair the wavy or straight hair typical of a European
charge card a means of making payment without using cash; similar to a credit card
chemical hair treatment a term that includes perming, colouring or tinting, bleaching, streaking, high- or low-lighting, frosting, lightening, permanent straightening or relaxing
cheque an order to a bank to pay a specified sum of money
cheque guarantee card a plastic card issued to an individual by a bank which guarantees payment of that person's cheques (up to a specified limit)
client a customer or patron of a shop or salon
client care looking after customers, ensuring that they are comfortable and confident, and that they will be satisfied with the service and/or treatment they receive

.t desires what a client wishes the results of a service or .reatment to be like

.ient record a method of storing information about a client, either on a slip or card, or on a computer

club-cutting or clubbing cutting straight across to produce level ends

cold permanent waving (perming) a perming process that does not rely on heat for its activation

cold sores *see* **herpes simplex**

colour filling *see* **pre-pigmentation**

colourant any type of colouring substance used on hair

communication giving and receiving information; understanding, and ensuring that one is understood

compensation a payment given to make amends for loss, damage, poor service etc.

compound colourings mixtures of vegetable and mineral dyes

conditioner a product used to correct or improve the state of the hair

confidentiality the maintenance and respect of an individual's privacy, including privacy (secrecy) of information

conjunctivitis inflammation of the conjunctiva (the membrane at the front of the eye)

consultation the process of interviewing a client; includes discussing, conferring, questioning, advising and counselling

contra-indication sign that some treatment or service is inadvisable or could be harmful

cornrowing fine plaits running continuously across the scalp

CPW abbreviation for **cold permanent waving**

credit card a means of making payment without using cash, allowing the card-owner a period of credit

crew cut short, spiky style with hair standing straight up

croquignole winding winding a curl from point to root

cross-infection the passing of an infection from one individual to another

cutting angle the angle at which hair is held and cut

cutting comb a flexible comb designed for use when cutting

cutting line the direction in which cutting is made to follow the contours of the head

cutting method a considered sequence of cutting techniques

cutting technique a special cutting skill aimed at producing a specific result

dandruff scales of dry dead skin flaking from the scalp

debit card a means of making payment without using cash, by which payment is made instantly from a bank account

decolouring removal of colour, especially artificial colour, from the hair

depth of colour a measure of how light or dark a colour is

dermatitis inflammation of the skin

dermis the layer of the skin underlying the epidermis; the thickest layer of the skin

detergent a cleansing agent, acting by reducing the surface tension of water and improving its wetting ability
development time the 'taking time' of a chemical action such as tinting
diagnosis identifying a disease or disorder by observing its symptoms
discoloration unwanted colour produced by a chemical
disinfectant a substance that kills disease-causing **micro-organisms**
dreadlocks long thin plaits
dressing the forming and blending of hair into a finished shape or style
dry cutting cutting hair while it is dry
dry shaving usually refers to electric shaving

eccrine gland a gland that emits a secretion to the surface of the body; most sweat glands are eccrine glands
eczema an inflammation of the skin, characterised by redness and irritation
effleurage light, soothing, stroking **massage** movement
EFTPOS Electronic Funds Transfer at Point of Sale: a means of making payment without using cash, by which payment is made instantly from a bank account
elasticity the ability of a material to return to the original length after stretching
emollient a substance used (e.g. in conditioners) to soften and enhance the appearance of hair
emulsion a suspension of tiny droplets of one liquid in another liquid (e.g. of oil in water)
end paper a tissue or wrap used during winding to secure a hair point
epidermis the outermost layers of the skin
epithelium a tissue of closely packed cells that covers a surface (internal or external) of the body
ethnic plaits *see* **cornrowing**
eumelanin black and brown pigment in the skin and hair

facial a face **massage**
feathering **tapering** action using scissor points
finger (hand) drying drying the hair using the fingers as a comb
finger waving forming waves in wet hair using the hands and a comb
fish hook a point of hair that has been bent back during rollering or winding
float sum of money that is kept in the till to ensure that adequate change is available; the sum that should be in the till when business opens each day
folliculitis inflammation of the hair follicles; may be caused by bacterial infection
fragilitas crinium splitting of the hairs at their ends
fraudulent dishonest, false or deceitful

freehand cutting cutting without forcing the hair out of its natural position

French roll a vertical fold of hair, usually on the back of the head

fringe hair that covers the forehead from side to side

frosting **shading** or **tinting** parts of the hair to enhance the style

fungi a large group of living organisms, plant-like in many respects; many cause disease

fungicide a substance that kills fungi

furunculosis an outbreak of boils and abscesses

glimmering **shading** or **tinting** parts of the hair to enhance the style

gown protective wrap

graduation the sloping line produced by layers of hair

guide (for cutting) any feature or previously cut section of hair that is used to indicate where the next cut should be made

hair shaper a razor-like cutting tool

hard water water that contains calcium and/or magnesium salts; produces scum with soap

haute coiffure *see* **high fashion**

head-hugging plaits plaits of hair lying close to the head

heat moulding shaping the hair while it is softened by heat (e.g. with heated tongs)

hepatitis inflammation of the liver

herb a herbaceous plant (one that dies back in winter); often refers to a plant that is used for medical or cosmetic purposes

hereditary passing from a parent to a child

herpes simplex a viral skin infection, the all-too-familiar 'cold sores'

herpes zoster a painful viral infection of the epidermis of the skin and of the nerve endings; usually called 'shingles'

high fashion the latest and newest shapes and trends

highlighting **shading** or **tinting** parts of the hair to enhance the style

HIV human imunodeficiency virus, believed to lead to the condition of **AIDS**

honing sharpening a razor using a stone (or hone)

humectant a substance that attracts and holds moisture (water)

humidity the amount of water (moisture) held by the air

hydrophilic attracted by water

hydrophobic repelled by water

hygiene the practice of procedures leading to cleanliness and the maintenance of good health

hygroscopic tending to absorb water from the air

hyperaemia flushing of the skin due to improved blood flow

illusionary effect a style that seems to diminish or accentuate certain facial features or shapes of the head

immune system the body's defence against disease
impetigo a bacterial infection of the **epidermis**
incompatibility inability to combine or coexist without ill effects
indicator a substance that changes colour at a certain pH value
infectious disease a disease that can be passed from one person to another
itch mite the animal **parasite** that causes **scabies**

job description a written specification of what is expected of someone who has to carry out a task
johoba oil a plant-based oil with moisturising properties

keratin the principal protein of hair, nails and skin

lanolin an **emollient** extracted from wool fat
lanugo hair the soft downy hair of an unborn child
lathering lubricating and softening the beard before shaving, using a foam, gel or cream
layering cutting hair at various angles to produce **graduation**
legal tender forms of money that are legally recognised as valid for making payments
level length *see* **bob cut**
lightening *see* **bleaching**
limescale hard deposit of calcium carbonate, separating from **hard water** when it is heated
lowlighting **shading** or **tinting** parts of the hair to enhance the style

massage the practice of moving skin and muscles by rubbing, kneading, etc. to promote relaxation and suppleness and improve blood flow
melanins the pigments that give colour to skin and hair
micro-organism a small living creature visible only with a microscope
mis-en-pli putting hair into set
moisturiser a substance that attracts and holds moisture (water)
Mongoloid hair the lank, straight hair typical of Asian or Amerindian people
monilethrix beaded hair
mousse a foam formulation used in setting or colouring

neckline the line of the hair across the nape of the neck
neutral having a pH close to 7
neutraliser a chemical formulation used to return hair to its normal condition after cold perming
nit an egg of the head louse
see also **pediculosis capitis**
normaliser *see* **neutraliser**

observation watching, noticing, studying, recording
once over shaving shaving once round the face

outlining marking out the boundaries of parts of the head and face (e.g. neckline, beard outline etc.)
overbooking making appointments for too many clients at the same time
oxidation reaction with oxygen, as in the neutralising of a perm

parasite an organism that lives on or in another organism, and may weaken it or cause symptoms of disease
pathogen a **micro-organism** or **virus** that produces harmful effects such as disease
pediculosis capitis an infestation of the head by the insect known as the head louse
performance criteria the standards by which one's work is judged and evaluated
permeable allowing other materials to penetrate or pass through
perming (permanent waving) the process that changes straight hair into waves or curls that last throughout the life of the hair
pétrissage deep, stimulating, kneading **massage** movement
petty cash cash kept on a firm's premises to meet minor items of expense
pH a measure of acidity or alkainity
pheomelanin red and yellow pigment in the skin and hair
pincurling forming hair into curl shapes which are held with pins or slips until dried
pityriasis capitis *see* **dandruff**
plaiting intertwining several sections of hair to form a single structure
pleat a folded roll of hair
pli shortened form of ***mis-en-pli***
polishing **shading** or **tinting** parts of the hair to enhance the style
porosity (of hair) the ability to absorb moisture or liquids (e.g. colour or perm lotion)
posterior towards the back
postiche hairpieces added for ornamentation or to disguise hair defects
pre-lightening bleaching hair before tinting it to a shade that is lighter than the original
pre-pigmentation adding a colour to porous hair before recolouring; allows the new colour (often a warm colour) to adhere to the hair and prevents patchy or greenish results
primary colours
of light: blue, green and red
of pigments: blue, yellow and red
processing time the 'taking time' of a chemical action such as tinting
psoriasis a condition that produces inflammation, irritation and scaling of the skin

quasi-permanent colour a long-lasting hair colour that fades gradually over time

rake a comb with widely spaced teeth
razor clubbing **club-cutting** with a razor
reception area where clients are received; the process of receiving people
reduction reaction with hydrogen, as in cold permanent waving
re-growth hair that has grown since the last treatment with colour or bleach
resistant hair hair that resists colour penetration
re-style to completely change the hair shape and style
retouching colouring re-growth
reverse graduation a cut in which the top layers are longer than those beneath
ringworm *see* **tinea**
roller a curler or former around which hair is wound to produce a curl or wave
rollerball a type of **accelerator** that incorporates a fan and provides a moving heat source

scabies a skin rash appearing as a reaction to an animal **parasite**
scalp the skin and subcutaneous tissue that covers the top of the head
scalp plaits *see* **cornrowing**
scrunch drying blow-drying while gripping and squeezing the hair; used to produce full effects
sebaceous cyst a swollen **sebaceous gland;** a wen
sebaceous gland a natural oil gland in the skin
seborrhoea over-production of sebum by the sebaceous glands, leading to greasy skin
sebum oily secretion of a sebaceous gland
secondary colours
of light: yellow, cyan and magenta
of pigments: violet, green and orange
sectioning hair dividing hair into manageable sections
self-appraisal, self-assessment judging and evaluating one's own level of achievement
semi-permanent colouring a hair colouring that lasts through several shampoos
setting placing wet hair into positions that will be temporarily held after drying, e.g. with rollers, pins or curlers
shading the lightening **(bleaching)** of small areas (ends or tips) of hair
shampoo a product used for cleaning hair
shaving the close removal of hair
shimmering shading or tinting parts of the hair to enhance the style
shingles *see* **herpes zoster**
shingling cutting a short layered style graduating from the nape of the neck
shrinkage theft of stock by members of staff
sideburns, sideboards names for men's side whiskers

soft water water that is free of calcium and magnesium salts
spectrum the colours contained in light that we see as white (many people can recognise red, orange, yellow, blue, green, indigo and violet)
stabiliser a chemical added to **bleach** to prevent deterioration
static electric charges on hair, producing 'flyaway' behaviour
steam setting setting hair while dry, then steaming, drying and dressing it
steamer a machine used to supply moist heat to the skin and/or hair
sterilisation killing all **micro-organisms** that may be present
stock in hand the stock available; re-ordering takes place at prearranged levels of stock in hand
stock rotation ensuring that old stock is used up before newer stock is brought out
stock taking checking the current levels of **stock in hand**
stropping sharpening a razor using a strip of leather called a strop
subcutaneous tissue the tissue lying immediately below the skin
sudoriferous gland an alternative name for a sweat gland
sycosis a bacterial infection of the hair follicles
symmetrical evenly balanced, the same shape on both sides
symptom a sensation or a change in the body or its functions by which a disease may be recognised
synthetic man-made

tailcomb a comb with an extension that is useful for sectioning and guiding hair
tapering (taper cutting) cutting a hair section to a tapered point (i.e. a point like that of a sharpened pencil)
tapotement tapping or patting **massage** movement
telogen the period during which a hair ceases to grow, before it is shed
temporary colouring a hair colouring that is washed away by shampooing
terminal hair the long, relatively coarse hair of the head and of men's beards
test a trial or experiment designed to find out the properties of, for example, skin or hair
texturising removing small amounts of hair without reducing the overall length
thinning reducing the bulk of hair without reducing its length
thinning scissors a pair of scissors with serrated blades (one or both) used for thinning the hair
tinea a fungal skin infection, often ringworm
tinea capitis ringworm of the head
tinea pedis ringworm of the feet (called 'athlete's foot')
tinting the process of adding artificial colour to hair
tipping **shading** or **tinting** parts of the hair to enhance the style
tone the overall visual impression given by a colour

toning the process of adding tint or colour to hair after **bleaching**
traveller's cheque a means of making payment without using cash
trichologist a scientist specialising in the treatment of diseases affecting the hair
trichorrhexis nodosa the development of nodules on the hair, leading to splitting
trimming removing small amounts of hair while retaining the original sytle
twice over shaving close shaving, shaving twice around the face

utilities the practical services essential to the running of a salon (gas, water, electricity etc.)

vein a blood vessel that carries blood towards the heart
vellus hair the fine, fluffy hair that covers skin; may be visible on the human face
venule a very small vein
verruca a type of wart, especially one that grows on the hand or foot
virgin hair hair that has never been treated by any chemical process
virus a very small particle, visible only with an electron microscope, able to reproduce itself but incapable of existing outside a cell of some other organism; many cause diseases
viscous thick and sticky; slow-flowing

wart a viral infection of the skin
water waving (water setting) *see* **finger waving**
wen *see* **sebaceous cyst**
wet cutting cutting hair while it is wet
wet shaving shaving after lathering or wetting the skin
winding rolling hair on to curl formers